MAGIC

STAGE ILLUSIONS AND SCIENTIFIC DIVERSIONS

THE SKIRT DANCE.

MAGIC

STAGE ILLUSIONS AND SCIENTIFIC DIVERSIONS

INCLUDING TRICK PHOTOGRAPHY

COMPILED AND EDITED BY

ALBERT A. HOPKINS

WITH AN INTRODUCTION BY

HENRY RIDGELY EVANS

WITH FOUR HUNDRED ILLUSTRATIONS

ARNO PRESS
New York · 1977

First Published New York 1897
Reissued 1967 by Benjamin Blom, Inc.

Reissued 1977 by Arno Press, Inc.

Library of Congress Catalog Card No. 67-12462

Manufactured in the United States of America

PREFACE.

It is believed that the present work occupies a unique field in the extensive literature of magic. There are already a large number of treatises on natural magic and legerdemain, but in most of them very little attention has been given to the *exposé* of stage illusions, which are of great interest as they are so largely based on ingenious applications of scientific principles. Optics, mechanics, sound, and electricity have all been pressed into service by the *fin de siècle* prestidigitateur. In the present work great attention has been paid to elaborate tricks of this nature, and in many cases the *exposés* have been obtained from the prestidigitateurs themselves. In the first few chapters many of the best illusions of Robert-Houdin, Dr. Lynn, Professor Pepper, Bautier de Kolta, Heller, Herrmann, Maskelyne and Cooke, and Kellar will be found clearly explained.

Conjuring tricks have been by no means neglected, but the number of them which are given has been limited, owing to the fact that many of the books on magic have gone into this subject quite extensively. Ventriloquism, shadowgraphy, mental magic, etc., will also be found treated in the present work.

The chapters relating to "Ancient Magic" take up the temple tricks of the ancient Egyptian, Greek, and Roman thaumaturgists, as well as a number of automata which are very interesting in view of their very early epoch. It is believed this will be found a particularly entertaining feature of the book.

There is always a great charm about the stage, and the methods of producing the effects which give realism to the drama. The chapters devoted to "Theatrical Science" will be found to contain a very large number of effects and illusions, many of which are here presented for the first time. Thus an entire opera, "Siegfried," is taken up, and the methods by which the wonderful effects are obtained are fully illustrated and described. Such amusements as cycloramas, the nautical arena, and fireworks with dramatic accessories are not neglected.

The chapters on "Automata" and "Curious Toys" describe many interesting tricks and mechanisms of an amusing nature.

The last few chapters of the book deal with "Photographic Diversions," and here will be found some of the most curious and interesting tricks and deceptions which may be performed by the aid of photography. The practical side of scientific photography will also be found represented. The chapter on "Chronophotography" describes the photography of moving objects of all kinds, and shows how the results obtained are of value to the savant. The projection of moving pictures upon a screen is thoroughly treated, a number of different forms of the apparatus being described.

The introduction is a unique feature of the work, being written by Mr. Henry Ridgely Evans, of Washington, D. C., author of "Hours with the Ghosts ; or, Nineteenth Century Witchcraft." It contains a brief but remarkably complete history of magic art from the earliest times to the present date, especial attention being given to amusing incidents in the careers of celebrated necromancers. This Introduction will be found one of the most entertaining parts of the present book. Mr. Evans has also contributed two chapters—one on "Shadowgraphy," or "Treweyism," as it has been called, in honor of M. Félician Trewey, the classic exponent of the art ; the other on "Mental Magic," or second-sight experiments. The chapter on "Shadowgraphy" is not only interesting because of the *exposé* of the art of theatrical silhouette-making, but on account of the sketch of the life and adventures of M. Trewey, who is a personal friend of the writer. Mr. Evans is also the compiler of the excellent Bibliography which concludes the book. Though this Bibliography makes no pretense to absolute completeness, it is believed to be more extensive than any other bibliography of the subject, and it will be found of great value to the student of psychology, as well as to the student of modern magic. Other acknowledgments are due to Mr. William E. Robinson, the well-known prestidigitateur, for many suggestions and favors and for important help in connection with the Bibliography; Mr. Robinson having a very remarkable collection of books upon magic, which he has gathered at home and abroad during a long period. We are also indebted to Mr. H. J. Burlingame, of Chicago, for permission to use extracts from his writings and for assistance in the Bibliography.

The matter for the present work is very largely compiled from articles which have appeared in the "Scientific American" and the "Scientific American Supplement," with the addition of much material hitherto unpublished. Especial acknowledgments are due to our French and German contemporaries, particularly "*La Nature.*" The section on "Ancient Magic" is taken almost wholly from the articles of Colonel A. de Rochas in "*La Nature.*" These articles were afterwards amplified by him and published in a most interesting book entitled "*Les Origines de la Science.*" It is hoped that the present work will prove entertaining to those who are fond of the *art magique.*

New York, *September,* 1897.

TABLE OF CONTENTS.

INTRODUCTION.

THE MYSTERIES OF MODERN MAGIC.

BOOK I.

CONJURERS' TRICKS AND STAGE ILLUSIONS.

CHAPTER I.

MYSTERIOUS DISAPPEARANCES.

CHAPTER II.

OPTICAL TRICKS.

CHAPTER III.

MISCELLANEOUS STAGE TRICKS.

CHAPTER IV.

CONJURING TRICKS.

CHAPTER V.

JUGGLERS AND ACROBATIC PERFORMANCES.

CHAPTER VI.

FIRE EATERS AND SWORD TRICKS.

CHAPTER VII.

CHAPTER VIII.

SHADOWGRAPHY.

CHAPTER IX.

MENTAL MAGIC.

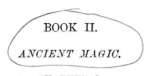

BOOK II.

ANCIENT MAGIC.

CHAPTER I.

TEMPLE TRICKS OF THE GREEKS.

CHAPTER II.

MIRACULOUS VESSELS OF THE GREEKS.

CHAPTER III.

THE ORIGIN OF THE STEAM ENGINE.

CHAPTER IV.

GREEK LAMPS, TOYS, ETC.

BOOK III.

SCIENCE IN THE THEATER.

CHAPTER I.

MAGIC:

STAGE ILLUSIONS AND SCIENTIFIC DIVERSIONS,

INCLUDING TRICK PHOTOGRAPHY.

INTRODUCTION.

THE MYSTERIES OF MODERN MAGIC.

By Henry Ridgely Evans.

I.

Far back into the shadowy past, before the building of the pyramids, magic was a reputed art in Egypt, for Egypt was the "cradle of magic." The magicians of Egypt, according to the Bible chronicle, contended against Aaron, at the court of Pharaoh. The Hebrew prophet "cast down his rod before Pharaoh and before his servants, and it became a serpent. Then Pharaoh also called the wise men and the sorcerers: now the magicians of Egypt, they also did in like manner with their enchantments. For they cast down every man his rod and they became serpents: but Aaron's rod swallowed up their rods." [Exodus vii. 10, 11, 12.]

The late Robert Heller, prestidigitateur, traveler in the Orient, and skeptic, once told me that he had seen this feat performed in Cairo many times by the Dervishes. The rods actually were serpents and hypnotized to such an extent as to become perfectly stiff and rigid. When thrown upon the earth and recalled to life by sundry mystic passes and strokes, they crawled away alive and hideous as ever. Said Heller: "It was in the open air that I saw this strange feat performed. Transferred to the gloomy audience chamber of some old palace, where the high roof is supported by ponderous stone columns painted with hieroglyphics, where rows of black marble sphinxes stare at you with unfathomable eyes, where the *mise en scène* is awe-inspiring —this trick of the rods turning into serpents becomes doubly impressive, and indeed to the uninitiated a miracle."

In the British Museum is an Egyptian papyrus, which contains an account of a magical séance given by a certain Tchatcha-em-ankh before King Khufu, B.C. 3766. In this manuscript it is stated of the magician: "He knoweth how to bind on a head which hath been cut off, he knoweth how to make a lion follow him as if led by a rope, and he knoweth the number of the stars of the house (constellation) of Thoth." The decapitation trick is thus no new thing, while the experiment performed with the lion, undoubtedly a hypnotic feat, shows hypnotism to be old.

The art of natural magic, then, dates back to the remotest periods of antiquity. It was an art cultivated by the Egyptian, Chaldean, Jewish, Roman, and Grecian priesthoods, being used by them to dupe the ignorant masses. Weeping and bleeding statues, temple doors that flew open with thunderous sound and apparently by supernatural means, and perpetual lamps that flamed forever in the tombs of holy men, were some of the thaumaturgic feats of the Pagan priests. Heron, a Greek mechanician and mathematician, who lived in the second century before Christ, wrote several interesting treatises on automata and magical appliances, used in the ancient temples. Colonel A. De Rochas, in an interesting work, *Les Origines de la Science,* has given in detail Heron's accounts of these wonderful automata and experiments in natural magic. St. Hippolytus, one of the Fathers of the early Christian Church, also described and exposed in his works many of these wonders.

Magic is divided, according to old writers on the occult, into: *White magic, Black magic,* and *Necromancy.* Modern magic, or conjuring, is divided by Robert-Houdin into five classes, as follows:

1. FEATS OF DEXTERITY. The hands and tongue being the only means used for the production of these illusions.
2. EXPERIMENTS IN NATURAL MAGIC. Expedients derived from the sciences, and which are worked in combination with feats of dexterity, the combined result constituting " conjuring tricks."
3. MENTAL CONJURING. A control acquired over the will of the spectator; secret thought read by an ingenious system of diagnosis, and sometimes compelled to take a particular direction by certain subtle artifices.
4. PRETENDED MESMERISM. Imitation of mesmeric phenomena, second-sight, clairvoyance, divination, trance, catalepsy.
5. MEDIUMSHIP. Spiritualism or pretended evocation of spirits, table-turning, rapping and writing, mysterious cabinets, etc.

In the Middle Ages magic was greatly in vogue and we read strange stories of ghosts, goblins, and gnomes in the literature of that period. Shriveled old women were burned at the stake for the crime of witchcraft, monks in their gloomy cells wrestled with Satan and the powers of darkness, and grimy alchemists toiled day and night over the red fires of their furnaces, seeking in vain for the talismanic philosopher's stone and wondrous elixir of life. With the aid of the concave mirror, magicians of the period were able to produce very fair ghost illusions to gull a susceptible public. Benvenuto Cellini chronicles one in his fascinating autobiography.

Cellini, as guileless as a child in matters of science, desiring to study sorcery, applied to a Sicilian priest who was a professed dabbler in the occult art. One dark night they repaired to the ruins of the Coliseum, at Rome; the monk described a circle on the ground and placed himself and the great goldsmith within its mystic outlines; a fire was built, intoxicating perfumes cast on it, and soon an impenetrable smoke arose. The man of the cowl then waved his wand in the air, pronounced sundry cabalistic words, and legions of demons were seen dancing in the air, to the great terror of Cellini. The story of this spirit séance reads like an Arabian tale, but it is easily explainable. The priest had a brother confederate concealed among the ruins, who manipulated a concave mirror, by means of which painted images were thrown on the smoke. Later on Nostradamus conjured up the vision of the future King of France for the benefit of the lovely Marie de Médicis. This illusion was accomplished by the aid of mirrors adroitly secreted amid hanging draperies.

II.

The history of magic would be incomplete without a sketch of Cagliostro, the arch-necromancer of the eighteenth century, who filled all Europe with his fame. Novels and plays have been founded on his strange career, as witness Goethe's " Grand Cophta " and Alexander Dumas' " Memoirs of a Physician." Thomas Carlyle has remorselessly dissected the character of Cagliostro in an immortal essay, " Count Cagliostro," which makes fascinating reading. Cagliostro like Nostradamus, and others of that ilk, as the Scotch say, was a pretender to magic and sorcery. He manufactured elixirs of life, raised the shades of the illustrious dead, pretty much after the fashion of our modern spirit mediums; told fortunes, predicted lucky numbers in the lottery, transmuted metals, and founded occult lodges of Egyptian Masonry for the regeneration of mankind. Joseph Balsamo—for such was the Count's real name—was born of poor parents at Palermo, Sicily, in the year 1743. He received the rudiments of an education, and a smattering of chemistry, at a neighboring monastery, and then started out to fleece mankind. He began by forging theater tickets, after that a will; then he robbed a goldsmith named Marano of a sum of money. Balsamo pretended that a secret treasure lay buried in a certain rocky chasm just outside the city of Palermo, and that he, for a consideration, was able to unearth the gold by means of certain magical incantations. Poor Marano like a susceptible gudgeon swallowed the bait, hook and all, paid the contingent fee, and accompanied by the amateur sorcerer (it was Balsamo's first attempt in the necromantic line) paid a visit on a certain dark night to the lonely spot where the treasure lay hid from mortal gaze. Joseph drew a magic circle of phosphorus on the earth, pronounced some spells in a peculiar gibberish known only to himself, which he denominated Arabic, and bade the goldsmith dig away for dear life. Marano went vigorously to work with pick and spade. Suddenly terrific yells were heard, whereupon a legion of devils (Joseph's boon companions with cork-blackened visages) rushed from behind the rocks, pounced upon the goldsmith, and nearly beat him to death with their pitchforks. The enchanter, in order to escape the vengeance of the furious Marano, was compelled to flee his native city. In company with a Greek, Althotas, he visited various places—Greece, Egypt, Arabia, Persia, Rhodes, Malta, Naples, Venice and Rome. According to his own account, he studied alchemy at Malta in the laboratory of Pinto, Grand Master of the Knights of Malta and St. John. At Rome he married a beautiful girl, Lorenza Feliciani, daughter of a girdle maker, who proved of great assistance to him in his impostures. They travelled over Europe in a coach-and-four with a retinue of servants garbed in gorgeous liveries. Balsamo changed his name to the high-sounding title of the Comte de Cagliostro, and scattered money right and left. "At Strasbourg," says one of his biographers, "he reaped an abundant harvest by professing the art of making old people young; in which pretension he was seconded by his wife, Lorenza Feliciani, who, though only twenty years of age, declared that she was sixty and that she had a son a veteran in the Dutch service." Cagliostro also pretended to be of a great age, and solemnly declared that he had hobnobbed with Alexander and Julius Cæsar; that he was present at the burning of Rome under Nero and was an eye-witness of the crucifixion of Christ. Cardinal de Rohan, of France, who became a firm believer in the pretensions of the charlatan, entertained him in Paris, introducing him to that gay world of the Old Régime which went out forever with the French Revolution. This was in 1785. All Paris went wild over the enchanter, and thronged to his magical soirées at his residence in the Rue St. Claude. Cagliostro coined money in the French capital with his spurious Egyptian Rite of Freemasonry, which promised to its votaries the length of life of the Noachites, and superhuman power over nature and her laws. Imbert Saint-Amand, the interesting author of "Marie Antoinette and the End of the Old Régime," says (Scribner Edition): "The mania for the supernatural, the rage for the marvelous, prevailed in the last years of the eighteenth century, which had wantonly derided every sacred thing. Never were the Rosicrucians, the adepts, sorcerers, and prophets so numerous and so respected. Serious and educated men, magistrates, courtiers, declared themselves eye-witnesses of alleged miracles. . . . When Cagliostro came to France, he found the ground prepared for his magical operations. A society eager for distractions and emotions, indulged to every form of extravagance, necessarily welcomed such a man and hailed him as its guide. Whence did he come? What was his country, his age, his origin? Where did he get those extraordinary diamonds which adorned his dress, the gold which he squandered so freely? It was all a mystery. . . . So far as was known, Cagliostro had no resources, no letter of credit, and yet he lived in luxury. He treated and cured the poor without pay, and not satisfied with restoring them to health, he made them large presents of money. His generosity to the poor, his scorn for the great, aroused universal enthusiasm. The Germans, who lived on legends, imagined that he was the Wandering Jew. . . . Speaking a strange gibberish, which was neither French nor Italian, with which he mingled a jargon which he did not translate, but called Arabic, he used to recite with solemn emphasis the most absurd fables. When he repeated his conversation with the angel of light and the angel of darkness, when he spoke of the great secret of Memphis, of the Hierophant, of the giants, the enormous animals, of a city in the interior of Africa ten times as large as Paris, where his correspondents lived, he found a number of people ready to listen and believe him."

The interior of Africa was an excellent place in which to locate all these marvels. Since no traveler in that age of skepticism and credulity had ever penetrated into the mysterious land of Ham, it was impossible to deny the Munchausen-like stories of the magician. All this bears a close analogy to the late Madame Blavatsky and her Tibetan Mahatmas. Cagliostro, like all successful and observant wizards, was keenly alive to the effects of *mise en scène* in his necromantic exhibitions; he was a strong believer in the spectacular. To awe his dupes with weird and impressive ceremonies, powerfully to stimulate their imaginations—ah, that was the great desideratum! His séance-room was hung with somber draperies, and illuminated with wax lights in massive silver candlesticks which were arranged about the apartment in mystic triangles and pentagons.

Says Saint-Amand: " As a sorcerer he had a cabalistic apparatus. On a table with a black cloth, on which were embroidered in red the mysterious signs of the highest degree of the Rosicrucians, there stood the emblems: little Egyptian figures, old vials filled with lustral waters, and a crucifix, very like, though not the same as the Christian's cross; and there too Cagliostro placed a glass globe full of clarified water. Before the globe he used to place a kneeling seer; that is to say, a young woman who, by supernatural powers, should behold the scenes which were believed to take place in water within the magic globe.

" Count Beugnot, who gives all the details in his Memoirs, adds that for the proper performance of the miracle the seer had to be of angelic purity, to have been born under a certain constellation, to have delicate nerves, great sensitiveness, and, in addition, blue eyes. When she knelt down, the geniuses were bidden to enter the globe. The water became active and turbid. The seer was convulsed, she ground her teeth, and exhibited every sign of nervous excitement. At last she saw and began to speak. What was taking place that very moment at hundreds of miles from Paris, in Vienna or Saint Petersburg, in America or Pekin, as well as things which were going to occur only some weeks, months, or years later, she declared that she saw distinctly in the globe. The operation had succeeded; the adepts were transported with delight."

Cagliostro became involved in the affair of the Diamond Necklace, and was thrown into the Bastille. Though eventually liberated, he was compelled to leave Paris. He made one remarkable prediction: That the Bastille would one day be razed to the ground. How well that prophecy was realized, history relates. In the year 1789 the enchanter was in Rome, at the inn of the Golden Sun. He endeavored to found one of his Egyptian Lodges in the Eternal City, but the Holy Inquisition pounced down upon him, adjudged him guilty of the crime of Freemasonry—a particularly heinous offense in Papal Territory—and condemned him to death. The sentence, however, was commuted by the Pope to perpetual imprisonment in the gloomy fortress of San Leon, Urbino. The manner of his death, nay the day of his death, is uncertain, but it is supposed to have taken place one August morning in the year 1790. The beautiful Lorenza Feliciani, called by her admirers the " Flower of Vesuvius," ended her days in a convent, sincerely repentant, it is said, of her life of impostures.

III.

With Cagliostro, so-called genuine magic died. Of the great pretenders to occultism he was the last to win any great fame, although there has been a feeble attempt to revive thaumaturgy in this nineteenth century by Madame Blavatsky. Science has laughed away sorcery, witchcraft, and necromancy. Prior to Cagliostro's time a set of men arose calling themselves *faiseurs,* who practiced the art of sleight-of-hand, allied to natural magic. They gave very amusing and interesting exhibitions. Very few of these conjurers laid claim to occult powers, but ascribed their *jeux,* or tricks, to manual dexterity, mechanical and scientific effects. These magicians soon became popular.

Towards the middle of the eighteenth century we hear of Jonas, Androletti, Carlotti, Pinetti, Katerfelto, Philadelphus Philadelphia, Rollin, Comus I. and II. Pinetti, when he arrived in London in 1784, displayed the following advertisement: " The Chevalier Pinetti with his Consort will exhibit most wonderful, stupendous, and absolutely inimitable, mechanical, physical, and philosophical pieces, which his recent deep scrutiny in those sciences, and assiduous exertions, have enabled him to invent and construct; among which Chevalier Pinetti will have the special honor and satisfaction of exhibiting various experiments of new discovery, no less curious than seemingly incredible, particularly that of Madame Pinetti being seated in one of the front boxes, with a handkerchief over her eyes, and guessing at everything imagined and proposed to her by any person in the company." Here we have the first mention of the second-sight trick, which in the hands of latter-day artists has become so popular. Houdin rediscovered it, passed it on to Robert Heller who improved it, and at the present time the conjurer Kellar makes it his *pièce de résistance.* Rollin had a romantic career. He accumulated a fortune at conjuring, and purchased the chateau of Fontenay-aux-Roses, in the department of the Seine. Says H. J. Burlingame, an interesting writer on magic:

" Rollin incurred the suspicions of the Committee of Public Safety in 1793, and suffered death by the guillotine. On the warrant for his execution being read to him, he turned to those about him, and observed, ' This is the first paper I cannot conjure away.' Rollin was the grandfather of the late political celebrity of that name, who was minister of the interior in the provisional government of France of 1848."

Comus II., who played in London in the year 1793, gave a curious exhibition of conjuring tricks and automata. His programme announced that the Great Comus would present " various uncommon experiments with his ' Enchanted Horologium,' ' Pyxidus Literarum,' and many curious operations in ' Rhabdology,' ' Stenaganagraphy,' and ' Phylacteria,' with many wonderful performances of the grand ' Dodecahedron,' also ' Chartomantic Deceptions ' and ' Kharamatic Operations.' To conclude with the performance of the ' Teretopæst Figure and Magical House ' ; the like never seen in this kingdom before, and will astonish every beholder."

In the height of the French Revolution, when the guillotine reeked with blood and the ghastly knitting-women sat round it counting the heads as they fell into the basket, a Belgian optician, named Etienne Gaspard Robertson, arrived in Paris, and opened a wonderful exhibition in an abandoned chapel belonging to the Capuchin convent. The curiosity-seekers who attended these séances were conducted by ushers down dark flights of stairs to the vaults of the chapel and seated in a gloomy crypt shrouded with black draperies and pictured with the emblems of mortality. An antique lamp, suspended from the ceiling, emitted a flame of spectral blue. When all was ready a rain and wind storm, with thunder accompanying, began. Robertson extinguished the lamp and threw various essences on a brazier of burning coals in the center of the room, whereupon clouds of odoriferous incense filled the apartment. Suddenly, with the solemn sound of a far-off organ, phantoms of the great arose at the incantations of the magician. Shades of Voltaire, Rousseau, Marat, and Lavoisier appeared in rapid succession. Robertson, at the end of the entertainment, generally concluded by saying: " I have shown you, citizens, every species of phantom, and there is but one more truly terrible specter—the fate which is reserved for us all." In a moment a grinning skeleton stood in the center of the hall waving a scythe. All these wonders were perpetrated through the medium of a phantasmagoric lantern, which threw images upon smoke. This was a great improvement on the simple concave mirror which so terrified Cellini. The effect of this entertainment was electrical; all Paris went wild over it. Robertson, lucky fellow, managed to save his neck from " *La Guillotine,*" and returned to his native province with a snug fortune to die of old age in a comfortable feather bed.

Clever as was Robertson's ghost illusion, performed by the aid of the phantasmagoric lantern, it had one great defect: the images were painted on glass and lacked the necessary vitality. It was reserved for the nineteenth century to produce the greatest of spectral exhibitions, that of Prof. Pepper, manager of the London Polytechnic Institution. In the year 1863, he invented a clever device for projecting the images of living persons in the air. The illusion is based on a simple optical effect. In the evening carry a lighted candle to the window and you will see reflected in the pane, not only the image of the candle but that of your hand and face as well. The same illusion may be seen while traveling in a lighted railway carriage at night; you gaze through the clear sheet of glass of the coach window and behold your " double " traveling along with you. The apparatus for producing the Pepper ghost has been used in dramatizations of Bulwer's " Strange Story," Dickens' " Haunted Man " and " Christmas Carol," and Dumas' " Corsican Brothers." In France the conjurers Robin and Lassaigne presented the illusion with many novel and startling effects.

One of the most famous of the eighteenth-century magicians was Torrini, a French nobleman, whose real name was the Comte de Grisi. His father, a devoted adherent of Louis XVI., lost his life at the storming of the Tuileries, on that fatal day in August, ever memorable in the annals of French history. Profiting by the disorders in the French capital, the young De Grisi was enabled to pass the barriers and reach the family chateau in Languedoc. He dug up a secret treasure his father had concealed for any emergency, and proceeded to Italy to study medicine. He established himself at Naples, where he soon became a physician of note. Here his noble birth and aristocratic manners gave him the entrée into the best society of the city. Like many enthusiastic amateurs he became interested in legerdemain, and performed for the amusement of his friends. A peculiar incident led him to adopt the profession of a magician. At the Carnival of 1796, the Chevalier Pinetti arrived in Naples to give a series of magical entertainments. Pinetti was the idol of the Italian public. The Comte de Grisi, having unraveled the secrets of most of Pinetti's illusions, performed them for his friends. Pinetti, who was furious at having a rival, set about revenging himself on the audacious amateur. Without much difficulty he succeeded in ingratiating himself with De Grisi, and complimented him on his success as a prestidigitateur. One evening, he persuaded the young Count to take his place at the theater and give a performance for the benefit of the poor of the city. Intoxicated with flattery, to say nothing of numerous glasses of champagne, De Grisi consented. The greater number of Pinetti's tricks were performed by the aid of confederates in the audience, who loaned various objects of which the magician had duplicates. A diabolical trap was laid for De Grisi. One of the accomplices declared that he had loaned the young magician a valuable diamond ring to use in a trick, and had had returned to him a pinchbeck substitute. Here was a dilemma, but De Grisi put the man off with an excuse until after the entertainment. Approaching the box where the king and his family were seated, De Grisi begged the monarch to draw a card from a pack. No sooner, however, had the king glanced at the card he had selected, than he threw it angrily on the stage, with marks of intense dissatisfaction. De Grisi, horror-struck, picked up the card and found written on it a coarse insult. The conjurer rushed off the stage, picked up his sword, and searched in vain for the author of the infamous act of treachery; but Pinetti had fled. De Grisi was so utterly ruined, socially and financially, by this fiasco, that he came near dying of brain fever, the result of overwrought emotions. On his recovery he vowed vengeance on Pinetti, a most unique vengeance. Says De Grisi: " To have challenged him would be doing him too much honor, so I vowed to fight him with his own weapons, and humiliate the shameful traitor in my turn. This was the plan I drew up: I determined to devote myself ardently to sleight-of-hand, to study thoroughly an art of which I as yet knew only the first principles. Then, when quite confident in myself—when I had added many new tricks to Pinetti's repertoire—I would pursue my enemy, enter every town before him, and continually crush him by my superiority."

De Grisi sold everything he possessed, took refuge in the country, and toiled for six months at sleight-of-hand. Then with splendid apparatus and elaborate printing, he took the field against his hated enemy. He succeeded in accomplishing his ends: Pinetti had to retire vanquished. Pinetti died in a state of abject misery at the village of Bastichoff, in Volhynia, Russia. De Grisi determined to proceed to Rome as a finish to his Italian performances. Pinetti had never dared to enter the Eternal City, since he laid claims to genuine necromancy to encompass his tricks. Remembering the fate of the Comte de Cagliostro, he apprehended a trial for sorcery, and a possible *auto da fé*.

De Grisi, however, had no such fears, as his entertainment was professedly a sleight-of-hand performance and did not come under the denomination of witchcraft and necromancy. The Frenchman set his wits to work to concoct a trick worthy to set before a Pope. Happening one day to drop into a jeweler's shop, he espied a magnificent watch lying on the counter undergoing repairs. " Whose chronometer? " inquired the wizard nonchalantly. " His Eminence, the Cardinal de ——'s watch, worth ten thousand francs, and made by the renowned Brègnet of Paris," said the jeweler. " Is there another timepiece similar to this in Rome? " continued De Grisi, examining the watch. " But one," replied the jeweler, " and that owned by an improvident young noble who spends his time in the gambling hells wasting his ancestral estates."

That was enough for the juggler. He commissioned the jeweler to purchase the watch at any cost and engrave the Cardinal's coat-of-arms inside of the case. The expensive recreation cost De Grisi a thousand francs. When the evening of the performance arrived the magician appeared before the Pope and a brilliant assemblage of red-robed Cardinals and executed his astonishing experiments in conjuring. As a culminating feat he borrowed the Cardinal's chronometer, which had been returned by the jeweler. After many promises to handle it carefully, he dropped it on the floor of the audience chamber as if by accident and set his heel upon it. Smash went the priceless timepiece. The Cardinal turned pale with rage, and all were horror-struck at the unfortunate fiasco. But the Frenchman smiled at the consternation of the spectators, picked up the fragments of the watch, had them fully identified in order to preclude any idea of substitution, and then proceeded to pulverize them in a big brass mortar. A detonation took place and red flames leaped up from the mortar in the most approved order of diabolism; all crowded around to watch the result. Watching his opportunity, the wizard surreptitiously slipped the duplicate chronometer into a pocket of the Pope's cassock. The mystification was complete when De Grisi pretended to pass the ingot of melted gold from the mortar into the pocket of His Holiness, resulting in the discovery of the watch, which was produced intact. This seeming marvel made the lifelong reputation of the French artist. The Pontiff presented him the day after the séance with a magnificent diamond-studded snuff-box as a mark of esteem.

Years after this event, De Grisi's son was accidentally shot by a spectator in the gun trick. A real leaden bullet got among the sham bullets and was loaded into the weapon. The wretched father did not long survive this tragic affair. He died in the city of Lyons, France, in the early part of this century. De Grisi was a superb performer with cards, his "blind man's game of piquet" being a trick unparalleled in the annals of conjuring.

After De Grisi came a host of clever magicians, among whom may be mentioned Döbler, whose principal trick was the lighting of one hundred candles by a pistol shot; Philippe, the first European performer to present the "bowls of gold fish" and the "Chinese rings"; Bosco, expert in cup and ball conjuring; and Comte, ventriloquist and expert in flower tricks. Comte was the most distinguished of these artists, being noted for his wit and audacity. He was a past master in the art of flattery. The following good story is told of him: During a performance at the Tuileries given before Louis XVIII, Comte asked the king to draw a card from a pack. The monarch selected the king of hearts, by chance, or by adroit forcing on the part of the magician. The card was torn up, and rammed into a pistol.

"Look, your majesty," said Comte, pointing to a vase of flowers which stood upon a table in the center of the stage. "I shall fire this pistol at the vase and the king of hearts will appear just above the flowers."

The weapon was fired, whereupon a small bust of Louis XVIII appeared instantaneously out of the center of the bouquet.

"Ah," exclaimed the king to the conjurer, in a slightly sarcastic tone of voice, "I think, Monsieur Magician, that you have made a slight mistake. You promised to make the king of hearts appear, but——"

"Pardon me, your majesty," interrupted the conjurer, "but I have fulfilled my promise to the letter. Behold, there is your likeness!—and are you not the acknowledged king of all our hearts, the well-beloved of the French people?"

The king bowed his royal head benignly, while the assembled courtiers made the salon ring with their applause. The journals next morning reported this little scene, and Comte became the lion of the hour.

Comte was in the zenith of his fame when a new performer entered the arena of magic—Robert-Houdin. One day the following modest handbill appeared on the Parisian bulletin-boards:

Aujourd'hui Jeudi, 3 *Juillet* 1845.

PREMIÈRE REPRÉSENTATION

DES

SOIRÉES FANTASTIQUES

DE

ROBERT-HOUDIN.

AUTOMATES, PRESTIDIGITATION, MAGIE

IV.

In the year 1843 there was situated in the Rue du Temple, Paris, a little shop, over the door of which was displayed the unpretentious sign, " M. Robert-Houdin, Pendules de Précision." It was the shop of a watchmaker and constructor of mechanical toys. The proprietor was destined to be the greatest and most original fantaisiste of his time, perhaps of all times, the founder of a new and unique school of conjuring, and the inventor of some marvelous illusions. No one who stopped at the unpretentious place could have prophesied that the keen-eyed little Frenchman, in his long blouse besmeared with oil and iron filings, would become the premier prestidigitateur of France, the inventor of the electrical bell, improver of the electrical clock, author, and ambassador to the Arabs of Algeria. During his spare moments Houdin constructed the ingenious automata that subsequently figured in his famous *Soirées Fantastiques.* When he went abroad on business or for pleasure he wore the large *paletot* of the period and practiced juggling with cards and coins in the capacious pockets.

About the time of which I write he invented his " mysterious clock "—a piece of apparatus that kept admirable time, though apparently without works —and he sold one of them to a wealthy nobleman, the Count de l'Escalopier. The Count, who was an ardent lover of the *art amusante,* or science wedded to recreation, made frequent visits to the shop in the Rue du Temple, and sat for hours on a stool in the dingy workroom watching Houdin at work. A strong friendship grew up between the watchmaker and the scion of the Old Régime. It was not long before Houdin confided the secret of his hopes to the Count—his burning desire to become a great magician.

The nobleman approved the idea, and in order to give the conjurer opportunities for practice, so that he might acquire the confidence which he lacked, constantly invited him to pass the evening at the De l'Escalopier mansion, for the purpose of trying his skill in sleight-of-hand before a congenial and art-loving company. On one occasion, after a dinner given in honor of Monseigneur Affré, Archbishop of Paris, who was killed at the barricades during the Revolution of 1848, Houdin performed his clever trick of the " burnt writing restored." In the language of Houdin, the effect was as follows: " After having requested the spectators carefully to examine a large envelope sealed on all sides, I handed it to the Archbishop's Grand Vicar, begging him to keep it in his own possession. Next, handing to the prelate himself a small slip of paper, I requested him to write thereon, secretly, a sentence, or whatever he might choose to think of; the paper was then folded in four, and (apparently) burnt. But scarcely was it consumed and the ashes scattered to the winds, than, handing the envelope to the Archbishop, I requested him to open it. The first envelope being removed a second was found, sealed in like manner; then another, until a dozen envelopes, one inside another, had been opened, the last containing the scrap of paper restored intact. It was passed from hand to hand, and each read as follows:

" ' Though I do not claim to be a prophet I venture to predict, sir, that you will achieve brilliant success in your future career.' "

Houdin preserved this slip of paper as a religious relic for many years, but lost it during his travels in Algeria.

The Count de l'Escalopier, after the incident at the memorable dinner, urged Houdin to start out immediately as a conjurer. One day the watchmaker, after considerable hesitation, confessed his inability to do so on account of poverty.

" Ah," replied the nobleman, " if that's all, it is easily remedied. I have at home ten thousand francs or so which I really don't know what to do with. Accept them, my dear Houdin, and begin your career."

But Houdin, loath to incur the responsibility of risking a friend's money in a theatrical speculation, without some guarantee of its being repaid, refused the generous offer. Again and again De l'Escalopier urged him to take it, but without success; finally the nobleman, annoyed at the mechanician's obstinacy, left the shop in a state of pique. But after a few days he returned, saying, as he entered: " Since you are determined not to accept a favor from me, I have come to ask one of you. Listen! For the last year an escritoire in my sleeping-apartment has been robbed from time to time of large sums of money, notwithstanding the fact that I have adopted all manner of precautions and safe-guards, such as changing the locks, having secret fastenings placed on the doors, etc. I have dismissed my servants, one after another, but, alas! have not discovered the culprit. This very morning I have been robbed of a couple of thousand-franc notes. There is a dark cloud of suspicion and evil hanging over my house that nothing will lift till the thief is caught. Can you help me?"

"I am willing to serve you," said Houdin; "but how?"

"What!" replied De l'Escalopier; "you a mechanician, and ask how? Come, come, my friend; can you not devise some mechanical means for appre-hending a thief?"

Houdin thought a minute, and said quietly: "I'll see what I can do for you." Setting to work feverishly, he invented the apparatus, and aided by his two workmen, who remained with him the whole of the night, he had it ready at eight o'clock the next morning. To the nobleman's house Houdin went. The Count under various pretexts had sent all his servants away, so that no one should be aware of the mechanician's visit.

While Houdin was placing his apparatus in position, the Count frequently expressed his wonderment at the heavy padded glove which the conjurer wore on his right hand.

"All in good time, my dear Count," said Houdin. When everything was arranged, the mechanician began his explanation of the working of the secret detective apparatus. "You see, it is like this," he remarked. "The thief un-locks the desk, but no sooner does he raise the lid, ever so little, than this claw-like piece of mechanism, attached to a light rod, and impelled by a spring, comes sharply down on the back of the hand which holds the key, and at the same time the report of a pistol is heard. The noise is to alarm the household, and——"

"But the glove you wear!" interrupted the nobleman.

"The glove is to protect me from the operation of the steel claw which tattooes the word *Robber* on the back of the criminal's hand."

"How is that accomplished?" said De l'Escalopier.

"Simplest thing in the world," replied Houdin. "The claw consists of a number of very short but sharp points, so fixed as to form the word; and these points are shoved through a pad soaked with nitrate of silver, a portion of which is forced by the blow into the punctures, thereby making the scars in-delible for life. A *fleur de lys* stamped by an executioner with a red-hot iron could not be more effective."

"But, M. Houdin," said the Count, horror-stricken at the idea, "I have no right to anticipate Justice in this way. To brand a fellow-being in such a fashion would forever close the doors of society against him. I could not think of such a thing. Besides, suppose some member of my family through carelessness or forgetfulness were to fall a victim to this dreadful apparatus."

" You are right," answered Houdin. " I will alter the mechanism in such a way that no harm can come to any one, save a mere superficial flesh wound that will easily heal. Give me a few hours."

The Count assented, and the mechanician went home to his work-shop to make the required alterations. At the appointed time, he returned to the nobleman's mansion, and the machine was adjusted to the desk. In place of the branding apparatus, Houdin had arranged a kind of cat's claw to scratch the back of the thief's hand. The desk was closed, and the two men parted company.

The Count did everything possible to excite the cupidity of the robber. He sent repeatedly for his stock-broker, on which occasions sums of money were ostentatiously passed from hand to hand; he even made a pretense of going away from home for a short time, but the bait proved a failure. Each day the nobleman reported, " no result," to Houdin, and was on the point of giving up in despair. Two weeks elapsed. One morning De l'Escalopier rushed into the watchmaker's shop, sank breathlessly on a chair, and ejaculated: " I have caught the robber at last."

" Indeed," replied Houdin; " who is he? "

" But first let me relate what happened," said the Count. " I was seated this morning in my library when the report of a pistol resounded in my sleeping-apartment. ' The thief! ' I exclaimed excitedly. I looked around me for a weapon, but finding nothing at hand, I grasped an ancient battle-ax from a stand of armor near by, and ran to seize the robber. I pushed open the door of the sleeping-room and saw, to my intense surprise, Bernard, my trusted valet and factotum, a man who has been in my employ for upwards of twenty years. ' What are you doing here? ' I asked; ' what was that noise? '

" In the coolest manner he replied: ' I came into the room just as you did, sir, at the explosion of the pistol. I saw a man making his escape down the back stairs, but I was so bewildered that I was unable to apprehend him.'

" I rushed down the back stairs, but, finding the door locked on the inside, knew that no one could have passed that way. A great light broke upon me. ' Great God! ' I cried, ' can Bernard be the thief? ' I returned to the library. My valet was holding his right hand behind him, but I dragged it forward, and saw the imprint of the claw thereon. The wound was bleeding profusely. Finding himself convicted, the wretch fell on his knees and begged my forgiveness.

" ' How long have you been robbing me? ' I asked.

" ' For nearly two years,' he said.

" ' And how much have you taken? ' I inquired.

" ' Fifteen thousand francs, which I invested in Government stock. The scrip is in my desk.'

" I found the securities correct, and in the presence of another witness, made Bernard sign the following confession:

" ' I, the undersigned, hereby admit having stolen from the Count de l'Escalopier the sum of 15,000 francs, taken by me from his desk by the aid of false
keys.

" ' Bernard X——.

" ' Paris, *the — day of* ——, 18—.

" ' Now go,' I exclaimed, ' and never enter this house again. You are safe
from prosecution; go, and repent of your crime.'

" And now," said the Count to Houdin, " I want you to take these 15,000
francs and begin your career as a conjurer; surely you cannot refuse to accept
as a loan the money your ingenuity has rescued from a robber. Take it——"

The nobleman produced the securities, and pressed them into Houdin's
hands. The mechanician, overcome by the Count's generosity, embraced him
in true Gallic style, and this embrace, Houdin says, " was the only security De
l'Escalopier would accept from me."

Without further delay the conjurer had a little theatre constructed in the
Palais Royal, and began his famous performances, called by him: " *Soirées
Fantastiques de Robert-Houdin*," which attained the greatest popularity. He
was thus enabled within a year to pay back the money borrowed from the
Count de l'Escalopier.

Jean Eugène Robert, afterwards known to fame by the cognomen of Robert-
Houdin, was born at Blois, the birthplace of Louis XII, on the sixth of
December, 1805. His father was a watchmaker. At the age of eleven
Robert was sent to a Jesuit college at Orleans, preparatory to the study of
law, and was subsequently apprenticed to a notary at Blois, but finding the
transcribing of musty deeds a tiresome task, he prevailed on his father to let
him follow the trade of a watchmaker. While working in this capacity, he
chanced one day to enter a bookseller's shop to purchase a treatise on mechanics, and was handed by mistake a work on conjuring. The marvels contained in this volume fired his imagination, and this incident decided his
future career, but he did not realize his ambition until later in life, when De
l'Escalopier came to his aid.

In his early study of sleight-of-hand Houdin soon recognized that the
organs performing the principal part are the sight and touch. He says in
his memoirs: " I had often been struck by the ease with which pianists can
read and perform at sight the most difficult pieces. I saw that, by practice, it
would be possible to create a certainty of perception and facility of touch,
rendering it easy for the artist to attend to several things simultaneously,
while his hands were busy employed with some complicated task. This faculty
I wished to acquire and apply to sleight-of-hand; still, as music could not
afford me the necessary element, I had recourse to the juggler's art." Resid-
ing at Blois at the time was a mountebank who, for a consideration, initiated
the young Houdin into the mysteries of juggling, enabling him to juggle four

balls at once and read a book at the same time. "The practice of this feat," continues Houdin, "gave my fingers a remarkable degree of delicacy and certainty, while my eye was at the same time acquiring a promptitude of perception that was quite marvelous."

On Thursday evening, July 3, 1845, Houdin's first Fantastic Evening took place in a small hall of the Palais Royal. The little auditorium would seat only two hundred people, but the prices of admission were somewhat high, front seats being rated at $1 or five francs, and no places were to be had under forty sous. The stage set represented a miniature drawing-room in white and gold in the Louis XV style. In the center was an undraped table, flanked by two small side tables of the lightest possible description; at the side wings or walls were consoles, with about five inches of gilt fringe hanging from them; and across the back of the room ran a broad shelf, upon which were displayed the various articles to be used in the séances. A chandelier and elegant candelabra made the little scene brilliant. The simplicity of everything on the conjurer's stage disarmed suspicion; apparently there was no place for the concealment of anything. Prior to Houdin's day the wizards draped all of their tables to the floor, thereby making them little else than ponderous confederate boxes. Conjuring under such circumstances was child's play, as compared with the difficulties to be encountered with the apparatus of the new school. In addition, Houdin discarded the long, flowing robes of many of his predecessors, as savoring too much of charlatanism, and appeared in evening dress. Since his time, no first-class prestidigitateur has dared to offend good taste, by presenting his illusions in any other costume than that of a gentleman habited *à la mode*, nor has he dared to give a performance with draped tables. In fact, modern professors of the *art magique* have gone to extremes on the question of tables and elaborate apparatus, many of them using simple little guéridons with glass tops, unfringed. Houdin's center table was a marvel of mechanical skill and ingenuity. Concealed in the body were "vertical rods each arranged to rise and fall in a tube, according as it was drawn down by a spiral spring or pulled up by a whip-cord which passed over a pulley at the top of the tube and so down the table leg to the hiding place of the confederate." There were "ten of these pistons, and the ten cords, passing under the floor of the stage, terminated at a keyboard. Various ingenious automata were actuated by this means of transmitting motion." The consoles were nothing more than shallow wooden boxes with openings through the side scenes. The tops of the consoles were perforated with traps. Any object which the wizard desired to work off secretly to his confederate behind the scenes was placed on one of these traps and covered with a paper, metal cover, or a handkerchief. Touching a spring caused the article to fall noiselessly through the trap upon cotton batting, and roll into the hands of the conjurer's *alter ego*, or concealed assistant.

Let us now look at some of the illusions of the classic prestidigitateur of

France. By far his best and greatest invention is the " light and heavy chest," of which he himself wrote: " I do not think, modesty apart, that I ever invented anything so daringly ingenious." The conjurer came forward with a little wooden box, to the top of which was attached a metal handle, and remarked as follows to the audience: " Ladies and gentlemen, I have here a cash box which possesses some peculiar qualities. I place in it, for example, a lot of bank-notes, for safe-keeping, and by mesmeric power I can make the box so heavy that the strongest man cannot lift it. Let us try the experiment." He placed the box on the run-down, which served as a means of communication between the stage and the audience, and requested the services of a volunteer assistant.

When the latter had satisfied the audience that the box was almost as light as a feather, the conjurer executed his pretended mesmeric passes, and bade the gentleman lift it a second time. But try as he might, with all his strength, the volunteer would prove unequal to the task. Reverse passes over the demon box restored it to its pristine lightness. This extraordinary trick is performed as follows: Underneath the cloth cover of the run-down, at a spot marked, was a powerful electro-magnet with conducting wires reaching behind the scenes to a battery. At a signal from the magician a secret operator turned on the electric current, and the box, which had an iron bottom, clung to the electro-magnet with supernatural attraction. It is needless to remark that the bottom of the cash box was painted to represent mahogany, so as to correspond with the top and sides.

The phenomena of electro-magnetism were entirely unknown to the general public in 1845, when this trick of the spirit cash-box was first presented. As may be well imagined, it created a profound sensation. When people became more enlightened on the subject of electricity, Houdin added an additional effect, in order to throw the public off the scent as to the principle on which the experiment was based. After first having exhibited the trick on the " run-down," he hooked the box to one end of a rope which passed over a pulley attached to the ceiling of the hall. Several gentlemen were now invited to hold the disengaged end of the rope. They were able to raise and lower the box with perfect ease, but at a wave of the magician's wand the little chest descended slowly to the floor, lifting off their feet the spectators who were holding the rope, to the astonishment of everyone. The secret lay in the pulley and block. The rope, instead of passing straight over the pulley, in on one side and out on the other, went through the block and through the ceiling, working over a double pulley on the floor above, where a workman at a windlass held his own against the united power of the five or six gentlemen below. It is a simple mechanical principle and will be easily understood by those acquainted with mechanical power.

Houdin's orange tree, that blossomed and bore fruit in sight of the audience, was a clever piece of mechanism. The blossoms, constructed of tissue paper, were pushed up through the hollow branches of the tree by the pistons rising in the table and operating against similar pistons in the orange-tree box. When these pedals were relaxed the blossoms disappeared and the fruit was gradually developed—real fruit, too, which was distributed among the spectators. The oranges were stuck on iron spikes affixed to the branches of the tree and hid from view by hemispherical wire screens painted green and secreted by the leaves. When these screens were swung back by pedal play the fruit was revealed. In performing this illusion Houdin first borrowed a handkerchief from a lady in the audience, and caused it to pass from his hand into an orange left on the tree. When the disappearance was effected, the fruit opened, revealing the handkerchief in its center. Two mechanical butterflies, exquisitely made, then took the delicate piece of cambric or lace and flew upwards with it. The handkerchief of course was exchanged in the beginning of the trick for a dummy belonging to the magician. It was worked into the mechanical orange by an assistant, before the tree was brought forward for exhibition.

Houdin was very fond of producing magically bon-bons, small fans, toys, bouquets, and bric-à-brac from borrowed hats. These articles he distributed with liberal hand among the spectators, exclaiming : " Here are toys for young children and old." There was always a great scramble for these souvenirs. The conjurer found time to edit and publish a small comic newspaper, " Cagliostro," copies of which were handed to every one in the theatre. The contents of this *journal pour rire* were changed from evening to evening, which entailed no small labor on the part of the hard-worked prestidigitateur. It was illustrated with comic cartoons, and was eagerly perused between the acts.

Here is one of Houdin's *bon mots : Le Ministre de l'Intérieur ne recevra pas demain, mais le Ministre des Finances recevra tous les jours   . . .   et jours suivants.*

The crowning event of Houdin's life was his embassy to Algeria to counteract the influence of the Marabout priests over the ignorant Arabs. The Marabouts are Mohammedan miracle workers, and are continually fanning the flames of rebellion and discontent against French domination. The French Government invited Robert-Houdin to go to Algeria and perform before the Arabs in order to show them that a French wizard was greater than a Marabout fakir. It was pitting Greek against Greek! The marvels of optics, chemistry, electricity, and mechanics which Houdin had in his repertoire, coupled with his digital dexterity, were well calculated to evoke astonishment and awe. How well the famous French wizard succeeded in his mission is a matter of history. A full account of his adventures among the Arabs is contained in his memoirs and makes very entertaining reading. After his successful embassy to the land of the white bournous and turban, Houdin returned to France and settled down at St. Gervais near Blois, giving his time to electrical studies and inventions.

He received several gold medals from the French Government for the successful application of electricity to the running of clocks. The conjurer's house was a regular Magic Villa, being full of surprises for the friends who visited the place. There were sliding panels in the walls, trap doors, automatons in every niche, descending floors, and electric wires from attic to cellar. Houdin died at St. Gervais in June, 1871. His son-in-law, M. Hamilton, continued to carry on the Temple of Enchantment at Paris, and at the present time there is a little theater on the Boulevard des Italiens called "Théâtre Robert-Houdin," where strolling conjurers hold forth. It was a great disappointment to Houdin when his two sons refused to take up magic as a profession; one entered the French army, and the other became a watchmaker.

V.

One of the best sleight-of-hand artists that ever lived was Carl Herrmann, who styled himself the "Premier Prestidigitateur of France and First Professor of Magic in the World." He died at Carlsbad, June 8, 1887, at the advanced age of seventy-two. Of him Burlingame says: "Without using much mechanical or optical apparatus, he produced many wonderful effects by a sharp observation of the absence of mind of the human auditor, assisted by a hand as firm as steel and capable of the most deft movement." Carl Herrmann traveled extensively, and many conjurers adopted his name as a *nom de théâtre*. Magicians seem to have a *penchant* for this sort of thing, as witness the case of Signor Blitz. Antonio Blitz, a very clever performer, no sooner arrived in the United States than imitators sprang up like mushrooms in a single night. In his "Fifty Years in the Magic Circle," he gives a list of eleven of these impostors, who not only had the impudence to assume his name, but circulated verbatim copies of his handbills and advertisements—

Signor Blitz.
Signor Blitz, Jr.
Signor Blitz, The Original.
Signor Blitz's Son.
Signor Blitz's Nephew.
Signor Blitz, The Great.
Signor Blitz, The Wonderful.
Signor Blitz, The Unrivaled.
Signor Blitz, The Mysterious.
Signor Blitz, By Purchase.
Signor Blitz, The Great Original.

A clever entertainer was Robert Heller. He was a magician, a mimic, and a musician—a combination of talents rarely seen in one individual. He was, indeed, the Admirable Crichton of fantaisistes. As a pure sleight-of-hand artist, Heller was not the equal of some of his contemporaries, but he made up for all deficiencies in this respect by his histrionic abilities. By the power of his address and wit he invested the most insignificant feats of legerdemain with a peculiar charm. In this regard he was like Robert-Houdin. Robert Heller, or Palmer, was born in London, in the year 1833. Early in life he manifested a unique talent for music, and won a scholarship at the Royal Academy of Music at the age of fourteen. Having witnessed several performances of the conjurer Houdin, in London, he became enamored of magic, and devoted his time to perfecting himself in the art of legerdemain, subsequently traveling around giving entertainments in the English provinces. In the year 1852 he made his bow to a New York audience at the Chinese Assembly Rooms, on which occasion he wore a black wig and spoke with a decided Gallic accent, having come to the conclusion that a French prestidigitateur would be better received in the United States than an English wizard. I have this on the authority of Henry Hatton, the conjurer, who wrote an article on Heller's " second-sight " trick for the " Century Magazine " some years ago. Hatton also says that Heller began his magical soirée with an address in the French language. Not meeting with the desired financial success, Heller abandoned conjuring, and settled in Washington, D. C., as a teacher of the piano and organist of one of the large churches of the city. Eventually he married one of his music pupils, a Miss Kieckhoffer, the daughter of a wealthy German banker, and abandoned music for magic. He went to New York, where he opened Heller's Hall, in a building which then stood opposite Niblo's Garden, on Broadway. His second début as a conjurer was an artistic and financial success. After a splendid run in New York he returned to London, opening what is now Pool's Theater. Subsequently he visited Australia, India, and California, returning to New York in 1875. He died November 28, 1878, at the Continental Hotel, Philadelphia, at the height of his fame. Like most of his *confrères,* Heller was a clever advertiser. His theatrical posters usually bore the following amusing verse:

> " Shakespeare wrote well,
>   Dickens wrote Weller ;
>   Anderson was ——,
>   But the greatest is Heller."

His entertainments consisted of magic, music, and an exhibition of pretended clairvoyance. Those who were not interested in his feats of legerdemain flocked to hear his superb performances on the piano.

Heller, like Houdin, made great use of electricity in his magical séances. Many of his electrical tricks were of his own invention. In his will he directed his executors to destroy all of his apparatus, so that it might not come into the possession of any other conjurer.

The most popular performer in this country was Alexander Herrmann, a European by birth, but an American by adoption. I am indebted to Mr. Wm. Robinson, for years an assistant to Herrmann, for the following account of the great conjurer's career:

"The late Alexander Herrmann was born in Paris, France, February 11, 1843, and died in his private car on December 17, 1896, while *en route* from Rochester, N. Y., to Bradford, Pa. He came of a family of eminent prestidigitateurs, his father, Samuel Herrmann, being the most famous conjurer of his day. Samuel Herrmann was a great favorite with the Sultan of Turkey, who frequently sent for him to give entertainments in the royal palace at Constantinople.

"The next in the family to wield the magic wand was Carl Herrmann, who was the first of the Herrmanns to visit America, and the first to use and introduce the name 'prestidigitateur' in this country. Carl, Alexander's eldest brother, achieved great success in the world of magic. He

ALEXANDER HERRMANN.

died June 8, 1887, at Carlsbad, Germany, possessed of a large fortune. There were sixteen children in the Herrmann family, Carl being the eldest, and Alexander the youngest. After Carl adopted magic as a profession, the father abandoned it, and began the study of medicine. It was the father's fondest hope that Alexander, his favorite son, should be a physician, but fate decreed otherwise. Alexander's whole desire and ambition was to become a magician like his father and his brother. He persuaded his brother to take him as an assistant. One day young Alexander was missing from the parental roof; he had been kidnapped and taken away by Carl, with whom he made his first public appearance, at the age of eight, at a performance in St. Petersburg, Russia. Even at that early age his great dexterity, ingenuity, and presence of mind were simply marvelous. The sudden appearance of the father dispelled the visions of the embryonic magician, and he was compelled to return home. But the youth's attention could not be diverted from his purpose, and again he became his brother's assistant. This time, the father compromised by consenting to Alexander's remaining on the stage, provided his education were not neglected. Carl engaged two competent tutors to travel with the company and instruct the young prodigy. For six years the brothers worked together, visiting Spain, France, Germany, Russia, and the surrounding countries. Again the parents claimed Alexander, and placed him in the University of Vienna. At the age of sixteen, the old desire and fascination took possession of him. He accepted his brother's proposal to make a tour of the world, and ran away from home and studies. Their first appearance in America was at the Academy of Music, New York, Monday, September 16, 1861. Their last joint engagement was in this country in the year 1869. On the opening night, in New York, Monday, September 20, Carl introduced Alexander to the audience as his brother and successor. When this engagement terminated, the brothers separated; Carl made a short tour of this country, but Alexander went to Europe, where he appeared in the principal cities, subsequently visiting the Brazils and South America. After that he made a remarkable run of one thousand performances at the Egyptian Hall, London, England. From England he returned to the United States in the year 1874, and from that period made this country his home, becoming a naturalized citizen in Boston, 1876. His career as a magician was one uninterrupted success. The many lengthy and favorable notices of him in the leading journals of this country, immediately after his death, showed that he was regarded as a public character.

"Herrmann bore a remarkable resemblance to 'His Satanic Majesty,' which he enhanced in all possible ways, in recognition of human nature's belief in the superhuman powers of the arch enemy. Despite this mephistophelian aspect, his face was not forbidding; his manner was ever genial and kind. 'Magicians are born, not made' was a favorite paraphrase of his, and Dame Nature certainly had him in view for one when she brought him to this sphere.

"His success lay in his skill as a manipulator, in his witty remarks and ever-running fire of good-natured small talk. He was a good conjurer, a clever comedian, and a fine actor. His 'misdirection,' to use a technical expression, was beyond expression. If his luminous eyes turned in a certain direction, all eyes were compelled (as by some mysterious power) to follow, giving his marvelously dexterous hands the better chance to perform those tricks that were the admiration and wonder of the world.

" Alexander Herrmann's pet hobby was hypnotism, of which weird science he was master, and to its use he attributed many of his successful feats. His great forte was cards; he was an adept in the ordinary tricks of causing cards to disappear, and reappear from under some stranger's vest or from a pocket. With the greatest ease and grace, he distributed cards about a theater, sending them into the very laps and hands of individuals asking for them. On one occasion he gave a performance before Nicholas, the Czar of all the Russias. The Czar complimented the conjurer upon his skill, and decorated him, at the same time smilingly remarking: ' I will show you a trick.' The Czar tore a pack of cards into halves, and good-humoredly asked: ' What do you think of that? Can you duplicate it? ' His surprise was great to see Herrmann take one of the halves of the pack and tear *it* into halves. Herrmann was as clever with his tongue as with his hands, having mastered French, German, Spanish, Italian, Russian, Dutch, and English. He also had a fair knowledge of Portuguese, Chinese, Arabic, and Swedish.

" He was decorated by almost every sovereign of Europe, and many of them gave him jewels. The King of Belgium and the late King of Spain each presented him with a cross; there was a ring from the King of Portugal, one from the Prince of Wales, and various other gems.

" At private entertainments and clubs Herrmann was especially felicitous as a prestidigitateur. I will enumerate a few of his numberless sleight-of-hand tricks: He would place a wine glass, full to the brim with sparkling wine, to his lips, when suddenly, to his apparent surprise and consternation, the glass of wine would disappear from his hand and be reproduced immediately from some bystander's coat-tail pocket. He would place a ring upon the finger of some person, and immediately the ring would vanish from sight. A silver dollar would change into a twenty-dollar gold piece. A magnum bottle of champagne, holding about two quarts, would disappear, to reappear from under a gentleman's coat. He was a capital ventriloquist, an imitator of birds, and quite clever at juggling and shadowgraphy, but he did not exhibit these talents in public.

" The lines in Herrmann's hands were studies for adepts in chirography. There were three lines of imagination, instead of one, which indicates an imaginative faculty little less than miraculous, and denotes a generous heart, genius for friendship, a determined nature, and an artistic temperament. The accompanying impression of his right hand, taken a few days after he died, represents a *short* hand, owing to the fact that in death the fingers had curled inward somewhat. In life his hands were long, slender, and tapering."

Leon Herrmann, a nephew of the great Herrmann, is now performing in the United States with success. In personal appearance he resembles his uncle. He is very clever at palmistry—the cardinal principle of conjuring.

One of the most original and inventive minds in the domain of conjuring is M. Bautier de Kolta, a Hungarian, who resides in Paris. He is almost a gentleman of leisure, and only appears about three nights in a week. He is the inventor of the flying bird cage, the cocoon. the vanishing lady, and the trick known as the "black art," reproduced by H e r r m a n n and Kellar.

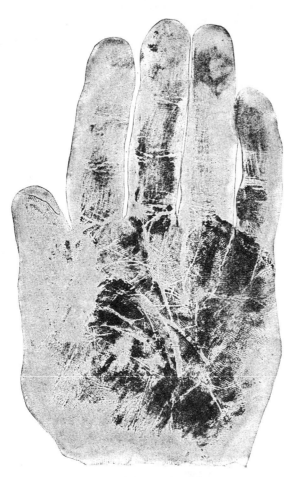

IMPRESSION OF HERRMANN'S HAND.

In England, t h e leading exponent of the magic art is J. N. Maskelyne, who has held forth at Egyptian Hall, London, for many years. He has done more to unmask bogus spirit mediums than any conjurer living. Apprenticed like Houdin to a watchmaker, Maskelyne became acquainted with mechanics at an early age. He is the inventor of some very remarkable a u t o m a t a and illusions, for example "Psycho" and the "Miracle of Lh'asa." At the juggling feat of spinning dessert plates he has but few rivals. To perform t h i s requires the greatest skill and delicacy.

One of the best performers in the United States of anti-spiritualistic tricks and mind-reading experiments is Mr. Harry Kellar, a Pennsylvanian, who at one time in his career acted as assistant to the famous Davenport Brothers, spirit mediums. Kellar is exceedingly clever with handkerchief tricks, and his "rose-tree" feat has never been surpassed for dexterous and graceful manipulation. Like Houdin, De Kolta, and Maskelyne, he is an inventor, always having some new optical or mechanical illusion to grace his entertainments.

Of late years he has made the fatal mistake of exposing the methods of palmistry to the audience, thereby offending one of the cardinal principles of the art of legerdemain—never explain tricks, however simple, to the spectators. People go to magical entertainments to be mystified by the pretended sorcery of the magician, and when they learn by what absurdly simple devices a person may be fooled, they look with indifference at the more ambitious illusions of the performer. Palmistry is the very foundation stone of prestidigitation. No magician, unless he confines himself to mechanical tricks, can do without it in a performance.

Last but not least in the list of modern fantaisistes is the French entertainer, M. Trewey, an exceedingly clever juggler, sleight-of-hand artist, and shadowgraphist.

VI.

In his advertisements, Robert-Houdin was extremely modest. His successors in the *art magique*, however, have not imitated him in this respect. We have Wizards of the North, South, and West, White and Black Mahatmas, Napoleons of Necromancy, Modern Meriins, etc. Anderson, the English conjurer, went to the extreme in self-laudation, but managed to draw crowds by his vainglorious puffery and fill his coffers with gold, though he was but an indifferent performer. The following is one of his effusions:

"Theatre Royal, Adelphi ——. The greatest wonder at present in London is the Wizard of the North. He has prepared a Banquet of Mephistophelian, Dextrological, and Necromantic Cabals, for the Wonder seekers of the approaching holidays. London is again set on fire by the supernatural fame of the eximious Wizard; he is again on his magic throne; he waves his mystic scepter, and thousands of beauty, fashion, and literature, rush as if charmed, or spell-commanded, to behold the mesteriachist of this age of science and wonder! Hundreds are nightly turned from the doors of the mystic palace, that cannot gain admission; this is proof, and more than proof, of the Wizard's powers of charming. During the last six nights, 12,000 spectators have been witnesses of the Wizard's mighty feats of the science of darkness, and all exclaim, 'Can this be man of earth? is he mortal or super-human?'

"Whitsun-Monday, and every evening during the week, The Great Delusionist will perform his Thousand Feats of Photographic and Alladnic Enchantments, concluding every evening with the Gun Delusion! ! "

The Theosophical craze of recent years has had its influence on prestidigitation. A modern conjurer who does not claim some knowledge of the occult, or, at least, who has not traveled in the Orient, cuts but little figure in public estimation. Every now and then some enterprising wizard rushes into print and exploits his weird adventures in Egypt and India, the birthplaces of magic and mystery. Every intelligent reader reads between the lines, but the extravagant stories of Oriental witchery have their effect on certain impressionable minds. The magician Kellar is a reputed Oriental tourist. He has journeyed, according to his own account, in the wilds of India, witnessed fakir-miracles at the courts of Mohammedan Rajahs, hobnobbed with Mahatmas in Tibetan lamaseries, and studied the black, blue, and white art in all its ramifications. In one of his recent advertisements he says: " Success crowns the season of Kellar, the .Great American Magician. His Oriental magic, the result of years of original research in India, enables him to present new illusions that are triumphs of art, and attract enormous houses—dazing, delighting, dumbfounding, and dazzling theater-goers."

BOOK I.

CHAPTER I.

MYSTERIOUS DISAPPEARANCES.

The fascination which the general public finds in clever tricks and illusions is little to be wondered at, but it is a mistake to suppose that all the outfit which the modern magician needs is a few paper roses, a pack of cards, some coins, and a wand. The fact of the matter is, that usually the most entertaining tricks are those which are produced at considerable expense in the way of apparatus and stage fittings. It is for this very reason that the secret of the illusion is always so closely guarded by the prestidigitateur. After a series of sleight-of-hand tricks the magician usually leads up to what might be called "set pieces" in contradistinction to the sleight-of-hand tricks. Chief among the more important illusions are the wonderful cabinets and other articles of furniture which enable the wizard to make away with his assistants. We will describe a number of these arrangements for "mysterious disappearances" before proceeding with the mirror and other optical tricks to which the *fin de siècle* magician is so largely indebted. All of these illusions, as they depend upon pre-arranged machinery, afford an introduction to the tricks which, though much simpler, require a certain amount of aptness in manipulation.

"VANITY FAIR."

The first illusion presents the disappearance of a lady, apparently through a solid looking glass. The method used is remarkably ingenious.

A large pier glass in an ornamental frame is wheeled upon the stage. The glass reaches down within about two feet of the floor, so that every one can see under it. The only peculiarities which a skilled observer would be apt to notice are a wide panel extending across the top of the frame and a bar crossing the glass some four feet from the floor. The first is ostensibly for artistic effect—it really is essential to the illusion. The horizontal piece purports to be used in connection with a pair of brackets to support a glass shelf on which the lady stands—it also is essential to the illusion.

Brackets are attached to the frame, one on each side, at the level of the transverse piece, and a couple of curtains are carried by curtain poles or rods extending outward from the sides of the frame. Across the ends of the brackets a rod or bar is placed and a plate of glass rests as a shelf with one end on

SCREENING THE LADY.

the rod and the other on the horizontal piece, thus impressing upon the audience the utility of the crosspiece. Its real function is not revealed.

A lady steps upon the shelf, using a step-ladder to reach it. She at once turns to the glass and begins inspecting her reflection. The exhibitor turns her with her face to the audience and she again turns back. This gives some byplay, and it also leaves her with her back to the audience, which is desirable for the performance of the deception. A screen is now placed around her. The screen is so narrow that a considerable portion of the mirror shows on each side of it. All is quiet for a moment, and then the screen is taken down and the lady has disappeared. The mystification is completed by the removal of the portable mirror, it being thus made evident that the performer is not hidden behind it.

Two of our cuts illustrate the performance as seen by the audience, the second explains the illusion. The mirror is really in two sections, the appar-

THE DISAPPEARANCE EXPLAINED.

ently innocent crossbar concealing the top of the lower one. The large upper section is placed just back of the lower piece, so that its lower end slides down behind it. This upper section moves up and down in the frame like a window sash, and to make this possible without the audience discerning it the wide panel across the top of the frame is provided. When the glass is pushed up, its upper portion goes back of the panel, so that its upper edge is concealed.

Out of the lower portion of the same mirror a piece is cut, leaving an opening large enough to admit of the passage of the person of the lady. The second cut, with this description, explains everything. The mirror as brought out on the stage has its large upper section in its lowest position. The notched portion lies behind the lower section, so that the notch is completely hidden from the audience. When the glass shelf is put in place, the performer steps upon it and is screened from view. The counterpoised glass is raised like a window

THE LADY HAS VANISHED.

sash, exposing the notch. The screen is just wide enough to conceal the notch, the fact that a margin of the mirror shows on each side of the screen still further masking the deception. From the scene piece back of the mirror an inclined platform is projected to the opening in the mirror. Through the opening the lady creeps and by the assistant is drawn away behind the scene; then the platform is removed, the glass is pushed down again, and, the screen being removed, there is no lady to be seen. The fact that some of the mirror was visible during the entire operation greatly increases the mystery. The lady passes through the notch feet foremost, and her position, facing the mirror, makes this the easier.

"AFTER THE FLOOD."

In this illusion the curtain rises and shows upon the stage what is to be interpreted as a representation of Noah's ark, a rectangular box with ends added to it, which, curving upward, give it a boat-like aspect. It stands upon two horses or trestles. The cut, Fig. 3, shows the ark in its entirety. The exhibitor opens it on all sides, swinging down the ends and the front and back lids, and raising the top as shown in Fig. 1. It will be noticed by the observant spectator that the back lid is first dropped and that the assistant helps throughout, the reason of which will

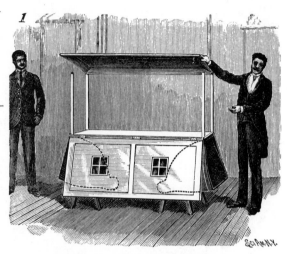

THE ARK OPENED FOR INSPECTION.

be seen later. The skeleton or frame of the structure is now disclosed and it is seen to be completely empty. It is now closed, this time the back lid being

THE FLOOD.

swung into place last, and all is ready for the flood. This is represented by the water poured in *ad libitum* through a funnel inserted in an aperture in the upper corner. To the audience it seems as if the ark were being filled with water. In reality, the water simply runs through a pipe, carried through one of the legs of the trestle, and so down beneath the stage. The management of the flood is illustrated in our cut, Fig. 2.

After the flood the exit of the animals from the ark is next to be attended to. Opening windows in its front, a quantity of animals and birds are taken out as shown in Fig. 3. Ducks, chickens, pigeons, cats, dogs, and a pig are removed and run around on the stage or fly about, and it

TAKING OUT THE BIRDS AND ANIMALS.

is wondered how so small an inclosure could contain such a collection. It is also to be observed that none of the animals are wet—the water has not reached them. More, however, is to follow, for the exhibitor now lets down the front, and a beautiful Eastern woman, Fig. 4, reclines gracefully in the center of the ark, which has only room enough to accommodate her. Where the animals came from, and how they and the woman could be found in the ark, which, when opened before the audience, seemed completely

THE LADY TENANT OF THE ARK.

empty, and how they escaped the water, are the mysteries to be solved.

Our cut, Fig. 5, completes the explanation. The ends which are swung up and down in the preliminary exhibition of the ark are the receptacles which accommodate the animals and birds. They are stowed away in these, are swung up and down with them, and are taken out through apertures in their fronts.

The woman, the other tenant, is fastened originally to the back lid. When the ark is opened for inspection, this lid is swung down, ostensibly to enable the audience to see through the ark—in reality to prevent them from seeing through the illusion. For, as stated, it is swung down before the front is

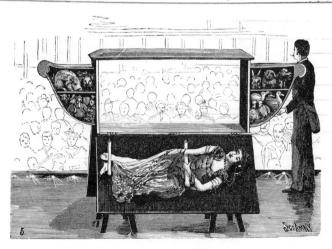

THE MYSTERY EXPLAINED.

3

opened, and as it goes down the woman goes with it, and remains attached to it and out of sight of the audience, who only see the rear side of the door as it is lowered. Fig. 5 shows the rear view of the ark when open, with the woman in place on the rear lid, and also shows the animals in place in the side compartments.

The illusion is exceedingly effective, and is received with high appreciation by the audience. To those who understand it, the performance is of heightened interest.

"THE MAGIC PALANQUIN."

The heroine in this play was presented on the stage in a palanquin carried by four slaves. At a given moment the curtains were drawn and then immediately opened, when it was seen that the actress had disappeared; and yet the

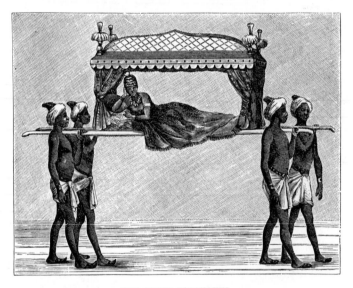

THE MAGIC PALANQUIN.

palanquin was well isolated on the shoulders of the carriers, who resumed their journey and carried it off the stage.

This trick, which preceded by many years Buatier de Kolta's experiment, in which also a woman was made to disappear, but by an entirely different process, as will be explained later on in this chapter, was performed as follows: The four uprights arranged at the four corners of the apparatus were hollow, and each contained at the top a pulley over which a cord passed. These cords were attached by one end to the double bottom of the palanquin, and by the other end to a counterpoise concealed in the canopy.

At the precise moment at which the curtains were drawn, the carriers disengaged the counterpoises, which, sliding within the uprights, rapidly raised the double bottom, with the actress, up to the interior of the canopy. The person thus made to disappear was quite slender and took such a position as to occupy as little space as possible. By making the shadows of the mouldings of the canopy and columns more pronounced through painting, and by exaggerating them, the affair was given an appearance of lightness that perplexed the most distrustful spectator.

"CASSADAGA PROPAGANDA."

One of the most mysterious among Kellar's repertory of successful illusions is the "Cassadaga Propaganda," an explanation of which is herewith presented.

THE CABINET OPEN FOR INSPECTION.

The effect as produced on the spectators will first be outlined. A sheet of plate glass about sixteen by sixty inches in size is placed upon the backs of two chairs, and on it is erected a small beautifully finished cabinet consisting of four pieces, of which the sides are hinged to the back, and which, with the front, are seen resting on a chair at the side of the stage. When erected, the cabinet is forty-two inches high, thirty-six inches wide, and fourteen inches deep.

Tambourines and bells are placed in the cabinet and the doors closed, when the instruments instantly began playing and are then thrown out at the top of the cabinet. The cabinet is now opened and found to be empty. A slate placed in the cabinet has a message written thereon.   In fact, all manifestations usually exhibited in the large cabinets are produced, and yet this cabinet is apparently not large enough to contain a person.   We say apparently not large enough; for, in reality, the whole secret consists in a small person, or an intelligent child of ten or twelve years of age, being suspended by invisible wires behind the back of the cabinet, where there is a small shelf on which the concealed assistant is sitting Turkish fashion.   This folded cabinet is hung on two fine wires which lead up to the " flies " and over rollers or pulleys to the counterweights.   When proper wire is used on a brightly illuminated stage the wires are absolutely invisible.

THE SPIRIT MANIFESTATIONS.

After showing the chairs and placing the glass plate upon them, the performer picks up the folded part of the cabinet and places it on the glass, the counterweights overcoming the extra weight of the concealed assistant.   He then opens out the sides, places the front containing the doors in position, fastening same by hooks to the sides.

The inside of the cabinet and panels of doors are lined with pleated gold silk.   There is a concealed opening in the silk at the back of the cabinet, for the assistant to pass his arm through, in order to handle whatever is placed within it.

Everything being in readiness, the tambourine and bell are placed in the cabinet and the doors are closed.   The assistant now passes his hand and arm

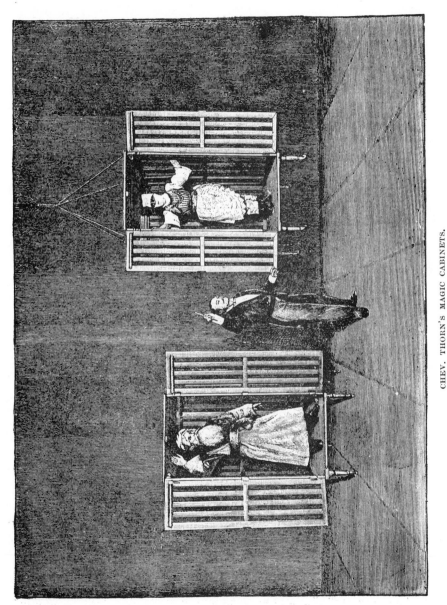

CHEV. THORN'S MAGIC CABINETS.

through the opening in the back and shakes the tambourine, rings the bell, and throws both out over the top of the cabinet. When the doors are opened the cabinet is shown to be empty. Clean slates placed in the cabinet are removed with messages written on them; in fact, the manifestations that can be produced in the cabinet are limited only by the intelligence of the concealed assistant.

One of the cuts shows the cabinet with open doors as seen by the audience. The second cut is an end view looking from the side of stage, showing the assistant on a shelf at the rear of the cabinet, and the wires leading up and over to the counterweights.

The clever illusionist Chev. E. Thorn made great use of a variation of the " Cassadaga Propaganda." He used two cabinets, each large enough to receive a person in an upright position. They were constructed of slats and were provided with curtains. Screens of the same color as the rear of the stage served to close the space between the slats. The magician deceived the audience by walking behind the cabinet or cage as often as possible when the screens were open so that the audience could see him through the slats. The carpet on the stage, the back of the stage, and the screen were all of the same shade of green.

The performers, usually a caliph and an odalisk, appear and disappear at will, really taking up the place on the wooden stage at the back of the cabinet. Usually two cages were used, one being suspended, and by the use of confederates who were dressed alike some very clever illusions were produced.

When the curtain rises the caliph stands on a little platform on the cage at the left, hidden by the cage and the screens. Attention is then called to the cage at the right whose screen is open so that the performer can be seen when he passes behind it.

After the performer has demonstrated this he pulls down red silk curtains over the side walls and the doors; the rear wall, however, remains uncovered. Now a brilliantly dressed odalisk steps into the box at the left. The doors have scarcely closed behind her when they open again, the curtains fly up, and it is seen that the woman has disappeared, and in her place stands a white-bearded caliph, while she appears at the rear door of the parquette smiling behind her veil. She passes down through the audience to the stage again. In the meantime the caliph has left the stage.

What follows is even more surprising. The curtains of both cages are pulled down, the caliph goes into the cage at the left and the odalisk into that at the right. The cage containing the odalisk is raised on a hoisting rope so that it hangs in midair with the doors open. The doors are closed, a shot is fired; at the same instant the doors of both cages spring open and the curtains are raised; the odalisk has disappeared from the cage, which stands again on the floor of the stage, but, at the same instant, she steps, as smiling as ever, from the cage at the left, from which the caliph has vanished. The two cages stand open and the audience can see right through them. The curtain falls and the spectators rub their eyes in bewilderment.

The pulling down of the curtains serves to conceal the entrance of the caliph in the box. When the odalisk is to vanish and the caliph to appear he slips in from the board on the outside, while the odalisk takes her place on the board behind the screen. The odalisk who appears at the door of the auditorium and walks down through the audience is an exact double of the real odalisk who is standing invisible behind the screen on the board of the cage at the left. Owing to the peculiar costume of the odalisk this disguise is rendered very easy. While the real odalisk is standing behind the screen on the board of the cage at the left, the caliph installs himself in the cage. The false odalisk is then raised in the air in the second cage, through which the audience has been able to see up to this time. A shot is now fired and just at that time the odalisk moves very quickly on a board behind the screen and the cage is let down and stands firmly on the floor, at the same moment the odalisk in the other cage changing places with the caliph. The swinging cage appears to be empty and apparently the odalisk has passed through the air to the other cage. The success of the trick depends upon making the spectators believe that everything is done in cages through which they can see.

"THE APPEARING LADY."

Of the many new illusions recently presented in Europe, an ingenious one is that of the appearing lady, the invention of that clever Hungarian magician Buatier de Kolta.

On the stage is seen a plain round top four-leg table, which the magician has been using as a resting place for part of the apparatus used in his magic performance. Eventually, the performer removes all articles from the table and covers it with a cloth that does not reach the floor. Our first engraving represents the table in this condition. On command, the cloth gradually rises

TABLE READY FOR THE APPEARANCE.

from the center of the table as though something were pushing it up. In a few moments it becomes very evident that some one, or something, is on the table covered by the cloth.   The magician now removes the cloth and a lady is seen standing on the table, as shown in our second illustration.

The secret of this, as in all good illusions, is very simple, as the third illustration will show.   In the stage there is a trap door, over which is placed a fancy rug that has a piece removed from it exactly the same size as the trap, to which the piece is fastened.   When the trap is closed the rug appears to be

THE APPEARING LADY.

an ordinary one.   The table is placed directly over the trap.   Below the stage is a box, open at the top, with cloth sides and wood bottom.   To this box are attached four very fine wires, that lead up through the stage by means of small holes where the trap and floor join, over small pulleys in the frame of the table and down through the table legs, which are hollow, through the stage to a windlass.   In the table top is a trap that divides in the center and opens outward.   The top of the table is inlaid in such a manner as to conceal the

Now can use hydraulic lift – no need for wires →table can be moved while on stage before this part

edges of the trap. The lady takes her place in the box in a kneeling position, the assistant stands at the windlass, and all is ready. Fig. 1 of our third engraving shows the arrangement beneath the stage, and Fig. 2 the under side of the table top.

  The magician takes a large table cover, and, standing at the rear of table, proceeds to cover it by throwing cloth over table, so that it reaches the floor in front of the table, then slowly draws it up over the table top. The moment that the cloth touches the floor in front of the table, the trap is opened and the

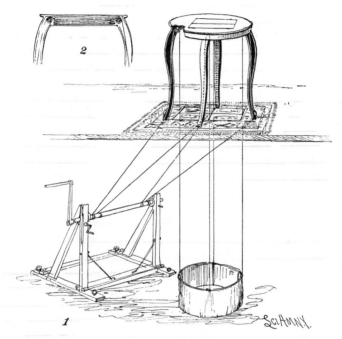

DETAILS OF THE APPARATUS.

box containing the lady is drawn up under the table by means of the windlass, and the trap closed. This is done very quickly, during the moment's time in which the magician is straightening out the cloth to draw it back over the table. All that now remains to be done is for the lady to open the trap in table and slowly take her place on top of the table, and close the trap.

  The top and bottom of the box by means of which the lady is placed under the table are connected by means of three strong elastic cords placed inside of the cloth covering. These elastics are for the purpose of keeping the bottom and top frame of box together, except when distended by the weight of the lady. Thanks to this arrangement of the box, it folds up as the lady leaves it for her position on the table top, and is concealed inside of the frame of table after her weight is removed from it. A somewhat similar trick is called " The Disappearing Lady." In this illusion the process is worked in the reverse order.

" THE DISAPPEARING LADY."

The accompanying figures illustrate a trick in which the prestidigitateur, after placing a chair upon an open newspaper and seating a lady thereon, covers her closely with a silk veil, and after the words " one, two, three," lifts the veil and shows that the lady has disappeared.

The newspaper is provided with a trap, which is concealed by the printed characters (Fig. 1). This trap is of the same size as the one that must exist in the floor upon which one operates. As for the chair, that is generally an

FIG. 1.

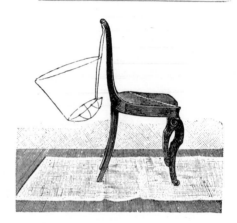

FIG. 2.

old affair, without any cross rod in front (Fig. 2). It is provided with a movable seat that lowers in order to allow the lady to pass between the two front legs. It is provided, besides, with a frame of wire which is invisible on account of the feeble diameter of the latter, and which, attached to the back, is turned backward on the side opposite the spectator. As soon as the lady who is to be made to disappear is seated (Fig. 3), she causes the frame to tilt and cover her head and shoulders. This operation is hidden by the veil that the prestidigitateur spreads out at this moment in front of the lady.

At this instant the operator actuates a spring, which opens the trap in the floor. The lady passes between the legs of the chair (Fig. 4), and then through the two traps, the one in the paper and the one in the floor. As soon as she reaches the floor beneath the stage she closes the trap in the newspaper with gummed paper, and shuts the one in the floor, and it might be thought that she was still on the stage, although she has disappeared. In fact, the veil, on account of the wire frame, seems always to outline the contours of the vanished subject.

After the operator has said " one, two, three," he lifts the veil and causes the wire frame to fall back.

Since this trick was first introduced it has been more or less perfected or modified in its form, but the preceding description states the methods generally employed in performing the trick. In some cases if the newspaper is carefully

FIG. 3.   FIG. 4.

examined, it will be found to be made of India rubber and to contain a large rent at about the center. In the next chapter will be described an interesting illusion called " She," in which the lady disappears while being supposed to be cremated. This ingenious trick depends for a portion of the effect upon mirrors, so it is placed with the other illusions requiring the aid of mirrors.

"THE MYSTERIOUS TRUNK."

A trick known by the name of the Indian Trunk, the Mysterious Trunk, the Packer's Surprise, etc., formerly had much success in theaters of prestidigitation. This trick, which may be presented in several ways, is executed by different means, one of which we shall describe.

The following is in what the experiment consists: The prestidigitateur has a trunk brought to him, which he allows the spectators to examine. When every one is certain that it contains no mechanism, a person comes upon the stage and enters the trunk. It is found that he fills it entirely, and the cover is shut down. A spectator locks the trunk and guards the padlock.

The trunk is afterward wound in all directions with rope, the intersections of the latter are sealed, and the whole is introduced into a bag provided with leather straps, and which may in its turn be sealed at each of its buckles. When the operation is finished, the spectators who have aided in the packing remain on the spot to see that nothing makes its exit from the trunk, which has been placed upon two wooden horses. The prestidigitateur then fires a pistol over the trunk, which, when divested of its covering, ropes, and unbroken seals, is found to be entirely empty.

The whole credit of the trick is due to the cabinet maker who constructed the trunk. The latter, in the first place, is exactly like an ordinary trunk, and the closest examination reveals nothing out of the way about it. Yet one of the ends, instead of being nailed, is secured by a pivot to the two long sides, so that it can swing. The swinging motion is arrested by a spring plate bolt. When the person in the interior presses upon a point corresponding to this bolt, the pivot turns freely and the end of the trunk swings.

The following is the way that the operation is performed in order that the spectators may not perceive the opening of the trunk. The operator's assistant takes his place in the trunk, which is closed and locked and the padlock sealed. Some obliging spectators then aid in tying the trunk, around which the rope is passed twice lengthwise, beginning at the side opposite the opening part. The rope is then passed over this part and runs in the axis of the pivots. Then the trunk, for the convenience of tying, is tilted upon the end where the rope passes. It is then that the assistant inclosed in the interior presses the bolt. The end of the trunk then has a tendency to open, and as the prestidigitateur has taken care to tilt the trunk at a carefully marked point of the stage floor, the movable end meets in the latter with an exactly similar trap that opens at the same time, and it is through these two traps that the invisible vanishing takes place. As soon as the assistant has passed through the trap, he pushes up the latter, and consequently the movable end of the trunk, which closes upon its spring plate bolt.

The time that it takes the man to pass through the trap is insignificant,

THE MYSTERIOUS TRUNK.

and while the ropes are being crossed the operation might be performed several times.✦ Afterward, there is nothing to be done but to proceed with the experiment as we have said, care being taken, however, not to abuse the complaisance of the spectators, and not to allow them to try the weight of the trunk.

When the vanished person descends beneath the stage, he is supported by some other individual if the theater is not well appointed, and by a trap with a counterpoise if the construction of the stage admits of it. This trap permits of expediting things in certain cases of the reappearance of the confederate, but is useless in the process described above.

Such is one of the artifices employed. Whatever be the process, the presentation of it is often complicated by causing the person who has vanished to reappear in a second trunk that has previously been ascertained to be empty and that has been sealed and enveloped under the eyes of the spectators. It will be easily comprehended that the operation here is reversed, and that the confederate beneath the stage awaits the proper moment to be lifted into the interior of the second trunk, whose movable end is opened outwardly by the prestidigitateur at the desired moment.

Boxes with glass sides also have been constructed. The management is the same, but, as the person inclosed is visible up to the last moment, care must be taken to so pass the ropes as not to interfere with the trap of the trunk, which then consists of one of the sides, and which operates at the moment when the trunk, bound with ropes, sealed and laid upon this side, is about to be wrapped up. This presentation has still more effect upon the spectators than the preceding, and seems to present greater difficulties.

✦ *new person may enter trunk or animal*

"THE INDIAN BASKET TRICK."

Among the most remarkable experiments performed by prestidigitateurs should be cited that of the Indian basket, which, as its name indicates, is of Asiatic origin. Travelers in Hindostan have often told us that the Indians practice this wonderful trick upon the public places. The Indian magician makes use of an oblong osier basket provided with a cover. He takes a child and incloses it in this basket, and around the latter buckles a belt. Grasping a sword, he thrusts it into the basket here and there, and pulls out the blade all dripping with blood.

The spectacle is shocking, and the feelings of the spectators become wrought up to a high pitch. The magician then opens the basket, which, to the surprise of all, is empty.

At a few yards distance cries are heard proceeding from the child who had been inclosed in the basket, and who is now running forward sound and happy. Robert-Houdin, who studied this juggler's trick, explained it perfectly, and was able to perform it himself. The basket used by the Indian prestidigitateurs is represented herewith.

Fig. 1 shows the basket open ready to receive the child. For the sake of the explanation we have cut away one end. This basket is provided with a double movable bottom, A C B, the center of motion of which is at C. In order to make the child disappear, the cover being closed, the top of the basket is lowered by turning it toward the spectators (Fig. 2). But the bottom, B, and the part A, that depends upon it, do not take part in this motion. The weight of the child lying upon the bottom forces the latter to remain in place, and by this fact the part A C shuts off the bottom of the basket (Fig. 2).

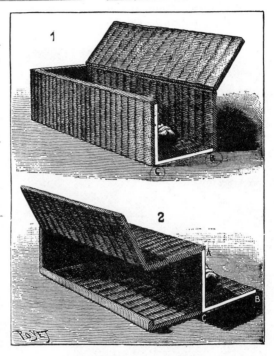

THE INDIAN BASKET TRICK.

In order to turn the basket over, the Indian fastens it with strips of leather, and, to facilitate this operation, places his knee on it. The child can then easily hide himself under the robe worn by the magician. Replacing the basket in its first position, the Indian inserts his sword and sticks the blade into a small sponge fixed within and saturated with a red liquid. While the attention of the spectators is absorbed by this exciting operation, the little Indian escapes from beneath the robe, and runs a short distance from the spectators without being seen. Houdin says that when this trick is well performed, it has a startling effect. In all the preceding tricks the magician has made way bodily with assistants, we now come to a case of mutilation in which the luckless clown must suffer decapitation.

DECAPITATION.

The means employed in this illusion is the old-fashioned "defunct" method of decapitation, and although this lacks the refinement and scientific interest of execution by electricity, it has a certain precision.

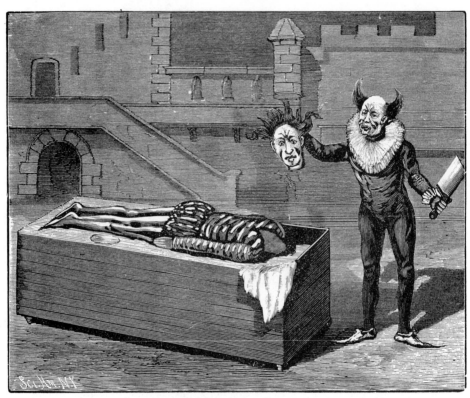

A NOVEL STAGE TRICK—DECAPITATION.

The poor clown who suffers the death penalty twelve times a week usually enters the circus ring, or appears on the stage, as the case may be, and after performing certain acrobatic feats, commits some crime against his fellows, for which he is condemned to die. He is placed upon the block; his head is covered with a cloth. Harlequin approaches as executioner, and begins to cut with a huge knife across the victim's neck. In a moment all is over, the cloth is removed, and Harlequin lifts in the air the severed head. Delighted with his trophy, he carries it about under his arm, places it in a charger in the center of the ring, and finally takes it back to the block wrapped up in the cloth, and places it by the side of the headless trunk. He removes the cloth, and then in sport places a lighted cigarette in its mouth. In a little while you notice that the cigarette begins to glow, smoke comes from the nose, and the eyes roll. Evidently the head has come to life. Not able to bear the horrible sight, he throws the cloth again over the head, seizes it, places it in its original position on the shoulders of the victim, kneads it to the body, and suddenly the figure rises, head and all, and bows to the audience—an orthodox clown.

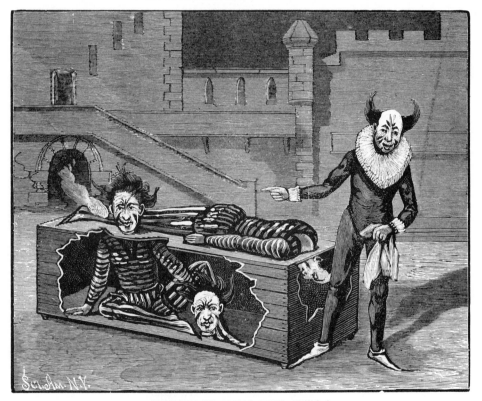

EXPLANATION OF THE DECAPITATION TRICK.

The trick is a good one, and takes with the audience. The way in which it is done is explained in the second cut.

As soon as the clown lies on the box and his head has been covered with the cloth, he passes his head through an invisible opening in the top of the box. An assistant inside of the box passes up the dummy head, which is an exact facsimile of the clown's head and face. This is seized by Harlequin, who makes such sport of it as he sees fit. When he places it by the side of the trunk, in reality he passes it through an opening in the top of the box to the assistant within, who substitutes his own head (which is painted to match the other two) in place of it. The other steps in the performance readily follow.

4

The cloth which the harlequin always carries conceals all the sleight of hand, and the whole performance is a series of surprises.

Another performance of a somewhat similar character was recently performed at a theater in New York, in which a clown throws himself on a sofa and is cut in two by a harlequin. One part of the sofa with the body remains in one part of the stage while the other part with the legs and feet (which are all the time vigorously kicking) disappear through a wing at the other end of the stage. The action is very sudden and the effect startling. Of course, in this case there are two men similarly dressed. The head and body of one of them appears at the head of the sofa, while the body of the second clown is concealed in the box under the seat at the other end of the sofa, the feet and legs alone being exposed.

SPIRITUALISTIC TIES.

The following article is not written with the intention or desire to antagonize any believer in Spiritualism, but merely to explain how anti-spiritualists, as well as several professional " mediums," secured their release after being fastened in their cabinet. During the years the writer (Mr. Caulk) has been before the public as a magician and cabinet performer, he has met a number of cabinet test " mediums," and can safely say that all of these people who have come under his observation have been imposters. This may be due, however, to the bad fortune of the writer.

The writer has been tied with ropes, fastened with handcuffs, brass collars, and chains, many times in many different cities, and by people who were just as alert as any investigator of spiritualistic phenomena, yet, unlike many " mediums " he has met with, was never exposed.

The methods used are many, some simple, others complicated, but all mystifying. To the average auditor the most wonderful point is, how does the performer release himself after being so securely bound? For the benefit of the curious the writer will explain a few of the methods by which he has secured his release after being fastened by a committee from the audience. All anti-spiritualists, as well as several " mediums " personally known to the writer, make use of these same methods of release, or others founded on the same principle.

Among the many successful rope tests, the following is about the best. A piece of soft cotton rope about six feet long, and of the size known as sash cord, is securely tied around the performer's left wrist, dividing the rope so that the ends will be of an equal length. When the committee is satisfied that they have made the knots secure, the performer places his hands behind him, with the right wrist resting over the knots on the left wrist, and the ends of the rope are securely tied together, bringing the knots down tight on the right wrist. This appears fair enough, but it is not as fair as it appears, because, while the knots are secure enough, there is sufficient slack between the wrists to enable the performer, by giving his right wrist a half turn, to withdraw this hand from the rope encircling it.

The reader may say, "That is all well enough, but how and by what means does he secure this slack?"

In placing his hands behind him after the rope is tied about the l e f t wrist, he gives the rope a twist and knot with over the other, pressing the twist down on the knot and covering t h e t w i s t and **knot with** the right wrist, which is

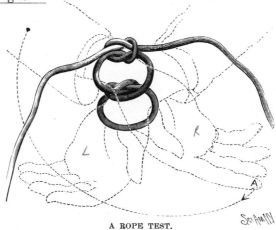

A ROPE TEST.

then tied. When ready to release himself, the performer gives his right hand and wrist a half turn, releasing the twist lying on the knot, which thus becomes a part of the loop tied around the right wrist, and enlarging it sufficiently to enable the performer to pull the right hand free from the rope, when he can perform any trick he chooses with the free hand. Our first and second engravings show the formation of t h e twist, thus making the above explanation clear. By replacing the hand in the loop and giving the hand a half turn the knots can be shown as secure as when first tied.

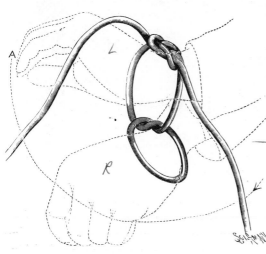

EXPLANATION OF THE ROPE TEST.

The "Spiritualistic Post Test" is among the latest and most successful of mechanical fastenings. A piece of wood f o u r inches square and three feet long is given to the committee, who bore a hole through it near one end, and then pass an ordinary rope through the hole, tying a knot in the rope on each side of the post, pressing the knots against the post so that the rope cannot be drawn through the post.   The ends of the rope are now unraveled, and the post secured to the floor of the cabinet.

The performer, standing behind the post, places his wrists against the knots

THE SPIRITUALISTIC POST TEST.

in the rope, one on each side of the post, and the unravelled ends of the rope are bound around his wrists and tied securely, and all knots are sealed with wax.   A large nail is driven in the top of the post, to which are fastened cords that are passed out through the cabinet and held by members of the committee in order that they may know if the performer moves the post in any manner during the performance of any test, such as the ringing of bells, etc.   Fig. 2

of our third engraving shows the performer tied to the post and the committee holding the cords. The curtains of the cabinet are closed and the usual manifestations take place.

Before the performance a hole is bored in the center of the end of the stick or post, in which is placed a chisel-shaped piece of steel sharpened at the lower end and blunt at the upper end, as shown in Fig. 3 The opening in the end of the post is now carefully closed and all signs of such an opening are concealed by the aid of glue, sawdust, and a little dirt rubbed over it.

When the committee are invited to bore a hole in the post, the performer takes care to start the bit, in order that there will be no mistake about getting the hole directly beneath the chisel concealed in the post. When the rope is passed through the hole and knotted it is directly under the sharp edge of the chisel, with a thin layer of wood between. When the nail is driven in the top of the post it strikes the chisel, forcing it through the thin shell of wood above the rope and through the rope, thus releasing the performer, who can withdraw his hands from the post and do any trick he chooses, and when finished, by merely replacing the ends of the rope in the holes from which he removed them, and holding the hands tight against the post, can allow a most rigid examination of the seals to show that it was not possible for him to have released his hands, and the persons holding the cords that are fastened to the nail testify that they did not feel any movement of the performer or the post.

The Handcuff Test is a great favorite of the " medium." In this test the performer uses any pair of handcuffs furnished by the audience, and by them put on him. Yet, in a very few moments after he takes his place in the cabinet, his coat is thrown out, but on examination the handcuffs are found to be on his wrists just as they were placed by the audience. As a final test, the performer comes out of the cabinet holding the handcuffs in his hand, removed from the wrist but locked.

The explanation of this trick is very simple, but, like many simple tricks, very mysterious. There are only a few styles of handcuffs made in this country, and all that a " medium " has to do is to secure the proper key for each style, which keys

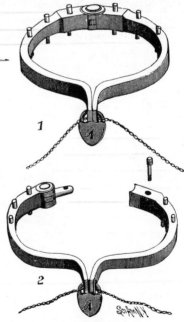

THE SPIRIT COLLAR.

are concealed about the person, and by the aid of fingers and teeth the proper key can be fitted to the handcuffs. In some types of handcuffs it is impossible to get the fingers to the key-hole.   If such a pair is placed on the performer and he cannot use his teeth to hold the key, he slips the key in a crack in the chair or cabinet, which crack he makes sure is there before undertaking the test, thus holding the key and unlocking the handcuffs.

As the space allotted for this article is limited, the writer will explain but one other piece of apparatus used to secure the " medium," which is known as the Spirit Collar.

The collar is made of brass, and fits closely about the performer's neck. Through the openings in the ends of the collar is passed a chain, after the collar is on the performer's neck, and this chain is passed around a post, carried back and through the padlock which is used to lock the collar.   By this arrangement the performer is fastened securely to a post, at least it appears so to the audience.   This collar is shown in our fourth engraving.   As seen by the cut, the collar is decorated with a number of small bolts, which impart to it an additional appearance of strength.

These bolts are all false with one exception.   This genuine bolt can be removed by the performer when the collar is on his neck, thus allowing the collar to come apart at the hinge, as shown in the cut, thus releasing the performer, allowing him full liberty to perform any trick he wishes, and permitting him to again apparently fasten himself securely.   This loose bolt fits so securely that there is no danger of any of the committee removing it with their fingers.   The performer uses a small wrench to remove the bolt.

CHAPTER II.

OPTICAL TRICKS.

The prestidigitateur has always been indebted more or less to the use of reflection from mirrors and plate glass as an important adjunct in conjuring. Many of the illusions in the succeeding pages have often been used as an entertainment in themselves so that it might really be termed " side show science." Without doubt the most famous of all the illusions in which effects of lighting are used is " Pepper's Ghost " which was devised by that eminent experimentor on physical and chemical science, John Henry Pepper. There are a number of variations of the Pepper Ghost of which the " *Cabaret du Neant* " is an excellent example.

THE " CABARET DU NEANT."

The name " *Cabaret du Neant*," or " Tavern of the Dead " (" non-existing "), has been given by the proprietors to a recent Parisian sensation; it was also exhibited in New York. The interest of course centers in the ghost illusion.

The spectators on entering the *Cabaret* pass through a long hall hung with black and find themselves in a spectral restaurant. Along the walls coffins are placed for tables, and on the end of each coffin is a burning candle. From the center of the ceiling hangs what is termed " Robert Macaire's chandelier," made to all appearances of bones and skulls. The spectators are here at liberty to seat themselves at the tables and are served with what they desire by a mournful waiter dressed like a French mourner with a long crape streamer hanging from his silk hat. Around the walls of the room are placed pictures to which the spectator's attention is called by the lecturer. Seen by the light of the room these pictures are ordinary scenes, but a new aspect is given to each when lights directly behind it are turned on; the figures in it appear as skeletons, each picture being in fact a transparency giving a different effect as it is lighted from the rear or as seen simply by reflected light. The second chamber is now entered; it is hung with black throughout. On the walls tears are painted, and in close juxtaposition are two somewhat incongruous inscriptions, " *Requiescat in pace*," and " No smoking." The reason for the latter admonition, which is also given by the lecturer, is that for the success of the illusion an absolutely clear atmosphere is essential.   At the end of this second chamber, at the back of a stage, is seen a coffin standing upright, in which one of the audience is requested to place himself.   Entering the stage by the side door, he is conducted by an attendant to the coffin and placed in it.   Blocks of wood are placed for him to stand on in quantity sufficient to bring his head to the right height so that the top of it just presses against the top of the coffin, and the attendant with great care adjusts his height according to the predetermined

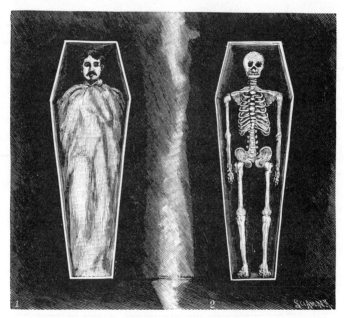

THE SUBJECT AND HIS SKELETON.

position.   Two rows of Argand burners illuminate his figure, which is then wrapped in a white sheet.   Now, as the spectators watch him, he gradually dissolves or fades away and in his place appears a skeleton in the coffin. Again, at the word of command the skeleton in its turn slowly disappears, and the draped figure of the spectator appears again.   The illusion is perfect to the outer audience; the one in the coffin sees absolutely nothing out of the common.   His interest, if he knows what is going on, is centered in watching the changing expression of the spectators, being increased by the fact that at their period of greatest astonishment he is absolutely invisible, although directly before them and seeing them more plainly than ever.   After the restoration to life one or more auditors are put through the same performance, so that the recent occupant of the coffin can see what he has gone through.

The third chamber is now entered, somewhat similar to the second, but on its stage is a table and seat, all the walls being lined with black. One of the auditors is invited to seat himself at the table on the stage. He does it, and, as before, sees nothing. While the description of the lecturer and the appearance and comments of the audience tell him that something very interesting is going on, the remarks will probably disclose to him the fact that this time at least he is never out of their sight. He leaves the stage and his place is taken by another, and then he understands the nature of the drama in which he has been an unconscious participator. He sees the other spectator seated alone at the table. Suddenly a spirit,

THE SHEETED GHOST.

perhaps of an old man, appears at the other side of the table, while a bottle and glass are seen upon the table. When exhorted to help himself to the liquid, the performing spectator's idle gestures show that he certainly does not see the glass, through which his hand passes unobstructed. Or perhaps it is a woman who appears and makes the most alluring gestures toward him who never sees her. This concludes the exhibition, which as accessory has the strains of a funeral march, the ringing of deep-sounding bells as room after room is entered, and the appearance of a brown-robed monk who acts as Charon to introduce the spectator to his place in the coffin. In one of our illustrations we show, side by side, the coffin with its living occupant draped in a sheet and in the other the skeleton which appears in his place. Two other cuts show the scenes between the spectator at the table and the specters, illustrating how active a part the specters take, they being no mere painted appearances, but evidently living, moving things. Our large illustration shows precisely how it is done and so clearly that an explanation is hardly needed. The floor of the stage is represented. To the left are seen the spectators and the performer at the piano discoursing his lugubrious melodies. To the right is seen Charon, and directly in front of him the coffin with its living occupant. When lighted up by the burners shown near him, the other burners being turned down, the coffin with its occupant is all that is seen by the spectator.

AN X-RAY ILLUSION UPON THE STAGE—CONVERSION OF A LIVING MAN INTO A SKELETON.

Directly in front of the coffin, crossing the stage obliquely, is a large sheet of the clearest plate glass, which offers no impediment to the view of the coffin with its occupant, when the latter is fully illuminated. At one side of the stage, in the back of the picture, is a painting of a skeleton in a coffin with its own set of Argand burners. It is screened from view. When strongly illuminated, and when the lights of the real coffin are turned down, the spectators see reflected from the glass a brilliant image of the pictured coffin and skeleton. By turning up one set of burners as the others are turned down a perfect dissolving effect is obtained, skeleton replacing spectator and *vice versa* at the will of the exhibitor.

THE FEMALE SPIRIT.

The magic lantern operator always realizes that to secure a good dissolving effect perfect registration is essential. In the securing of this lies the secret of the coffin exhibit of the *Cabaret du Neant.* By the blocks on which the occupant of the coffin stands, and by the adjustment of his head by the attendant, the head is brought into perfect registration with the reflected head of the skeleton. The wrapping with the sheet, presumably the enveloping in a shroud, is done with a purpose. It covers the body from the shoulders down and extends to the very bottom of the coffin, covering the blocks also, thus doing away with all defects of registration which would be incurred in the persons of spectators of different heights. In other words, the exhibition fits out everybody with a skeleton of precisely the same height, however tall or short he may be, the draping of the sheet and accurate position of the head concealing from the spectators this inaccuracy, the skull occupying precisely the place of the head, the rest taking care of itself.

Still referring to the large cut, it will be seen that it serves to explain the exhibition in the other chamber. Instead of the coffin there is the table and chair, and in place of the pictured skeleton a live performer is placed. In this act there is no dissolving effect; by turning up the lights at the side of the stage any object desired and performers dressed as spirits are made to appear upon the stage, being reflected from the glass plate. The spectators simultaneously see their companion sitting at the table and the reflections of the ghosts apparently executing their movements about him.

From the scientific as well as scenic aspect, the exhibition is most interesting, and to one who knows how it is performed, the interest is vastly enhanced. To properly enjoy it, the stage position should be taken during one or both performances.

THE THREE-HEADED WOMAN.

In this illusion the spectators are separated from the stage by a balustrade —behind which is seen the curtain. In a few moments the latter is drawn back and there is distinctly seen a woman's body the lower part of which is hidden by a basket of flowers. This body has three heads, one in the middle and two others grafted at the base of the neck of the first. The heads move their eyes, answer questions and sing, and finally salute the audience, and the curtains are drawn together and the performance is over. As in many tricks of this kind the showman usually announces that for an additional admission the secret of the illusion will be divulged. The visitor then enters the side scene and perceives that on the little stage where the phenomenal woman just appeared, nothing is visible but a large plate of glass slightly inclined towards the audience and its edges hidden by drapery. Behind the mirror there is a recess whose sides are covered with a jet black fabric. In front of the mirror on the stage sits the basket of flowers from which issued

THE THREE-HEADED LADY.

the woman's body. On an inclined board which rests against the screen or balustrade lie three young girls; one of these, the middle one, is clothed in a brilliant costume of light-colored silk, and it is she who in the exhibition makes trunk, arms, and the middle head. The lower part of her body is covered over with a black fabric and she is supported by a cushion which permits the two other girls to place their necks closely against hers. The bodies of these two girls at the sides are completely covered with fabric of a dead black color. In front of these three young women are placed powerful lights. The heads, hair, and arms of the "body" are covered with powder so as to present completely white surfaces. All the white or light-colored surfaces being strongly lighted by the lamps reflect the light; the image is thus made upon the spectator.

"AMPHITRITE."

This illusion, which is presented under the name of "Amphitrite," is as follows: When the representation is about to begin, the curtain of a small stage

AMPHITRITE.

rises. There is observed a circular aperture, cut in a screen, over which is stretched transparent muslin.

About six feet behind the latter there is a scene representing the sky with clouds; below, in the foreground, there is a canvas representing the sea.

"Amphitrite, come forth!" exclaims the person in charge of the show. All at once, a woman in the costume of an opera nymph rises from the sea without anything being visible to support her in space, in which she turns round and round, gracefully moving her legs and arms, now in one direction, and then in another. When the exhibition is at an end, she straightens out in the position of a swimmer about to make a dive, and plunges behind the curtain representing the ocean.

The illusion that we have just described may be performed as follows: Amphitrite is an image—a specter analogous to those of Robin. If we im-

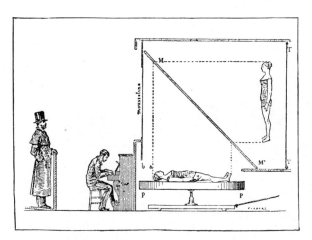

agine that a transparent glass, M M., in our diagram, is inclined 45° with respect to the stage, a person clad in light clothing, lying horizontally upon a black background beneath the stage, and well illuminated, will exhibit an upright image behind the glass.

This image will appear to be formed in front of the back canvas, T T. Now,

DIAGRAM EXPLAINING THE AMPHITRITE ILLUSION.

as Amphitrite is lying upon a table, P P, she will be able to go through her evolutions and bend herself in a circle; and if, during this time, the table, movable upon its axis, A, is revolved, her image will turn in all directions. Finally, to cause Amphitrite to appear or disappear, it will suffice to slide the table upon rails, thus bringing it in front of or behind the glass. Amphitrite should be placed upon an absolutely black background. Her costume should be of a light color with metallic spangles, and she should be illuminated by a powerful electric light.

The muslin stretched in front of the screen is designed to arrest anything that jesters might throw against the glass, and which, sticking thereto might explain a part of the mystery.

"THE MYSTERY OF DR. LYNN."

In this illusion which was presented at the "Folies Bergères," at Paris, the stage is rather larger than in most of the talking heads and other analogous tricks. At a short distance from the spectator is observed a woman cut off at the thighs and resting on a small swinging shelf. The showman moves the shelf laterally, and at a signal the exhibitor removes the shelf, and the half-length body appears suspended in the air. The question which every visitor asks is, where is the rest of the body? In many of the tricks of talking heads, isolated busts, etc., the illusion is obtained by the aid of mirrors, but the mystery of Dr. Lynn is obtained in a much simpler manner. All painters know that in a very strongly lighted picture the bright colors stand out at the expense of the half-tones and dark colors, and this effect is greater as the light becomes brighter. It is upon this principle that the Dr. Lynn trick is based. The lower part of the bust seen is a dummy upon which the upper part of the woman's body lies, the remainder of her body being extended nearly horizontally upon a board which is capable of swinging and following the motion of the shelf. All this portion is hidden by o p a q u e black drapery so arranged as not to reflect the light at any point. The bust and shelf receive a very intense light ; then immediately behind there is seen intense darkness, forming an absolutely dark background. The latter is rendered still darker by the brilliant cords

THE ILLUSION EXPLAINED.

of the shelf, a metallic chain and a dagger suspended beneath it, as well as a white handkerchief which seems to have been dropped upon the stage by accident. At least six powerful gas burners or electric lights with reflectors are turned towards the spectators, so that it will be seen that the latter are in a manner dazzled by everything that strikes the eye in the foreground, and that beyond this they see absolutely nothing but a black background.

Another variation of the illusion of the "Decapitated Princess," which will be described later on, is obtained without the aid of mirrors. A young girl appears before the audience, accompanied by an executioner clad in red, and armed with the traditional axe of his profession. The curtain then drops, and rises in a few moments, the stage being somewhat darkened. Near the executioner can be perfectly distinguished the girl's head lying on a round table at the back of the stage. The body is seen lying on the bed a few feet from her head and at her side is the fatal block that had served for execution. The trick is the same as the preceding one; it requires, however, two persons of the same size, wearing the same costume, to carry out the illusion successfully. One of these, the one who shows herself to the public, makes the head, her body being hidden behind the cloth in the rear of the stage, which is in darkness, as has just been explained. The other, who makes the body, has her head bent far back and hidden in a sort of box, a false cardboard neck contributing to increase the illusion.

"BLACK ART."

To the Yogi and Mahatmas of India, the magicians and illusionists of Europe and America are indebted for the ideas of many of their best tricks and illusions. While the published reports of many of the alleged marvelous effects produced by the "wonder workers" of India must be taken with a very large amount of salt, yet we must give these people due credit for being the originators of many tricks from which the modern magician has taken principles on which he has founded and created several of the grandest and most successful illusions of modern times.

Take, for instance, the illusion known as "Black Art," or the "Midnight Mysteries of the Yogi," made famous in this country by those master minds of magic, Harry Kellar and the late Alexander Hermann. The weird illusion is founded on an idea advanced by the Yogi of India.

No doubt nearly all of the readers of this article have seen "Black Art" presented by one of the above named magicians, yet the number who could advance a plausible explanation of how it was done, are very few, because as soon as one thinks that he has discovered the secret, the performer produces an effect in direct variance with the principle on which the illusion appears to be founded.

In this illusion the entire stage from the first groove to the rear is hung with black velvet, the floor covered with black felt, and the top is covered with black velvet, thus forming a large room lined entirely in black. The regular footlights are turned out, and a special set are used, that consist of a row of open gas jets placed on a line with the boxes, and carried up the outside of the black room, as shown in the large engraving.

The lights throughout the entire house are either turned very low or put out, with the exception of the special lights mentioned above.

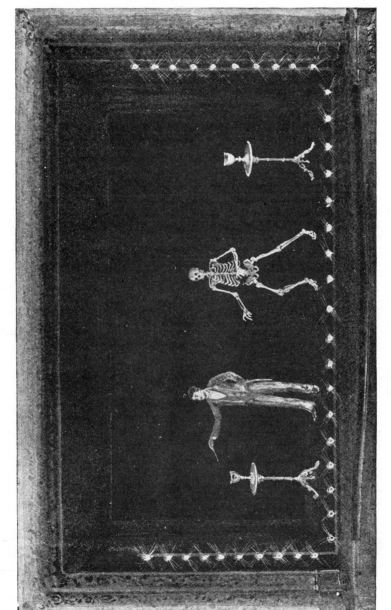

THE STAGE SETTING FOR BLACK ART.

The curtain rises, disclosing the black chamber. In a moment the magician appears, dressed in a white suit; a wave of his hand, and a white wand appears floating in the air, which the magician secures. A wave of the wand, and a table appears on the right, then a second table appears on the left. A large vase appears on one of the tables, and a second vase appears on the magician's outstretched hand. Both of the vases are shown and proven empty, and in one is placed a few orange seeds, and the wand is passed over the vase, which instantly becomes filled with oranges. The oranges are poured into the second,

AN ASSISTANT REMOVING THE TABLE COVER.

then returned to the first vase, when they disappear as quickly and as mysteriously as they appeared, and the vases are again shown empty, and again placed one on each of the tables. A borrowed watch is placed in one of the vases, from which it disappears and is found in the vase on the other table. A life-size skeleton now appears and dances around the stage, becomes dismembered, the separated parts floating about, but they finally rearticulate themselves, and the skeleton vanishes. Now a rabbit is seen in one of the vases, from which it is taken by the performer, and in his hands it becomes two, which are tossed in the air and disappear.

The number and style of tricks performed in the mysterious black chamber are almost unlimited, but an explanation of the ones mentioned above will suffice to show how " Black Art " is performed.

While the stage is draped in black, everything that appears is painted white, and the magician is dressed in white. There is an assistant on the stage all through the act, but as he is dressed in black, with gloves on his hands and a hood over his head, made of black velvet, he is not seen by the spectators, whose sight is somewhat dazzled by the open gas jets. The tables are on the stage,

THE DISARTICULATED SKELETON.

but covered with pieces of black velvet, rendering them invisible. The second engraving shows how the assistant removes the piece of velvet and causes a table to appear at the magician's command.

The vases are also sitting on the stage, but covered with pieces of black velvet. By picking up the covered vases the assistant can cause them to appear, by removing the velvet, one on the table and the other on the performer's hand. The oranges are in a black velvet bag, from which the assistant pours them into the vase. To cause the oranges to vanish, the magician, instead of pouring them into the vase, pours them into the open mouth of a large black bag held by the assistant just over the lower vase. The transposition of the watch from one vase to the other is just as easy. The assistant merely removes it from the vase in which the performer placed it, and places it in the second vase. The manipulation of the rabbit is equally simple. The assistant places the first one in the vase by means of a black bag in which it was concealed, then places the second one in the performer's hands from a second small bag. In vanishing the rabbits the performer merely tosses them up into a large open-mouthed black bag held by the assistant.

THE JOINTED PAPER SKELETON.

The skeleton is made of *papier maché*, painted white, and fastened on a thin board that is sawed to shape and covered with black velvet. One arm and one leg are jointed so as to be readily removed and replaced by the assistant when he is operating the skeleton. The last two illustrations fully explain the method of construction and manipulation of the skeleton.

The tables are made either of wood or *papier maché* and painted white. The vases are made of *papier maché*, painted white on the outside and black on the inside. The reason the inside of the vases are painted black is to prevent the hand of the assistant being seen when he places it in the vase.

This is one of the most expensive of stage illusions, costing several hundred dollars to properly stage it with the best drapery and accessories, and unless such are used the proper illusory effect is lost. In magic as well as in other business, cheap apparatus is dear at any price.

THE TALKING HEAD.

Probably the most common of all of the illusions which depend upon mirrors is the Talking Head upon a table. The illustration is almost self-explanatory. The apparatus consists only of a mirror fixed to the side legs of the table. The mirror hides the body of the girl, who is on her knees and seated on a small stool, and reflects the straw which covers the floor so as to

THE TALKING HEAD.

make it appear continuous under the table; likewise it reflects the front leg of the table so as to make it appear at an equal distance from the other side and thus produce the illusion of the fourth leg. It also reflects the end of the red fabric hanging in front of the table and thus makes it appear to hang down from behind. The visitor stands only a few inches away from the table and head. Such proximity of the spectator and actor would seem to favor the discovery of the trick, but on the contrary it is indispensable to its success.

THE LIVING HALF-WOMAN.

This illusion is a very ingenious improvement on the "Talking Head." On entering the small booth in which it is usually exhibited, we perceive

THE LIVING HALF OF A WOMAN.

an elegant little room decorated with flowers and lights and hung with tapestry. In front there are two railings and the floor is covered with a carpet. In the center is seen a small table on which rests a kind of three-legged stool supporting a cushion and the half body. The lady shows she has arrived by moving her arms and head and speaking and singing. The visitor can see the four legs of the table and can perfectly distinguish the space under the stool, the whole scene being brilliantly lighted, contrary to the usual custom in any such illusions.

The secret of the illusion is as follows:

The stool is formed only of a hollowed out disk whose supports are connected by two mirrors that make with each other an angle of forty-five degrees. These mirrors rest on the top of the table which was decorated in regular designs in mosaic and reflect the latter in such a way that they seem to continue uninterruptedly under the stool. The table presents an analogous arrangement, its side legs being connected with the middle one by two mirrors. These mirrors

EXPLANATORY OF THE HALF-WOMAN.

reflect not only the designs of the carpet which by their continuity produce the illusion of a vacancy, but also two table legs located on each side behind the railing, as shown in our small engraving; the mirror to the left transmits to the spectators on that side the image of the leg placed on the left and this image seems to them to be the fourth leg of the table. The mirror to the right plays the same *rôle* with regard to the spectators on that side. These mirrors in addition hide the lower part of the girl's body.

" SHE."

During the season of 1891-92, among various interesting things to be seen at the Eden Musée, perhaps the most interesting, and at the same time the most scientific, was the weird spectacle entitled " She," exhibited by Powell, the

PREPARED FOR CREMATION.

well-known illusionist, and suggested by the Cave scene in H. Rider Haggard's celebrated novel " She."

In this scene a beautiful young lady mounts a table arranged in an alcove formed by a folding screen. Above the victim is suspended a cylindrical cloth screen. The screen is lowered to the level of the table, completely inclosing the subject. The table apparently has four legs, and four candles shown beneath it indicate that the space underneath the table is open and clear. The cylindrical screen is shown to be entire, with openings only at the upper

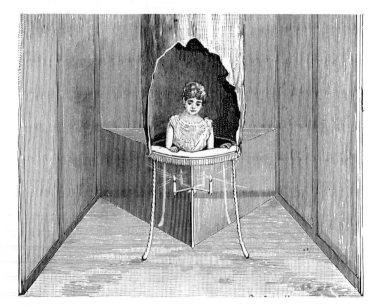

THE ESCAPE.

THE BURNING.

and lower ends, and no openings are seen in the folding screen which partly surrounds the table. Upon the firing of a pistol the occupant of the table is ignited, and smoke and flame bursting from the screen indicate that the work of destruction is going on within. When the fire is burned out the screen is lifted, and nothing remains upon the table but a few smouldering embers and a pile of bones surmounted by a skull. Close observation does not reveal any way of escape for the young woman. It is, however, obvious that the magician cannot afford to sacrifice such a subject every evening, and the spectators are forced to conclude that the whole affair is a very clever trick. In fact, it is simply a modification of the beheaded lady and numerous other tricks based upon the use of plane mirrors. The table has but two legs, the other two which appear being simply reflections. The central standard supports but two candles, the other two being reflections. Underneath the table, and converging at the central standard, are arranged two plane mirrors at an angle of 90° with each other and 45° with the side panels of the screen. By means of this arrangement the side panels, which are of the same color as the central or back panel, are reflected in the mirror and appear as a continuation of the back panel. The triangular box, of which the mirrors form two sides, has a top composed in part of the table top and in part of mirror sections for reflecting the back panel, or with a covering of the same color as the back panel.

THE FINISH.

The operation of the apparatus is now obvious. When the victim is inclosed by the cylindrical screen, she immediately escapes through a trap door in the table top, places the bones and the fireworks upon the table, and at the firing of the pistol ignites the latter and retires, closing the trap door after her.

"THE QUEEN OF FLOWERS."

One of Mr. Kellar's recent illusions is what he is pleased to call "The Queen of Flowers." Our first engraving represents the stage as the audience sees it, and the last cut will help to explain it to the reader. The background, set against curtains, is about ten feet long and eight feet high, and represents a mass of flowers and bushes indiscriminately thrown together, with

MR. KELLAR'S ILLUSION, "QUEEN OF THE FLOWERS."

blue sky above. There is a little flat roof which projects out about three feet from the bottom of the screen and is supported by four red poles. The bottom is a floor raised about a foot from the stage, and in front of each of the three divisions made by the poles between the stage proper and the floor of this improvised summer house is placed an electric light. The audience usually wonders what these lights are for in this strange place; but as audiences always accept anything shown them by the prestidigitateur, these lights do not disturb

ENTRANCE TO THE CABINET.

them very much except by dazzling them, as they are meant to do. So much for the setting. There being no doors or screens or curtains of any kind, the spectators have the satisfied feeling that there is no deception there, for they can see all there is to see. They can, that is true, only they don't realize how much they are seeing.

Mr. Kellar next brings a semicircular stand which he places in front of the middle panel at the height of the floor. At the roof is fixed a brass rod in the form of a semicircle, from which hangs a curtain inclosing the little stand. This, however, cannot do much good, for, as Mr. Kellar says, those on the extreme right and left of the audience can still see quite behind the curtain, through the summer house, and they believe him, not only because he told them so, but because they can see with their own eyes. What could be more convincing! In a moment the curtain is withdrawn and a beautiful lady surrounded by flowers is seen standing on the little platform.

The last engraving will explain matters. The lines extending from the two center poles to the background represent double mirrors; that is, each mirror consists of two mirrors back to back, running from the floor to the roof of the summer house. On account of the indefinite arrangement of the flowers painted on the back scene in monotonous design, the spectators do not notice the mirrors. These, of course, form a passageway through which anyone can walk from behind the scenes to the stand behind the curtain, while the audience is still keeping guard with its ever watchful eye.

"THE DECAPITATED PRINCESS."

In this illusion the exhibitor states that it is the head of an Egyptian Princess who was accused of treason and beheaded. The head is exhibited in

ILLUSION OF THE DECAPITATED PRINCESS.

a curtained recess and it reposes upon two swords lying across the arms of the chair.   The chair is upholstered in red plush and is placed close to the curtain at the back of the recess.   At the back of the chair is an opening just below the level of the tops of the chair arms.   This opening is not seen from the front, as it is concealed by a mirror that is placed between the arms of the chair at an angle of 45°.   The ends of the mirror rest in folds of the fan-shape

THE DECAPITATED PRINCESS—EXPLANATION OF ILLUSION.

upholstering on the inside of the chair arms.   The lower edge of the mirror is resting on the bottom of the chair and the upper edge is concealed by laying one of the swords on it, as may be seen in the other illustration.   At the proper angle the bottom of the chair is reflected in the mirror, leaving the impression that one is looking at the back.   The folds in the upholstering of the inside of the arms effectually conceal the ends of the mirror.   There is a hole in the rear curtain directly opposite the hole in the chair back, through which there passes a board supported at one end by resting on the seat of the chair and at the other end by a small box or any convenient article.

The lady who is to impersonate the princess takes her position on this board with her chin just above the edge of the mirror, the second sword is placed at the back of her head and a wide lace collar that she wears around her neck is adjusted so as to rest nicely on the two swords. The second illustration shows the board in position, passed through the curtain, with the lady lying on it, her head on the swords and the lace collar in position. The curtain in the rear must be close to the chair, but the side curtains are removed about five feet. The board is padded so as to make the lady as comfortable as possible.

"STELLA."

The following illusion is similar to the "Decapitated Princess." A small stage is partitioned off by curtains. In the center of the stage, suspended in

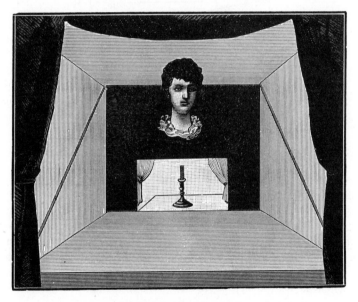

AN ISOLATED HEAD IN THE CENTER OF A STAGE.

space, is a young girl's head, the neck of which starts from a satin collar. This head is isolated on every side. One sees the rear of the stage, the sides, the top and the bottom, and the brilliant illumination leaves no portion in shadow. The head speaks and smiles and finally blows out a lighted candle. The exhibitor then disappears behind the side scenes with the candle.

He now, as it seems, draws out a panel in the back of the stage, and through the aperture thus formed the spectator very distinctly sees the top of a table and upon it a candle which the head has just extinguished. Now this aperture is directly under the head, but much farther off, and is in the direction the body would occupy if the head possessed one. The absence of the body is therefore apparently demonstrated to the visitors.

The illusion was obtained by means of a simple mirror which starting from the upper part of the back of the stage descended obliquely to the front. In the center of this there was an opening which was concealed by the satin collar and through this the young girl passed her head. The inclination of the mirror was, in fact, indicated by a gold rod designed to hide the junction of the mirror and the side. The arrangement will be better understood by reference to the annexed diagram, which belongs to the same illusion, only the clown is substituted for the girl's head.

Now, by virtue of the optical law that "an object reflected from a mirror appears to be behind the latter at a distance equal to that which separates it

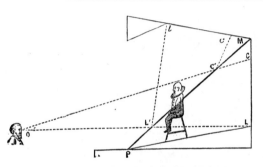

DIAGRAM EXPLANATORY OF THE PHENOMENON.

from it," every point of the line, M l, reflected from the mirror, P M, will appear to be situated upon the line, M L.

So, to the spectator located at O, the point, c, reflected at C' will appear to be the point, C; the distance, c C' equaling C C'. The point, l, reflected at L', will appear to be L. And it will be the same for all the intermediate points. The spectator, then, will believe that he sees the line, M L, when in reality he sees only the reflection of M l. Now, as we have just said, he will believe that he sees the back of the stage, when, in fact, he sees nothing but a reflection of the ceiling in the mirror. In the same way, the reflection from the front of the ceiling will produce the illusion of the stage floor. This fact still further contributes to increase the illusion, for the spectators are not aware of the difference that exists between the arrangement of the place where the bust appears and of that of the place where the showman is walking.

In the illusion of "Stella" the aperture through which the table was seen was in reality at the top. The table was vertical and the candle which was firmly fixed to it was horizontal. The farce of blowing out the candle and carrying it behind the scenes was only designed to make the spectators believe it was the same candle that was seen at the rear of the stage, when in reality it was only a duplicate.

HOUDIN'S MAGIC CABINET.

These apparatus were formerly much employed by magicians—Robert-Houdin, for instance. The following is an example of one of the scenes that may occur with them:

When the curtain rises, there is seen in the center of the stage a large, dark-colored cabinet, ornamented with mouldings, and mounted upon legs that are a little longer than those of ordinary cabinets, the object being to remove all possibility of a communication with the stage beneath. These legs are provided with casters. The showman turns this cabinet around and shows that there is nothing abnormal about it externally. He then asks some of the spectators to come up close to it, and lets them examine its interior, which is entirely empty. There is no double bottom, nor any hiding-place. When the witnesses have made themselves certain of this fact, they station themselves around the stage, and a certain number of them even consent to remain behind the cabinet and see nothing of the experiment. The cabinet being thus surrounded on all sides, and every one being able to look under it, fraud would seem to be an impossibility.

A young woman dressed as a *danseuse* then comes on the stage and enters the cabinet, and the doors are closed upon her. In a few moments the doors are opened again, when, lo and behold! the closet is empty, the young woman having disappeared. Then the doors are closed again, and then opened, and the *danseuse* makes her appearance; and so on. At the end of the experiment the witnesses examine the cabinet again, and finding nothing changed therein, are justly stupefied.

In another style of cabinet there is no bar in the center, as shown in our engraving, but there is observed on one of the sides in the interior a bracket a few centimeters in length, and, back and above this, a shelf. This arrangement permits of performing a few experiments more than does the one just described. Thus, when the woman has disappeared, the showman allows a young man to enter, and he also disappears, while the young woman is found in his place. This is a very surprising substitution.

The box into which the harlequin takes refuge, and which appears to be empty when Pierrot or Cassandra lifts the curtain that shields its entrance, is also a sort of magic cabinet.

In a series of lectures delivered a few years ago at the London Polytechnic Institution, a professor of physics unmasked the secret of some of the tricks employed on the stage for producing illusions, and notably that of the magic cabinet. The lecturer, after showing the cabinet, and causing the disappearance therein of an individual while the doors were closed, repeated the same experiment with the latter open. But, in the latter case, so quick was the

MAGIC CABINET.

disappearance that the spectators could not even then see how it was done. The illusion produced by the apparatus is the result of a play of mirrors.

In the first cabinet described, when the exhibitor has closed the doors upon the young woman, the latter pulls toward her two mirrors that are represented in our plan of the cabinet by the lines, G G. These mirrors a r e hinged at O O, and, when swung outward, rest by their external edges against the bar, P, and then occupy the position shown by the dotted lines, G' G'. When the cabi-

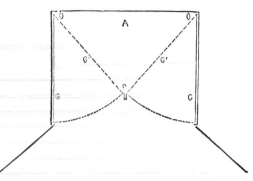

PLAN EXPLANATORY OF THE CABINET.

net is again opened, the woman placed at A is hidden by the two mirrors; but the appearance of the interior of the cabinet is not changed, since the spectators see the image of each side reflected from the corresponding mirror, and this looks to them like the back of the cabinet.

The illusion is perfect. When the experiment is ended and the mirrors are again swung against the sides, at G G, the spectators see nothing but the backs of them, which are covered with wood; the cabinet is really empty, and no one can discover what modification has taken place in its interior during the disappearance of the woman.

In the second arrangement, which is shown in vertical section in our last engraving, the young man gets up on the shelf, *c n*, at the upper part of the cabinet, by the aid of the bracket, T, and then pulls down over him the mirror, *b c*, which was fastened to the top of the cabinet. This mirror, being inclined at an angle of 45°, reflects the top, and the spectators imagine that they see the back of the cabinet over the shelf, as they did before.

The box which Harlequin enters is based upon precisely the same principle. Its interior is hung with paper banded alternately blue and white. When Harlequin enters it, he places himself in one of the angles and pulls toward him

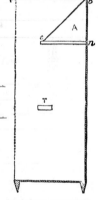

SECTION EXPLANA-
TORY OF THE
CABINET.

two mirrors which hide him completely, and which reflect the opposite side of the box, so that the spectator is led to believe that he sees the back of it. In this case, one of the angles at the back of the box is not apparent, but the colored stripes prevent the spectator from noticing the fact.

A MYSTIC MAZE.

We present an engraving of a very interesting optical illusion produced with only three mirrors. By multiplying the mirrors the large number of different effects can be obtained.

Let us imagine that three perfectly plain and very clear mirror glasses, as large as possible, form a prism whose base is an equilateral triangle. A person placed in the interior of this prism will see his image reflected a very large number of times. A very simple geometrical construction, and one which we recommend our young readers to carry out as an exercise in optics, by the simple application of the principle that the angle of incidence is equal to the angle of reflection, allows us to see that the image of any point whatever placed in the center of this triangle of glass plates will be reproduced indefinitely by groups of six images distributed symmetrically around points regularly spaced in the prolongations of the planes of the three glasses.

A person, therefore, sees his image reproduced indefinitely in groups of six until, the successive reflections attenuating the intensity of the images, the latter cease to be visible. Three or four persons massed in one of the angles present the illusion of a compact and mixed crowd standing upon a sidewalk and awaiting the passage of a procession. The hats waving in the air convert the peaceful waiting into an enthusiastic manifestation, which is so much the more surprising in that it is made by but half a dozen persons at the maximum.

The accompanying figure gives an idea of this remarkable effect, and the three persons, whose images reflected *ad infinitum* produce the curious result that we call attention to, would have much trouble to believe that they were the subject of an illusion.

Upon the whole, the experiment is nothing more than an application of the principle of the old kaleidoscope enlarged and revived, in the sense that the observer has before his eyes the successive reflections of his own image, and that the objects are replaced with living beings movable at will.

Five or six persons may occupy, at the same time, the triangular prism, of which the sides are about six feet wide, and which they enter through a trap in the floor. When these five or six persons are walking about in all directions, they present the aspect of a tumultuous and agitated crowd commenting upon grave events.

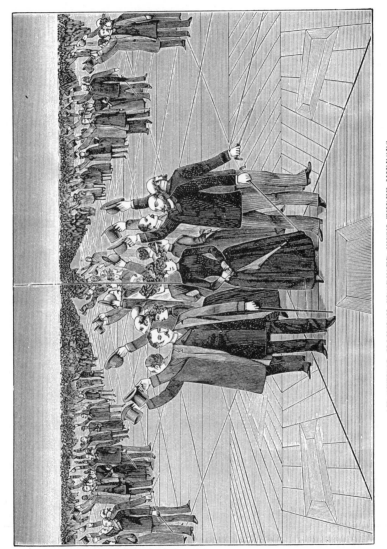

AN OPTICAL ILLUSION PRODUCED WITH THREE MIRRORS.

PLATINIZED GLASS.

Platinized glass plates are no longer a novelty, but the illusion is very effective. The mirrors give an image in the ordinary way when looked at by reflected light, but are transparent when observed by transmitted light. The metalization of glass with platinum was discovered a great many years ago by

FIG. 1.

the Messrs. Dodé. This property of transparency by transmitted light affords a very clever surprise. The mirrors are set in frames. In a panel behind the latter there is an aperture closed by a shutter. As the glass is transparent there may be seen through it, when the shutter is open, everything that is on the other side, so it occurred to the inventors to utilize this transparency by placing an image or photograph between the panel and the glass. On exposing the mirror to the light to look at one's self in the ordinary way, if the shutter is open, the human head will disappear and may be replaced by the photographic portrait or a horned devil, which is placed behind the mirror. In the illusion we illustrate the head of the devil whose body is hidden by two mir-

FIG. 2.

rors inclined at an angle of forty-five degrees, as in some of the illusions we have already described. As he moves his head and smiles, the effect is rather startling. Electric light is used to illuminate the trick.

STATUE GIVING A DOUBLE IMAGE.

At the Italian exhibition held a few wears ago in the Champ de Mars, Paris, there was a statue that attracted much attention from the visitors. It represented Goethe's Marguerite standing before a mirror. This latter gave by reflection the image of Faust, as shown in our engraving. The artifice was

MARGUERITE AND FAUST.

well concealed by the sculptor. In reality, it was not a double statue, but the figure of Faust was skillfully obtained by means of the folds of Marguerite's robe.

Marguerite holds her arms in front of her, and these same arms form those of Faust, who holds them crossed behind his back. Faust's face is carved in Marguerite's back hair, and the man's figure is obtained, as before stated, by means of the folds of the woman's robe.

CHAPTER III.

MISCELLANEOUS STAGE TRICKS.

The tricks in this chapter are no less interesting than those which have gone before, but are rather of a more miscellaneous nature. The first trick which we shall describe, is called "The Illusion of Trilby."

The late Professor Herrmann won for himself a firm place in the regards of the civilized world, representing the *fin de siècle* Houdin. His carefully executed work, with its perfect detail and finish, was a standard among performances of natural magic, and other exhibitions are referred to it as the gage

PREPARING TRILBY'S COUCH.

of their quality. In Herrmann's illusion of "Trilby," hypnotism is supposed to play a part. As will be seen, it is really an ingenious application of mechanics.

A plank is placed upon the backs of two chairs. A lady performer who is supposed to represent Du Maurier's "Trilby" enters and, stepping on a footstool, lies down upon the plank. She holds a bouquet in her hand, which bouquet, unknown to the audience, has its own part to play. The other performer, Herrmann, who is supposed to be Svengali, carefully arranges the drapery, walking around her as he does so. Then he makes some passes, and one by one removes the chairs, and the lady and board remain in the air. In response to his passes the lady, still resting on the board, rises, and the position changes to an inclined one and back to the horizontal one. Finally the chairs are replaced, the lady by passes is supposed to be waked from her trance and steps down, chairs and plank are removed, and nothing is to be seen further.

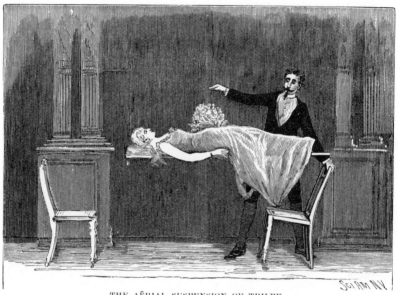

THE AËRIAL SUSPENSION OF TRILBY.

Two of the cuts show the progress of the performance as seen by the audience. The third cut explains the mechanism. Behind the scenes is a strong frame, up and down which a movable slide works. Tackle is provided to raise and lower the slide; and a workman behind the scenes is intrusted with its manipulation. A bar carrying at its rear end handles, and in front a socket, shown in the upper right-hand corner of the same cut, is journaled in the slide, and can also be thrust in and out through the journal box.

When Trilby has been placed upon her board couch, the bar is thrust forward, drapery at the back having hitherto concealed its socket end. The fair Trilby with her bouquet now effectually conceals it as it emerges from behind the curtains. The performer, while apparently sedulously arranging the drapery, guides the socket and causes it to grip the board. The assistant behind the scene pulls upon the tackle and works the handle, so that Trilby's weight leaves the chairs one by one, which are removed, and, supported by the bar, she seems to float in air. By manipulating the tackle she can be raised and lowered. By the handles she can be tilted about, giving a wonderfully good effect. Finally the chairs are replaced, and the assistant lowers Trilby upon them. During the waking passes the socket is detached and the bar is withdrawn. A close observer may notice a slight agitation of the drapery or curtains behind the stage as the bar is pushed out and withdrawn, but the attention of the audience in general is so taken up with the performance proper that this disturbance is overlooked by them.

THE ILLUSION EXPLAINED.

The magician, it will be seen, can only walk completely around the reclining lady before the bar is in place or after it is withdrawn. When the bar is in place, he can walk behind her, but cannot go completely around her. Hence his complete excursions are restricted to the time when she is resting on the chairs, before the bar is in place or after it has been withdrawn.

After the board is vacated, Svengali throws it down upon the stage, its fall, with accompanying noise and disturbance, showing that there is no deception about that portion of the display.

THE "HAUNTED SWING."

The supreme happiness of sitting in a swing which apparently whirls around its points of support, giving the occupant what is most properly described as a new sensation, may now be enjoyed by all. It is termed the "haunted swing," and has been in most successful operation at Atlantic City and at the Midwinter Fair near San Francisco. Those who are to participate in the apparent gyrations of the swing—and there may be quite a number who enjoy it simultaneously—are ushered into a small room.   From

TRUE POSITION OF THE SWING.

a bar crossing the room, near the ceiling, hangs a large swing, which is pro-vided with seats for a number of people.   After the people have taken their places, the attendant pushes the car and it starts into oscillation like any other swing. The room door is closed. Gradually those in it feel after three or

ILLUSION PRODUCED BY A RIDE IN THE SWING.

four movements that their swing is going rather high, but this it not all. The apparent amplitude of the oscillations increases more and more, until presently the whole swing seems to whirl completely over, describing a full circle about the bar on which it hangs.   To make the thing more utterly mysterious, the bar is bent crank fashion, so that it seems demonstrably impossible for the swing to pass between bar and ceiling.   It continues apparently to go round and round this way, imparting a most weird sensation to the occupants, until its movements begin gradually to cease and the complete rotation is succeeded by the usual back and forth swinging, and in a few seconds, as the children say, "the old cat dies."   The door of the room is opened and the swinging party leave.   Those who have tried it say the sensation is most peculiar and the deception perfect.

The illusion is based on the movements of the room proper.   During the entire exhibition the swing is practically stationary, while the room rotates about the suspending bar.   At the beginning of operations the swing may be given a slight push; the operators outside the room then begin to swing the room itself, which is really a large box journaled on the swing bar, starting it off to correspond with the movements of the swing.   They swing it back and forth, increasing the arc through which it moves until it goes so far as to make a complete rotation.   The operatives do this without special machinery, taking hold of the sides and corners of the box or "room."   At this time the people in the swing imagine that the room is stationary while they are whirling through space.   After keeping this up for some time, the movement is brought gradually to a stop, a sufficient number of back and forth swings being given at the *finale* to carry out the illusion to the end.

The room is as completely furnished as possible, everything being, of course, fastened in place.   What is apparently a kerosene lamp stands on a table, near at hand.   It is securely fastened to the table, which in its turn is fastened to the floor, and the light is supplied by a small incandescent lamp within the chimney, but concealed by the shade.   The visitor never imagines that it is an electric lamp, and naturally thinks that it would be impossible for a kerosene lamp to be inverted without disaster, so that this adds to the deception materially.   The same is to be said of the pictures hanging on the wall, of the cupboard full of chinaware, of the chair with a hat on it, and of the baby carriage.   All contribute to the mystification.   Even though one is informed of the secret before entering the swing, the deception is said to be so complete that passengers involuntarily seize the arms of the seats to avoid being precipitated below.

THE "SCURIMOBILE."

The peculiar gun shown in the cut is named after its inventor, Alessandro Scuri, of Liège, Belgium.   M. Scuri is also known as the inventor of a unicycle and a quadruple cornet.   The "scurimobile" is a gun with two barrels

THE SCURIMOBILE.

which can be aimed at different objects, the angle between the barrels being adjustable.   The adjustment is effected by moving a ring located on the under side of the gun.   The pivot of the barrels is so arranged that it is easy to sight two objects at the same time.   Both cartridges are automatically ejected after each shot fired.   It is also possible to use only one barrel in the ordinary way. In the cut the inventor is shown aiming at two balls placed about a yard apart. Another valuable feature of this new gun is its applicability as a range finder. The observer first sights two objects which are at about equal distances from him, and measures the distance or angle between the two barrels, a graduation being provided for this purpose.   Then the same operation is made from a point more distant from the objects first sighted.   If the observer steps back ten yards, and finds that the graduation indicates just one-half of the value obtained at first, he will know that in the second position he was just twice as far from the objects as in the first position, so that the objects are ten yards from the observer's first position.   This operation will give distances with sufficient accuracy in most cases, but more exact results can be obtained by means of a simple trigonometric formula when the angle between the barrels is measured.

" THE NEOÖCCULTISM."

The X rays, after becoming the indispensable coadjutors of surgeons, and even of physicians, are now competing with the most noted mediums in the domain of the marvelous.

M. Radiguet, the well known manufacturer of physical apparatus, has been devoting himself for a long time to experiments with the Roentgen rays in the laboratory, which is encumbered with electric lamps, lamp globes, and glass apparatus of all kinds.   One day he perceived that these glass objects, under the action of the X rays, shone in the darkness.   Here again was an amusing and perhaps a useful experiment due to accident.   Useful, because the radiographs obtained up to the present, by means of artificial screens, have been really good only when the sensitive bodies have been in small crystals.   In a pulverulent state they are nearly insensible to the X rays, and it is almost impossible to obtain the grain of the screen upon the photographic plate.   It is easy, on the contrary, to work the glass in such a way as to prevent any irregularity in the radiograph.   Such experiments will certainly be made ere long, but, for the present, it is the fantastic side of the discovery that we shall present to our readers.

Porcelain, enamels, and diamonds, and also objects covered with platino-cyanides (used by Roentgen) and with calcium tungstate, zinc sulphate, etc., have, like glass, the property of becoming luminous in darkness under the action of the X rays.   We have, therefore, only the trouble of selection in order to get up a " spirit séance " with every certainty of success, while genuine spiritual séances fail in most cases, as well known, because the spirits are in an ill mood and disposed to be coyish.

ARRANGEMENT FOR A STRIKING EXPERIMENT WITH THE X RAYS.

The following will prove a scene sufficiently weird to put the most intrepid worldlings in a flurry if some one of our friends takes it into his head to give them the mysterious spectacle thereof before they have read an exposure of the trick.

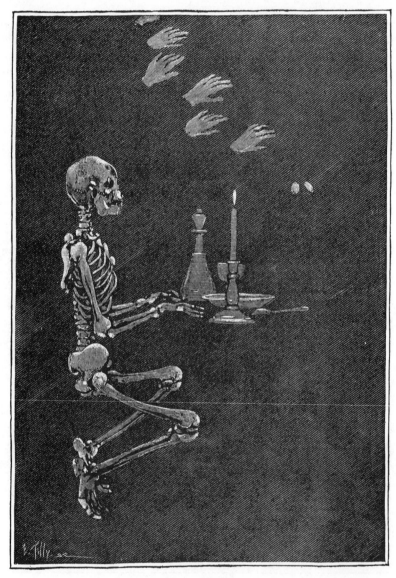

THE APPARITION.

The first figure that we present herewith exhibits a Ruhmkorff coil, which is placed here to show the operation in its entirety. But, as the first effect of its vibrations would be to attract the attention, and consequently the suspicions of the spectators, whom it is a question of transporting into the domain of the marvelous, this apparatus is relegated to some distant room. The current that produces the X rays is led into the Crookes tube by wires. This apparatus, moreover, which is not very bulky, may be placed behind a door or be concealed under black cloth. The objects designed to become luminous are placed as near to the tube as possible. In the experiment under consideration a diner (who is doubtless near-sighted, since he wears eyeglasses) is about to do justice to his breakfast. Armed with a knife and fork, he attacks his beefsteak; but he is assuredly a greater eater than drinker, since he contents himself with water, while his light consists of a single candle.

A black curtain on the other side of the table conceals from the spectators a skeleton covered with zinc sulphide.

Let us now put out the light and set the Ruhmkorff coil in action. What a surprise! A plate, a glass, a water bottle, and a candle shine in space with the light of glow-worms.

A sinister guest in the form of a skeleton sits opposite the place occupied by the near-sighted gentleman, who has disappeared, and whose eyeglasses alone have held their own before this ghastly apparition. Finally, to complete the illusion, hands are seen moving over the heads of the spectators, and those multiply, and then disappear, only to appear anew.

It must be remarked that, in order to render the experiment more conclusive, it is allowable for the most incredulous members of the party to tie the gentleman tightly to his chair, and, if they desire, to hold his hands and feet during the entire time of the experiment. It is scarcely necessary to explain how the latter is performed. The X rays pass through the black cloth on the door that conceals the Crookes tube and also through the body of the gentleman, and render luminous the glass objects covered with zinc sulphide. As for the mysterious hands, those are simply gloves covered with the same substance and fixed to the extremity of long sticks that are moved in all directions by confederates.

Such scenes may naturally be varied to infinity; and the spirit of invention is so fertile, there is no doubt that before long ladies will be giving a place in the programme of their soirées to this up-to-date spiritualism.

"THE MASK OF BALSAMO."

This illusion is a variation of the enchanted "death's head" which was for a long time the attraction of the Robert-Houdin Theater. Our engraving shows both the "death's head," the "mask of Balsamo," and the method of producing the illusion. Under the influence of the passes of the prestidigitateur the skull on the glass plate bends forward and seems to salute the spectators. The nodding of the "death's head" was utilized in a number of ways, as, to indicate the number when dice was thrown. This trick was per-

THEATRICAL SCIENCE.

Fig. 1.—The Enchanted Death's Head.   Fig. 2.—The Mask of Balsamo.

formed as follows: Upon a table near the magician was placed a ball of soft wax attached to a string which ran to the side scenes, where it could be pulled by a confederate. After passing the skull around to be examined, the prestidigitateur, in laying it upon the table, fixed the ball of wax at the top of it. After the experiment a simple scraping with the finger nail removed every trace of the trick. The Isola Brothers used electricity in a somewhat similar illusion. The skull is replaced by a wooden mask laid flat on a small table and the mask answers questions by rocking slightly. The magician then brings the table into the midst of the spectators, and the mask still continues to move, to the astonishment of the onlookers. The secret of the trick is that part of the wood which forms the chin is replaced by a small strip of iron which is painted the same color as the mask so that it cannot be seen; an electro-magnet is let into the top of the table so that the cores shall be opposite the strip of iron when the mask is laid upon the table. Contact is made by means of a push button somewhere in the side scenes, the wires run under the stage, and connection is made through the legs of the table when the legs are set on the foreordained place. Upon the same principle is Robert Houdin's heavy chest and magic drum. A rapping and talking table may be made by carrying out the same idea. The battery is carried in the lower part of the table, where the three legs join. The top of the table is in two parts, the lower of which is hollow and the top being very thin. In the center of the hollow part is placed an electro-magnet, one of the wires of which connect with one of the poles of the battery, while the other is connected with a flat metallic circle glued to the cover of the table. Beneath this circle and at a slight distance from it there is a toothed circle connected with the whole pole of the battery. When the table is pressed lightly upon, the cover bends and the flat circle touches the toothed one. This closes the circuit, and the electro-magnet attract-

ing the armature produces a sharp blow. When the hand is raised the circuit is broken, producing another sharp blow. By running the hand lightly over the table the cover is caused to bend successively over a certain portion of its circumference. Thus contact is made at a number of places, and the sharp blow is replaced by a quick succession of sounds. This table is very useful for spirit rappings; as the table contains all of the mechanism in itself, it can be moved to any part of the room. The table may be also operated from a distance by employing conductors passing through the legs of the table and under the carpet. By sub-

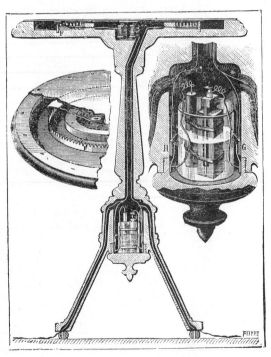

RAPPING AND TALKING TABLE.

stituting a small telephone receiver for the electro-magnet, the rapping spirits may be made talking ones.

Electric insects may be constructed on the same plan and give a very lifelike appearance when placed on an artificial bunch of flowers in a flower pot.

The battery is concealed in the top.   When the pot is raised a drop of mercury which occupies the bottom of the pot will roll over the bottom, closing the circuit successively on different insects, keeping them in motion until the pot has been set down.

THE INVISIBLE WOMAN.

At the end of the last century and the beginning of the present, a very curious experiment, and one which was looked upon as marvelous by the credulous, was wonderfully popular at Paris.   The representation took place

THE INVISIBLE WOMAN.

at the old Capuchin convent. The spectator entered a well lighted hall in which, in part of a window, there was a box suspended by four brass chains attached by bows of ribbon. The box, which was surrounded by a grating, was provided with two panes of glass that permitted of seeing that it was absolutely empty. To one of the extremities was fixed a speaking trumpet. When a visitor spoke in the latter, he was answered by a hollow voice; and when he placed his face near the box, he even felt upon it the action of a mysterious breath. When he presented any object whatever in front of the mouthpiece, and asked the voice to name it, an answer immediately came from the speaking tube. The box was suspended freely from the ceiling, and it could be made to swing at the extremity of the chains; it was empty and isolated in space. People were lost in conjecture as to the secret of the experiment. Among the unlikely theories that were put forth was that of the invisibility of a person obtained by unknown processes.

As usual in these kinds of impostures, there was here merely an ingenious application of a scientific principle. A physicist, E. J. Ingennato, revealed the mystery in a pamphlet published in 1800 under the title of "The Invisible Woman and Her Secret Unveiled." This tract, now rare, had for a frontispiece the engraving which we reproduce herewith and which explains the whole experiment. The invisible woman of the Capucmin convent was named Frances, and the following is the explanatory legend appended to the original engraving:

"Questioner: 'Frances, what is this that I have in my hand?'

"Frances (after looking through the little peep-hole, D): 'A stick with a crooked handle.'

"The entire assembly at once: 'It is incomprehensible!'"

Ingennato, in his pamphlet, explains that above the ceiling there was a low, darkish chamber, in which Frances was concealed, and that she looked at the object presented to her through a small aperture, D, which was skillfully hidden by a hanging lamp, and then answered through the speaking tube, B B B, hidden in the wall. The sound traversed a space of about six inches, that separated the speaking tube from the speaking trumpet.

MAGIC HARPS.

The experiment which we are about to describe, while it is thoroughly scientific, was taken up under the name of "Æolian Harps" by Robert-Houdin, who introduced several modifications of it. When the experiment was performed by Wheatstone in 1855, four harps were arranged in a semi-circle on the stage of the Polytechnic Institution. These harps, at the pleasure of the experimentor, vibrated as if they were made to resound by invisible hands.

This effect was produced by fixing to the sounding board of each of them vertical rods of fir-wood which passed through the floor of the stage and ceilings, into the cellar of the Institution, where one of them was fixed upon a sounding board of a piano, another upon the sounding board of a violoncello, and two others upon the sounding boards of violins. In order to render it possible

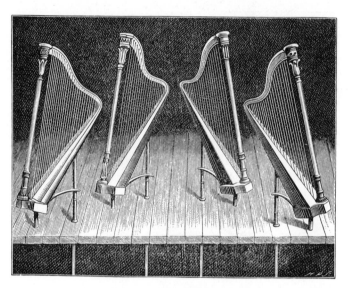

ÆOLIAN HARP EXPERIMENT.

to interrupt the vibrations between the instruments and the harps, the rods supporting the latter were divided at two inches above the floor. Each harp could be cut off from communication with the instrument below by turning it around upon its axis. When Robert-Houdin introduces the illusion, he used a stage elevated in the very midst of the spectators. This stage was traversed by two fir-wood rods which, after passing through the floor, rested upon harps placed in the hands of skillful players. At the command of the prestidigitateur two other harps supported upon the upper extremity of the rods executed a concert which was very successful, thanks to the careful preparations and the elegant *mise en scène*. Of course the harps were supposed to operate through the intervention of mediumistic spirits.

CHAPTER IV.

CONJURING TRICKS.

Having described some of the illusions which are produced with the aid of elaborate outfits, we now come to the more simple tricks which are produced with smaller and less expensive apparatus, and, sometimes, with no apparatus at all. In the old days the man of mystery appeared on the stage clad in a robe embroidered with cabalistic figures, the ample folds·of which could well conceal a whole trunkful of paraphernalia. The table in the center of the stage was covered with a velvet cloth embroidered with silver, and its long folds, which reached the ground, suggested endless possibilities for concealment. All of these things have now passed away, and the modern magician appears clad in ordinary evening dress, which is beyond the suspicion of concealment. The furniture is all selected with special reference to the apparent impossibility of using it as a storeroom for objects which the prestidigitateur wishes to conceal. Some of the easiest and simplest of modern tricks that anyone with little or no practice can perform are very effective. The tricks in this chapter are far from being all which have been published in the *Scientific American* and the *Scientific American Supplement*, but they are believed to be the best which have been published in those journals.

TRICK WITH AN EGG AND A HANDKERCHIEF.

In this trick we have an egg in an egg-cup, which the prestidigitateur covers with a hat, and then he rolls a small silk handkerchief between his hands, as shown in Fig. 1. As soon as the handkerchief no longer appears externally, he opens his hands and shows the egg, which has invisibly left the place that it occupied under the hat, while the handkerchief has passed into the egg-cup (Fig. 3). We shall now explain how these invisible transfers are effected.

Two eggs, genuine and entire, were truly placed in plain view in a basket, but it was not one of those that served for the experiment. Behind the basket was placed a half shell, C, of wood (Fig. 2), painted white on the convex side, so as to represent the half of an egg, and on the concave side offering the same aspect as the interior of the egg-cup, A, to which it can be perfectly fitted in one direction or the other, as may be seen in the section in Fig. 2. It is this shell, inclosing a small handkerchief exactly like the first, that the prestidigitateur placed upon the egg-cup (Fig. 2).   Then, while with the left hand he covered the whole with a hat with which he concealed the operation, he with the right hand quickly turned the shell upside down.   The shell, therefore, by this means disappeared in the egg-cup, and the handkerchief, spreading out, assumed the appearance that it presents in Fig. 3.

TRICK WITH AN EGG AND HANDKERCHIEF.

The prestidigitateur, having afterward secretly seized with his right hand a hollow egg of metal, containing an oval aperture (F, Fig. 2), stuffed into it the handkerchief that he seemed simply to roll and compress between his hands. It is almost useless to add that the metallic egg may be easily concealed either with the palm of the hand that holds it, or with the handkerchief.

THE CONE OF FLOWERS.

In prestidigitation flowers have in all times played an important part, and they are usually employed in preference to other objects, since they give the experiments a pleasing aspect.   But, in most cases, natural flowers, especially when it is necessary to conceal their presence, are replaced by paper or feather ones, the bulk of which is more easily reduced.   Such is the case in the experiment which we are about to present, and which, it must be confessed, requires to be seen from some little distance in order that the spectators may, without too great an effort of the imagination, be led into the delusion that they are looking at genuine flowers.   However, even seen close by, the trick surprises one to the same degree as all those that consist in causing the appearance of more or less bulky objects where nothing was perceived a few moments previous.

The prestidigitateur takes a newspaper and forms it into a cone before one's eyes. It is impossible to suppose the existence here of a double bottom, and yet the cone, gently shaken, becomes filled with flowers that have come from no one knows where. The number of them even becomes so great that they soon more than fill the cone and drop on and cover the floor.

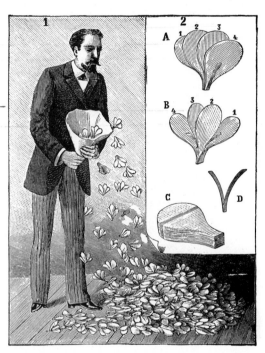

THE CONE OF FLOWERS.

The two sides of the flowers employed are represented in Fig. 2, where they are lettered A and B. Each flower consists of four petals of various colors, cut with a punch out of very thin tissue paper. Upon examining Fig. A, we see opposite us the petals 1, 2, 3, and 4 gummed together by the extremities of their anterior sides, while Fig. B shows us the petals 2 and 3 united in the same manner on the opposite side. A small, very light and thin steel spring, D, formed of two strips soldered together at the bottom, and pointing in opposite directions, is fixed to the two exterior petals, 1 and 4, of the flower, and is concealed by a band of paper of the same color, gummed above. It is this spring that, when it is capable of expanding freely, opens the flower and gives it its voluminous aspect.

Quite a large number of these flowers (a hundred or more), united and held together by means of a thread or a rubber band (Fig. 2, C) makes a package small enough to allow the operator to conceal it in the palm of his hand, only the back of which he allows the spectators to see while he is forming the paper cone.

THE MAGIC ROSEBUSH.

In lectures on chemistry, the professor, in speaking of aniline colors, in order to give an idea of the coloring power of certain of these substances, performs the following experiment:

Upon a sheet of paper he throws some aniline red, which, as well known, comes in the form of iridescent crystals. He shakes the surplus off the paper into the bottle, so that it would be thought that nothing remained on the

THE MAGIC ROSEBUSH.

paper. If, however, alcohol, in which aniline colors are very soluble, be poured over the paper, the latter immediately becomes red.

This experiment may be varied as follows: Instead of scattering the aniline over paper, it is dusted over the flowers of a white rosebush, and the flowers are shaken so as to render the dust invisible, and then when a visit is received from an amateur of horticulture, we tell him that we have a magic rosebush in our garden, the flowers of which become red when alcohol or cologne is poured over them. The experiment is performed with the aid of a perfumery vaporizer, and the phenomenon causes great surprise to the spectators who are not in the secret.

"MAGIC FLOWERS."

A trick that has contributed much toward making one of our leading magicians such a favorite with the fair sex, is one in which a bush filled with genuine rosebuds is caused to grow in a previously-examined pot that contained nothing but a small quantity of white sand.

After the bush is produced, the flowers are cut and distributed to the ladies, and by many recipients of the magician's favors these buds are looked upon as a production of fairy land. For many years this trick has occupied a prominent position on the programme of the magician in question, and mystifies the audience as much to-day as ever, thus proving how well magicians keep their secrets from the public. The trick is not a difficult one by any means, yet, regardless of its simplicity and the ease with which it may be performed, the florist would find it anything but an economical method of raising roses, as a perusal of the following will show.

On the stage is seen two stands with metal feet, and with long rich drapery trimmed with gold fringe. On each of the stands is a miniature stand on which are flower-pots.

The magician passes the pots for inspection, then places them on the stands, and plants a few flower seeds in each pot. A large cone, open at both ends, is shown, and can be carefully examined. One of the pots is covered for a moment with the cone, and on its removal a green sprig is seen protruding from the sand, the seed having sprouted, so the magician says. Now the second pot is covered for a moment with the cone, on the removal of which a large rosebush is seen in the pot, a mass of full-blown roses and buds. The first pot is again covered for a moment with the cone, and when uncovered a second rosebush is seen, equally as full of roses as the other. The cone is once again shown to be empty.

A small basket or tray is now brought forward, on which the roses and buds are placed as the performer cuts them from the bushes, after which they are distributed to the ladies.

The stands are not what they appear, as the drapery does not extend entirely around them, but quite a space at the back of the stand is open. There is a small shelf attached to the stand leg, near the bottom of the drapery. Three cones are used, of which the audience see but one.

The rosebushes are merely stumps to which are attached a base of sheet lead, cut of such a size as to fit nicely in the flower-pots, resting on the sand. To the stumps the genuine roses are attachd by tying with thread. When the bushes are prepared they are suspended inside of cones, by means of a stout cord that is fastened to the stump by one end and to the other end of which is attached a small hook, which hook is slipped over the edge of the upper opening of the cone. When the bushes are placed in the cones, these cones are placed on the shelves at the back of the stands. Reference to the second

MAGIC FLOWERS.

engraving will make the arrangement of the shelf, back of stand, and position of concealed cone plain to all. There is a variance in the size of the cones. The cone shown to the audience is slightly larger than the cone that is behind the first stand, and the cone behind the second stand is a fraction smaller than either of the others. Thus the cones will fit snugly one in the other, in the order named.

After the performer has shown the pots, planted the seed, and placed the pots on the small stands, which are used to convince the spectators that there is no connection between the pot and the large stand, he shows the large cone, which is nicely decorated, and covers the top of the pot on the first stand, as he says, to shut out the light, that the seed may germinate. Between the fingers of the hand holding the cone, he has concealed a small metal shape, painted green, which he drops through the cone into the pot. In a moment he removes the cone from over the pot, and in a most natural manner passes it down behind the stand and over the concealed cone containing the rosebush, and carries this cone away inside of the larger one. At the same moment he picks up the flower-pot and carries it down and shows the green sprout in the sand.

THE MYSTERY EXPLAINED.

The performer now steps to the second stand and covers the flower-pot on it with the cone. As soon as the pot is covered, he slips off the small hook supporting the rosebush, which drops into the pot; the weight of the lead base keeps it in position while the cones are being removed.

When the performer removes the cone—or cones, we should now say, as we have two now in place of one, although this fact is unknown to the audience— he passes it down behind the stand, over the concealed third cone, picking it up with the second rosebush inside. He now returns to the first stand, covers the pot, and by slipping off the hook holding the rosebush in position, and removing the cone, or cones, properly, from the pot, shows the second rosebush. He now turns the large cone so the audience can see through it, and as the upper and lower edge of each cone is blackened, there is no danger of the inside cones being seen. The rear of the stand tops are something of a crescent shape, to facilitate the passing of the large cone down behind the stand in a graceful manner.

THE "BIRTH OF FLOWERS."

The trick that we are about to describe, although old, is very interesting. The prestidigitateur comes forward, holding in his hand a small cardboard box which he says contains various kinds of flower seeds.

"Here there is no need of moisture, earth, or time to cause the seed to germinate, the plant to spring up, and the flower to bloom. Everything takes place instantaneously. Would not a rose in my buttonhole produce a charming effect? A stroke of the wand upon the seed deposited in the desired

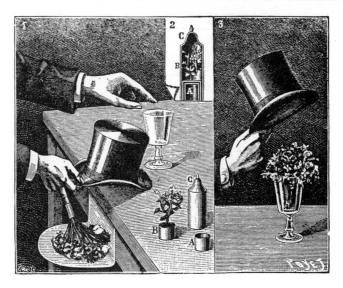

THE BIRTH OF THE FLOWERS.

place, and see! the rose appears. A few seeds are in this little box (Fig. 1, A) that we shall cover for an instant so that it cannot be seen how flowers are born. It is done; let us take off the cover; violets, forget-me-nots, and Easter daisies are here all freshly blown.

"You are suspicious, perhaps, and rightly, of the little tin box, and more so of its cover. Well, then, here is a small goblet, the transparency of which is perfect, and this borrowed hat with which I cover it can have undergone no preparation. Let us remove it quickly, for the flowers— What! no flowers? Ah! it is because I forgot to sow the seeds. Let us begin the operation over again. What flowers do you want—a mignonette, a violet, a marigold? Here is a seed of each kind, which I shall put into the glass. Now let each one tell me the flower that he prefers. Now I cover the glass and count three seconds. See the magnificent bouquet!" (Fig. 3.)

Finally the trick is finished by taking from the hat a number of small bouquets that are offered to the ladies. The following is an explanation of the various tricks, beginning with that which involves the *boutonnière* of the magician himself.

I. The Buttonhole Rose.

This is a stemless artificial rose of muslin, which is secured by a strong black silk thread arrested by a knot. To this thread, which should be five or six inches in length, is attached quite a strong rubber cord capable of being doubled if need be. The free extremity of the rubber traverses, in the first place, the left buttonhole of the coat, and then a small eyelet formed beneath, and then passes over the chest and behind the back, and is fixed by the extremity to one of the right-hand buttons of the waistband of the trousers.

When the prestidigitateur comes upon the stage, the rose is carried under his left armpit, where he holds it by a slight pressure of the arm. At the proper moment he raises his wand toward the right, and looks in the same direction in order to attract the eyes of the spectators to that side; but at the same time he separates his arms slightly, and the rose, held by the taut rubber, suddenly puts itself in place. The magic effect produced by the instantaneous appearance of this flower, coming whence no one knows where, could not be appreciated without having been seen.

II. The Flowers in the Small Box.

In the second appearance of flowers, produced by means of the small apparatus shown in Fig. 2, there is really nothing very mysterious. The special object of it is to bring into relief the experiment that is to follow, and in which, evidently, there can be no question of double bottom. Moreover, the diversity of the means employed contributes powerfully toward astounding the spectators.

Fig. 2 shows in section the three pieces of the apparatus, which are placed separately upon the table in Fig. 1. A is the cylindrical tin box in which the seeds are sown, and B another box of slightly larger diameter, but in other respects just like the first, which it entirely covers. To the bottom of B is fixed a small bouquet of artificial flowers. By slightly squeezing the cover, C (which is of thin brass), toward the bottom, the box, B, with the bouquet, is lifted. If, on the contrary, the box is left upon the table, the spectators do not perceive the substitution made, and think that they all the time see the first box, whence they believe the flowers started.

III. The Bouquet in the Glass.

This is the most interesting part of the experiment.

As we have said, the glass is first covered with a hat, and the prestidigitateur feigns astonishment upon seeing that the flowers have not appeared, but at the very instant at which the hat is lifted, when all eyes are fixed upon the glass, looking for the bouquet announced, the operator, who, with the right hand, holds the hat carelessly resting upon the edge of the table, suddenly sticks his middle finger in the cardboard tube fixed to the handle of the bouquet, which has been placed in advance upon a bracket, as shown in Fig. 1, and, immediately raising his finger, introduces the flowers into the hat, taking good care (and this is an important point) not to turn his gaze away from the glass to the bouquet or hat, as one might feel himself led to do in such a case. This introduction of the bouquet should be effected in less than a second, after which the hat is held aloft, while with the left hand some imaginary seeds, the kinds of which are designated in measure as they are taken, are selected from the cardboard box and successively deposited in the glass. So, this time, be certain of it, the flowers will appear.

IV. The Small Bouquets in the Hat.

There is not a second to be lost; the spectators are admiring the bouquet and are astonished to see it make its appearance. The operator very quickly profits by this moment of surprise to introduce, by the same process as before, a package of small bouquets tied together with a weak thread that will afterward be broken in the hat. We have not figured these bouquets upon the bracket, in order to avoid complication. Of course, a skillful operator will not hasten to produce the small bouquets. He will advance toward the spectators as if the experiment were ended, and as if he wished to return the hat to the person from whom he borrowed it. Afterward making believe answer a request, he says: "You wish some flowers, madam? And you too? And are there others who wish some? I will, then, empty into the hat the rest of my wonderful seeds, and we shall see the result." It is at this moment that the spectators are attentive and that all eyes are open to see the advent of the flowers.

TRICKS WITH A HAT.

Prestidigitateurs frequently borrow from their spectators a hat that serves them for the performance of very neat tricks which are not always easily explained. We shall describe some of the most interesting of these.

The operator will begin by proving to you that the felt of your hat is of bad quality, and, to this effect, he will pierce it here and there with his finger, his magic wand, an egg, and with a host of other objects.

This is all an illusion, the mystery of which is explained by our first engraving. (See the finger B.) It is either of wood or cardboard, and terminates in a long slender needle. The prestidigitateur, who has concealed the finger in his left hand, thrusts the point into the top of the hat, whose interior is turned toward the spectators. Afterward raising the right hand, the forefinger of which he points forward, he seems to be about to pierce the top of the hat, but instead of finishing the motion begun, he quickly seizes in the interior, between the thumb and forefinger, the point of the needle, wiggles it around in all directions, turns the hat over, and the cardboard finger, which moves, seems to be the prestidigitateur's own finger. The same operation is performed with the wooden half egg, C, and the rod, A, which, like the finger, appear to traverse the hat, in the interior of which are hidden the true rod and egg. We may likewise solder a needle to a half of a five-franc piece, and thus vary the objects employed for this recreation to infinity.

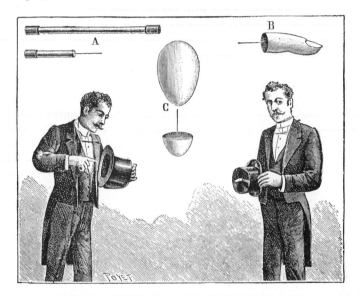

PASSING A FINGER, ROD, AND EGG THROUGH A HAT.

In order to take from a hat a large quantity of paper in ribbons, and then doves, and even a duck or a rabbit, there is no need of special apparatus nor of a great amount of dexterity, and still less of the revolving bobbin or of the mysterious machine whose existence is generally believed in by the spectators when they see the paper falling regularly from the hat, and turning gracefully of itself as the water from a new sort of fountain would do.

Nor is there here any need of a high hat; a simple straw hat (or a cap, at a pinch) will suffice. The prestidigitateur holds close pressed to his breast and hidden under his coat a roll of the blue paper prepared for the printing apparatus of the Morse telegraph, and which is so tightly wound that it has the aspect and consistence of a wooden disk with a circular aperture in the center. In turning around after taking the hat, the opening of which rests against his breast, the operator deftly introduces into it the roll of paper, which has the proper diameter to allow it to enter by hard friction as far as the top of the hat, and stay where it is put even when the hat is turned over.

Were it needed, the paper might be held by a proper pressure of the left hand exerted from the exterior. The introduction of the paper is effected in a fraction of a second.

" Your hat, my dear sir, was doubtless a little too wide for your head, for I notice within it a band of paper designed to diminish the internal diameter," says the prestidigitateur, while, at the same time, he draws from the hat the

THE ENDLESS PAPER RIBBON.

end that terminates the paper in the centre of the roll. Then he reverses the hat so that the interior cannot be seen by the spectators. The paper immediately begins to unwind of itself and to fall very regularly and without intermission to the right.

When the fall of the paper begins to slacken, that is, in general, when no more than a third of the roll remains, the prestidigitateur turns the hat upside down, and with the right hand pulls out and rapidly revolves in the air the paper ribbon, whose capricious contours, succeeding one another before the first have had time to fall to the floor, produce a very pretty effect, as shown in our second engraving. The quantity of paper extracted from the hat appears also in this way much greater than it really is, and at length forms a pile of considerable bulk.

This experiment may be completed in the following manner: The operator, approaching his table, which, upon a board suspended behind it, carries a firmly bound pigeon, quickly seizes the poor bird in passing, and conceals it under the pile of paper, while he puts the latter back into the hat in order to see, says he, whether all that has been taken out can be made to enter anew.

Having thus introduced the pigeon or any other object into the hat, the paper is taken out, and it is at the moment that the hat is restored to its owner that he pretends to discover that it still contains something.

A CAKE BAKED IN A HAT.

This old trick always amuses the spectators. Some eggs are broken into a porcelain vessel, some flour is added thereto, and there is even incorporated with the paste the eggshells and a few drops of wax or stearine from a near-by candle. The whole having been put into a hat (Fig. 1), the latter is passed three times over a flame, and an excellent cake, baked to a turn, is taken out of this new set of cooking utensils. As for the owner of the hat, who has

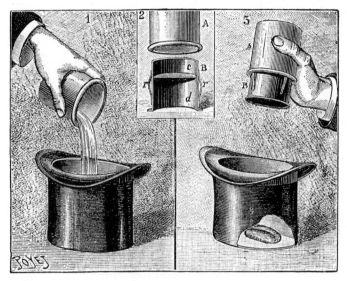

FIGS. 1-3.—A CAKE BAKED IN A HAT.

passed through a state of great apprehension, he finds with evident satisfaction (at least in most cases) that his head gear has preserved no traces of the mixture that was poured into it.

Fig. 2 shows the apparatus employed by prestidigitateurs to bake a cake in a hat. A is an earthen or porcelain vessel (it may also be of metal) into which enters a metallic cylinder, B, which is provided with a flange at one of its extremities and is divided by a horizontal partition into two unequal compartments, c and d. The interior of the part d is painted white so as to imitate porcelain. Finally, when the cylinder, B, is wholly inserted in the vessel, A, in which it is held by four springs, r, r, r, r, fixed to the sides, there is nothing to denote at a short distance that the vessel, A, is not empty, just as it was presented at the beginning of the experiment.

The prestidigitateur has secretly introduced into the hat the small cake and the apparatus, B, by making them fall suddenly from a bracket affixed to the back of a chair. That at least is the most practical method of operating.

The vessel, A, about which there is nothing peculiar, is, of course, submitted to the examination of the spectators. The object of adding the flour is to render the paste less fluid, and to thus more certainly avoid the production of stains.

The cake being arranged under the apparatus, B, in the space *d*, the contents of the vessel, A, poured from a certain height, fall into the part *c* of the apparatus; then the vessel, gradually brought nearer, is quickly inserted into the hat in order to seize therein, and at the same time remove, the receptacle, B, with its contents, and leave only the cake.

Fig. 3 shows this last operation. We have intentionally shown the part, B, projecting from the vessel, A, but it will be understood that in reality it must be inserted up to the base at the moment

FIG. 4.

at which the vessel, A, introduced into the hat, is concealed from the eyes of the spectators. The prestidigitateur none the less continues to move his finger all around the interior of the double vessel as if to gather up the remainder of the paste, which he makes believe throw into the hat, upon the rim of which he even affects to wipe his fingers, to the great disquietude of the gentleman to whom it belongs.

The experiment may be complicated by first burning alcohol or fragments of paper in the compartment *c* of the apparatus. Some prestidigitateurs even add a little Bengal fire. But let no one imitate that amateur prestidigitateur who, wishing to render the experiment more brilliant, put into the receptacle such a quantity of powder that a disaster supervened, so that it became necessary to throw water into the burning hat in order to extinguish the nascent fire.

FIG. 5.

The following method of baking a cake in a hat is a decided improvement over the old trick with the porcelain vessel. It has the advantage of being able to be employed anywhere and of producing a complete illusion.

Before beginning the experiment, take three eggs, and having blown two of them, close the apertures with white wax. Place the three eggs upon a plate.

Within the left-hand side of your waistcoat place a flat cake, and then make your appearance before the spectators.

Having borrowed a hat, place it upon the table, and, after secretly introducing the cake into it (Fig. 4), take an empty egg, crack the shell upon the edge of the plate, and, inserting your hands in the hat, make believe empty the contents of the egg into the latter (Fig. 5).

In order that the means employed may not occur to any one, take the perfect egg and let it fall upon the plate so that it will break and its contents flow out. Then take the remaining egg and operate as with the first. All you have to do then is to pass the hat back and forth a few times over the flame of a candle in order to cook the mass and then to serve the cake.

THE EGG AND HAT TRICK.

An effect due to an invisible thread is the following:

Some months ago, in a Parisian public establishment, a clown took a hat and a handkerchief, and then, after showing, by spreading it out, that the handkerchief was empty, drew an egg from the folds of the crumpled fabric and allowed it to drop into the hat. Then he took up the handkerchief, shook it out again, crumpled it up, found another egg, and let it drop into the hat, and so on. When it might have been supposed that the hat contained a certain number of eggs, he turned it upside down, and, lo and behold, the hat was empty! All the eggs from the handkerchief were reduced to a single one attached by a thread to one of the sides of the handkerchief, and which the amusing operator maliciously exhibited, after seeming to look·for the vanished eggs.

While the handkerchief was stretched out, the egg was behind it, and, although

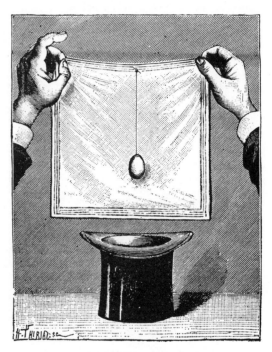

THE EGG AND HAT TRICK.

it was shaken, remained suspended by its thread. In crumpling the handkerchief it was easy to seem to find the egg in it, and to put it in the hat, where it did not remain, however, for, lifted by the thread, it resumed its place behind the handkerchief. Our engraving shows the handkerchief at the moment that the egg has been removed by the thread on the side opposite that of the spectators.

On attaching a black thread, sixteen or twenty inches in length, to an empty egg, and selecting the egg thus prepared from a lot of ordinary eggs, as if by chance, we have a ready means of amusing and mystifying spectators for a long time.   Having hooked the free extremity of the thread to a buttonhole of the waistcoat, let us lay the egg upon the table.   After apparently ordering it to approach us, it suffices to recede from the table to make the docile egg obey the command.   By the same means it may be made to make its exit alone from a hat; or, again, by bearing upon the invisible thread, it may be made to dance upon a cane or upon the hand; in a word, to perform various operations that eggs are not accustomed to perform.

MULTIPLICATION OF COINS.

Upon a small rectangular tray of japanned sheet iron, similar to those in common use, are placed seven coins (Fig. 1).   A spectator is asked to receive these in his hand and to put the coins back upon the tray, one by one, and to count them with a loud voice as he does so.   It is then found that the number

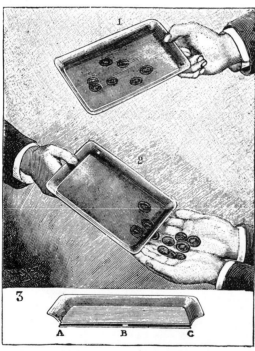

MULTIPLICATION OF COINS.

has doubled, there being fourteen instead of seven. The same operation repeated gives as a result twenty-one coins.

As may be seen in the section in Fig. 3, the tray has a double bottom, forming an interspace a little wider than the thickness of one of the coins, and which is divided breadthwise into two equal compartments by a partition, B.   These two compartments are closed all around, save at the ends of the tray, where there are two apertures, A and C, that in length are double the diameter of the coins.   In this interspace are concealed fourteen coins, seven on each side.   When the contents of the tray are emptied into the hand of a spectator, the coins concealed in one of the compartments drop at the same time (Fig. 2).   The operator then takes the tray in his other hand, and thus naturally seizes it at the end at which the now empty compartment exists, and this allows the seven coins that are contained in the other compartment to join the first ones, when the latter are rapidly emptied into the hands of the spectator for the second time.

A square tray, with a double bottom divided into four compartments by divisions running diagonally from one corner to another, would permit of increasing the number of coins four times.

Let us say, however, that skillful prestidigitateurs dispense with the double bottom. They hold the coins sometimes under the tray with their fingers extended, and sometimes on the tray, under their thumbs, and renew their supply several times from secret pockets skillfully arranged in various parts of their coats, where the spectators are far from suspecting the existence of them.

MAGIC COINS.

The street venders of Paris have for some time past been selling to pedestrians a coin that can be made to enter an ordinary wine bottle. This coin is a genuine ten centime piece, but, when it is handled, it is found that it bends exactly like the leaves of a dining-room table. Amateur mechanics, clock-makers, and copper turners can easily manufacture similar ones. The process is as follows:

FIG. 1.—MAGIC COINS.

By means of a very fine metal saw, cut the coin in three pieces, either by parallel cuts, or, better, by following the contours shown in Fig. 1. If the operation be skillfully performed, the marks of the cutting, too, will be

FIG. 2.—MODE OF INSERTING THE COIN IN A BOTTLE.

nearly invisible. Before the coin is sawed, a groove about a line in depth should be formed in the rim by means of a saw or file. In this channel or groove is inserted a very taut rubber ring, which, before it is stretched, should be, at the most, one and a half or two lines in diameter. If the rubber is well hidden in the groove, the cleft coin will appear to be absolutely intact.

Owing to this process, the coin can be easily inserted in a bottle by placing the hands as shown in Fig. 2. The hand that bends the coin covers the mouth. The coin is inserted, and then, by a smart blow given the bottle, it is made to pass through the neck. Owing to the tension of the rubber, the piece at once regains its flat form, and the operator makes it ring against the glass in order to show that it is really a piece of metal. In order to extract it, it is necessary to get the saw marks exactly in the direction of the bottle's axis, then the bottle is slightly inclined, neck downward, and through a few

FIG. 3.—THE DOUBLE SOU.

blows on the latter the coin is made to drop into the hand, where it will at once assume its original form.

We shall now have a few words to say about what is called the "double sou." The operator places the prepared coin in his hand, and calls strict attention to the fact that there is no companion piece. Then he covers it with his other hand for a moment, and finally shows two coins, instead of one, in the first hand.

Fig. 3 shows, not how the experiment is performed, but how the double coin is prepared. It is simply an ordinary sou, over which is placed a sort of hollow cover containing the impression of the coin, and which fits on the latter so accurately that the piece looks like an ordinary sou. This cover is lifted and made to slide alongside of the coin, thus showing two pieces instead of one.

The cover is stamped from a thin sheet of copper placed upon a sou serving as a mould. It might possibly be made by means of some electro-metallurgical process. The mutilation of United States coins is forbidden under penalty of the law.

THE DISSOLVING COIN.

Borrow a silver dollar, and have it marked, so that it can be identified. Ask some one to hold the coin horizontally between the thumb and forefinger of the right hand within the folds of a silk handkerchief, and over a glass full of water held in the left hand, Fig. 1. Your assistant's two hands being thus occupied, you will have no sort of indiscretion to fear. Stepping back a few feet, direct your assistant to let the coin drop; and the impact against the bottom of the glass will be heard by the entire assemblage. When the handkerchief is raised the coin is no longer in the glass, but has made its way to your hand or to the pocket of a spectator. Let it be examined, and it will be found to be really the coin that has been previously marked.

In order to perform this trick it is necessary to have a disk of glass of the same diameter as a silver dollar (Fig. 2).

Hide this disk, A (Fig. 3), in the palm of your right hand, turned toward you. This will not prevent you from holding the coin that has been confided to you between the thumb and forefinger of the same hand. While your hand is concealed by the handkerchief in which it is thought that you placed the coin, you shift the latter and give the assistant the glass disk to hold, by the

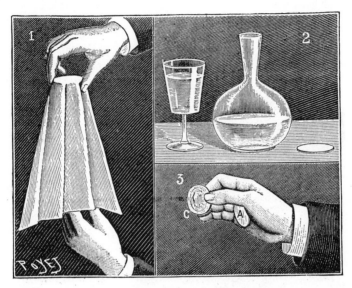

DISAPPEARANCE OF A SILVER DOLLAR.

edge, of course, and not by the flat surface, so that the substitution that you have made cannot be perceived by the touch.

After the trick has been performed, do not be afraid to let the person who has held the coin, and who is thoroughly astonished, examine the glass and its contents at his leisure. The glass disk is entirely invisible in the water, and if, as it is well to do, you have taken care to select a glass whose bottom is perfectly plane and of the same diameter as the disk (Fig. 2), the latter will remain adherent to the glass even when it is inverted to empty the water in order to prove once more to the spectators that it contains nothing but clear water.

THE SPIRIT SLATES.

Two ordinary wooden-framed slates are presented to the spectators, and examined in succession by them. A small piece of chalk is introduced between the two slates, which are then united by a rubber band and held aloft in the prestidigitateur's right hand.

Then, in the general silence, is heard the scratching of the chalk, which is writing between the two slates the answer to a question asked by one of the spectators—the name of a card thought of or the number of spots obtained by throwing two dice. The rubber band having been removed and the slates separated, one of them is seen to be covered with writing. This prodigy, which at first sight seems to be so mysterious, is very easily performed.

The writing was done in advance; but upon the written side of the slate, A, there had been placed a thin sheet of black cardboard which hid the char-

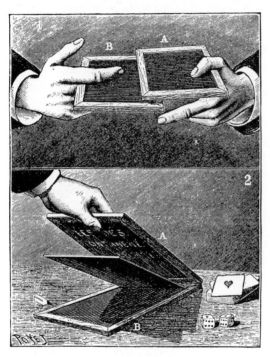

acters written with chalk. The two sides of this slate thus appeared absolutely clean.

The slate B is first given out for examination, and after it has been returned to him, the operator says: "Do you want to examine the other one also?" And then, without any haste, he makes a pass analogous to that employed in shuffling cards. The slate A being held by the thumb and forefinger of the left hand and the slate B between the fore and middle finger of the right hand (Fig. 1), the two hands are brought together. But at the moment at which the slates are superposed, the thumb and forefinger of the right hand grasp the slate A, while at the same time the fore and middle finger of the left hand take

SPIRIT SLATES.

the slate B. Then the two hands separate anew, and the slate that has already been examined, instead of the second one, is put into the hands of the spectator. This shifting, done with deliberation, is entirely invisible.

During the second examination the slate A is laid flat upon a table, the written face turned upward and covered with black cardboard. The slate having been sufficiently examined, and been returned to the operator, the latter lays it upon the first, and both are then surrounded by the rubber band.

It is then that the operator holds up the slates with the left hand, of which one sees but the thumb, while upon the posterior face of the second slate the nail of his middle finger makes a sound resembling that produced by chalk when written with. When the operator judges that this little comedy has lasted quite long enough, he lays the two slates horizontally upon his table, taking care this time that the non-prepared slate shall be beneath (Fig. 2). It is upon it that the black cardboard rests; and the other slate, on being raised, shows the characters that it bears, and that are stated to have been written by an invisible spirit that slipped in between the two slates.

SECOND SIGHT.

"The trick is performed as follows," says Judge James Bartlett in the *Popular Science News:* "Each person in the audience is presented with a slip of paper, upon which to write anything he or she may choose. The paper written upon is immediately secreted by the writer, as much care as possible being taken that no one else sees what is written upon it. The performer, who has been absent from the room while this is being done, is brought in and led, as if in a state of trance, to a chair within full view of every one present. A light piece of drapery is thrown over him so that he is completely covered by it, and yet it is thin enough to be translucent, and it can be seen he has not gone down through the floor or ascended up through the ceiling. The audience is told the drapery prevents the sphere or influence or spell that surrounds him from being dissipated. He now begins and repeats, word for word, the sentences written upon any or all the slips of paper. Nothing can be more astonishing; the paper has not left the possession of the writers; it is equally certain that it is impossible that another person could have seen what was thereon written, and yet the trick is as simple as it is surprising, and that is certainly saying a great deal.

"The explanation is as follows: In order to write anything upon the slip of paper given out, one must have something firm and flat upon which to place it, and for this purpose bits of pasteboard of a convenient size are handed about the audience. The pasteboard, however, is not solid, as it seems to be; the uppermost layer of paper can be separated at one of the edges from the layers beneath it, and into this slip white paper introduced. The uppermost layer of paper is blacked with crayon or soft pencil on its under side, and whatever is written upon the paper resting upon it is faithfully stenciled or traced upon the white paper inserted. The pasteboards, being collected, are taken out of the room and given to the performer by his assistant, who may or may not be a confederate. That is, if the performer is very skillful, he may dupe his assistant as well as his audience. He may tell him, for instance, it is necessary for him to have these pasteboard rests and pass his fingers over them so that he can become *en rapport* with the person with whom they were in contact. It is better, however, at least at first, to have a confederate. The rest is easy enough. The inserted slips of tell-tale papers are collected and carried with him by the performer, who manages to read them either through a hole in the drapery or by the light that sifts through it as he sits covered up in his chair with his back to the audience. It is well, sometimes, not to have enough pasteboard cards to go round the audience, and give apparently at haphazard a book, an atlas or portfolio, which, of course, has been neatly covered with paper or cloth and supplied with blackened and with white paper as are the pasteboard cards.

" If anything should happen that would prevent reading any particular strip of paper, the performer may at once say that he does not pretend to be able to read all, but only such sentences as appear to his mental vision. This will add to the effect and make the trick appear all the more mysterious. In supplying pencils to your audience be sure to give them good, hard ones, that will require some pressure to make the writing legible; be careful, too, that the paper with which you furnish them is rather thin, so that you will get a good tracing on that you have inserted in the pasteboard rest. As each slip is read by the performer the assistant should ask if any one in the audience wrote that sentence and if it is correctly repeated, and then, stepping to the writer and taking the slip from him or her, he should himself read it aloud and show it to any one desirous of seeing it; this enhances the wonder and interest of the performance, and also gives the performer time to decipher the next slip. It is well to have the sentences take the form of questions which the performer can read, comment upon, and answer in an oracular way, especially as this takes up time, and consequently gives fewer selected slips to read during the period allotted to the trick; for to read a few is quite as wonderful as to read many.

" Now let the master of occult art cap the climax. Let him again be led from the room, ostensibly to have his magic sphere renewed, and let some one among the audience write the name of a deceased person, together with their own, on a slip of paper. Lay a good deal of stress on the requirement that one name shall be that of a person deceased; this, of course, being only to mystify the audience. When the names have been written the performer is to enter the room. He does so with the sleeve of his coat rolled up, and his arm bared to the elbow. After showing there is nothing upon his arm, he turns down his sleeve, readjusts his cuff, and proceeds with his trick. He first names the person whom the audience has chosen, in his absence, to write the name; he requests that person to crumple up the slip of paper upon which the name is written and rub it well over his arm just above his cuff, ' so that the writing will penetrate through his sleeve,' he says; now turning up his sleeve he shows the writing that was upon the paper in blood-red letters upon his bared arm. The manner of performing this part of the trick is, having ascertained, as before, the writing upon the slip of paper by means of the tracing, to write or print it with red ink mixed with a little glycerine, or red printer's ink, or oil color and turpentine, upon paper which is to be fastened upon the inside of that part of the performer's coat sleeve which he instructs the person who has written the name upon the paper to rub with the paper. The paper may be neatly pinned to the lining of the sleeve, care being taken that the pins do not scratch when the sleeve is turned down."

MAGIC CABINETS.

The apparatus by means of which objects of various sizes—a card, a bird, a child, a woman, etc.—may be made to apparently disappear play a large part in the exhibitions of magicians, and also in pantomimes and fairy scenes. Among such apparatus there are some that are based upon ingenious mechanical combinations, while others bring in the aid of optics. We shall examine a few of them.

The Magic Portfolio.

This is an apparatus which an itinerant physicist might have been seen a few years ago exhibiting in the squares and at street corners. His method was to have a spectator draw a card, which he then placed between the four sheets of paper which, folded crossways, formed the flaps of his portfolio. When he opened the latter again a few instants afterward the card had disappeared,

MAGIC PORTFOLIOS, ENVELOPES, AND BOXES.

or rather had become transformed. Profiting then by the surprise of his spectators, the showman began to offer them his magic portfolio at the price of five cents for the small size and ten for the large.

The portfolio was made of two square pieces of cardboard connected by four strings, these latter being fixed in such a way that when the two pieces of cardboard were open and juxtaposed the external edge of each of them was connected with the inner edge of the other.

This constituted, after a manner, a double hinge that permitted of the portfolio being opened from both sides. To one pair of strings there were glued, back to back, two sheets of paper, which, when folded over, formed the flaps of the portfolio. It was only necessary, then, to open the latter in one direction or the other to render it impossible to open more than one of the two sets of flaps.

This device is one that permits of a large number of tricks being performed, since every object put under one of the sets of flaps will apparently disappear or be converted into something else, at the will of the prestidigitateur.

MAGIC ENVELOPES.

This trick is a simplification of the foregoing. The affair consists of several sheets of paper of different colors folded over, one upon the other. A card inclosed within the middle envelope, over which have been folded all the others, is found to have disappeared when the flaps are opened again. The secret of the trick is very simple. One of the inner sheets of paper—the second one, usually—is double, and, when folded, forms two envelopes that are back to back. It is only necessary, then, to open one or the other of these latter to cause the appearance or disappearance or transformation of such objects as have been inclosed within it.

MAGIC BOXES.

Magic boxes are of several styles, according to the size of the objects that one desires to make disappear.

There is no one who has not seen a magician put one or more pigeons into the drawer of one of these boxes, and, after closing it, open it to find that the birds have disappeared. Such boxes contain two drawers, which, when pulled out, seem to be but one; and it is only necessary, then, to pull out the inner one or leave it closed in order to render the inclosed birds visible or invisible.

In order to cause the disappearance of smaller objects, trick performers often employ a jewel box, and after putting the object (a ring, for example) into this, they hand it to some person and ask him to hold it, requesting him at the same time to wrap it up in several sheets of paper. But this simple motion has permitted the performer to cause the ring to drop into his hand through a small trap opening beneath the box. Yet, while he is doing this the spectators think that they hear the noise made by the ring striking against the sides of the box. But that is only an illusion; for the noise that is heard proceeds from a small hammer which is hidden within the cover under the escutcheon, and which is rendered movable when the latter is pressed upon by the performer. The box can thus be shaken without any noise being heard within it, and the spectators are led to believe that the object has disappeared.

Double-bottomed boxes are so well known that it is useless to describe them. Sometimes the double bottom is hidden in the cover, and at others it rests against one of the sides. Such boxes permit of the disappearance or substitution of objects that are not very thick, such as a note, an image, or a card.

THE TRAVELING BOTTLE AND GLASS.

Upon a table, at the rising of the curtain, are observed a bottle and a glass, the latter full of wine up to the brim. The prestidigitateur pours into the bottle half of the liquid, "which otherwise," he remarks, "might slop over during the voyage." Then two cylinders of the same diameter as the bottle are made before the eyes of the spectators out of two sheets of paper and four pins.

These are designed to cover the bottle and the glass, which have been separated from each other by a short interval (Fig. 1). Instantaneously, and in an invisible manner, the two objects change places twice, and yet there is never anything in the paper cylinders, which are, ostensibly, torn into a hundred bits.

Fig. 3 unravels the mystery. The bottle is of varnished tin, and bottomless. It covers a second bottle that is similar, but a little smaller, and in the center there is concealed a glass similar to the one that has been shown, but empty. It receives the half of the wine that was

TRICK WITH A BOTTLE AND GLASS OF WINE.

poured from the first glass. This operation necessarily contributes toward convincing the spectators that they have before them an ordinary bottle provided with a bottom and capable of containing a liquid.

The operator first covers the bottle with one of the paper cylinders as if to ascertain whether it has the proper diameter, but immediately removes it and places it upright upon the table.

What no one can suspect, however, he has at the same time lifted the first bottle by slightly compressing the paper. It is then the second bottle that is seen, and which is precisely like the other, the labels of both being turned toward the same side and exhibiting a slight tear or a few identical spots designed to aid in the deception.

The operator, having finished his palaver, places the empty cylinder upon the second bottle and covers the glass with the one in which the first bottle is concealed (Fig 2). The magic wand is then brought into play, and after this the paper cylinder alone is lifted at the side where the glass was in the first place seen, while at the opposite side, the bottle, on being removed, exposes the glass that it concealed.   The operation is begun over again in the opposite direction ; and, finally, under pretense of once again showing that either paper cylinder can be used indifferently, the operator replaces upon the second bottle the cylinder that still contains the first one, unbeknown to the spectators.

This is done so rapidly that the action is apparently a gesture, but nothing more is needed to free the cylinder of its contents and reëstablish things in their former state.

DISAPPEARANCE OF AN APPLE AND A NINEPIN.

To an apple and a ninepin, the principal objects with which this trick is performed, are added as accessories a napkin, a large vessel of dark blue glass, and a cone of coarse paper, which is made on the spot by molding it over the ninepin.

First Disappearance (Fig. 1).—The apple, "in order that it may be more in sight," is placed upon the inverted glass, V, under the paper cone, while

TRICK WITH AN APPLE AND A NINEPIN.

the inverted ninepin is covered with the napkin, S, through which it is held. All at once the napkin, quickly seized by the two corners, is vigorously shaken, and the ninepin has disappeared, or, rather, it is found upon the glass in place of the apple, which has passed into the prestidigitateur's pocket.

Second Disappearance (Fig. 2).—The apple, first placed upon the table, is thrown invisibly toward the paper cone, under which, in fact, it is found.

And the ninepin ? The prestidigitateur "had forgotten" to tell it where it was to go when he sent the apple in its place. As he gives up trying to find it and seizes the blue vessel in order to put it in place, it is seen that the ninepin, driven by the apple, has passed underneath.

Fig. 3 renders an explanation scarcely necessary. At the moment that the paper cone was made, the ninepin, A, was covered with a dummy, B, of thin metal, which remained in the cone when the latter was removed. In the napkin, formed of two napkins sewed together by their edges, was concealed, between the two fabrics, a small disk of cardboard of the same diameter as the base of the ninepin. The latter was allowed to fall secretly behind the table into a box lined with silk waste, only the cardboard disk being held, thanks to which the napkin preserved the same form that it possessed when the ninepin was beneath it, as shown in Fig. 1. There is no need of explanation in regard to the apple that comes out of the prestidigitateur's pocket and which is similar to the one that remained on the glass and was hidden by the false ninepin that covered it when the paper cone alone was removed.

For the second disappearance the apple, placed upon the table, is surrounded by the two hands of the prestidigitateur, who, while it is thus concealed, by a blow given with the little finger of the right hand, sends it rolling on to a shelf behind the table. His hands, nevertheless, preserve the same position as if they held the apple. It is the first one that is seen upon the foot of the glass, the false ninepin being removed this time with the paper cover. Under the glass there is a second false ninepin, C, of metal, painted dark blue in the interior and which has a narrow flange through which it rests upon the edge of the glass, of which it seems to form a part. Fig. 3 shows it in section with the glass, and also the different pieces as they are arranged at the beginning of the experiment.

A GOBLET OF INK CONVERTED INTO AN AQUARIUM.

Exhibit a goblet which is apparently nearly full of ink, and place it upon a table. In order to prove that the goblet really contains ink, partially immerse a visiting card in the liquid, and, on taking it out, show that it has been blackened. With an ordinary spoon dip out some of the ink and pour it into a saucer. Then, having borrowed a ring, pretend to dip it into the ink, but really allow it to drop into the saucer. Announce that you are going to make amends for your awkwardness, not by plunging your hand into the liquid, which would have the inconvenience of blackening it, but by rendering the ink colorless instantaneously. Take a white napkin or a large

FIG. 1.

sized silk handkerchief and cover the glass with it.   Upon removing the napkin or handkerchief, the glass will be found to contain clear water in which living fish are swimming. The hand may then be dipped into the liquid and the ring be taken out without fear.

FIG . 2.

The trick is performed as follows: Take a goblet containing water and some fish, and place against the inner surface a piece of black rubber cloth, to which attach a black thread that is allowed to hang down a few inches outside of the glass, and to the extremity of which is attached a small cork. Of course, the thread and cork must be placed at the side of the glass opposite the spectator.

Cover the glass with the napkin, and on removing the latter, grasp the cork, so as to raise it as well as the rubber cloth in the interior.

As for the card, that should have been previously blackened on one side for about three-quarters of its length, and, after being immersed in the liquid, with the white side toward the spectator, should be quickly turned around so as to show the blackened side. As for the liquid taken out with the spoon, care should have been taken to previously fix in the interior of the bowl a few particles of aniline black soluble in water, by breathing on the spoon before introducing the powder, this serving to fix it. Then the water taken out with the spoon will be converted into ink, which may be poured into a plate or saucer.

THE INVISIBLE JOURNEY OF A GLASS OF WINE.

Being given an ordinary glass half full of wine, which everybody can examine closely, and a hat situated at a distance, the question is to cover the glass with a piece of paper, and thence to send it invisibly into the hat.

A small piece of wood or paper that a spectator has put in the wine, or any mark whatever that has been made upon the glass, will permit of verifying the fact that it is really the same glass that was first exhibited, and that is afterwards found in the hat.

In order to perform this trick, it is necessary to have one of those double glasses (Fig. 4) that can be easily obtained in variety stores, and which contain between their double sides a red liquid that has been introduced through the foot of the glass, which is hollow. A small cork, *b*, which is absolutely invisible if it is not examined very closely, is inserted and withdrawn at will in order to change the liquid; but, for our trick, there is no occasion to occupy ourselves with these details. This double glass is kept concealed until the moment arrives for using it.

A second glass—this is a simple one (Fig. 4, B) and of the same appearance as the other—is filled with wine, in the presence of the spectators, to a level equal to that reached by the red liquid in the double glass.

The prestidigitateur, after exhibiting the interior of the hat so as to allow it to be seen that the latter is empty, introduces into it, while he turns his back to the spectators, the double glass which he had concealed under his arm, and which can be handled without any fear of spilling the liquid that it contains. The hat is then placed upon the table.

Afterward, taking the simple glass in his hands, the prestidigitateur asks the spectators whether he shall make it pass visibly or invisibly into the hat. As a usual thing suggestions are divided, and so, in order to please every-

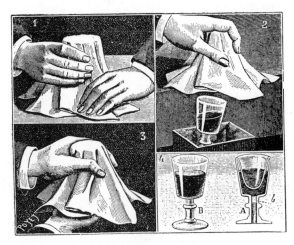

TRICK PERFORMED WITH A GLASS OF WINE.

body, the glass is first put ostensibly into the hat and then immediately taken out; that, at least, is what is thought by the spectators, who are very ready to laugh at the little hoax played upon those who perhaps expected to see the glass carried through the air upon the wings of the wind. But the prestidigitateur has taken care to leave the simple glass in the hat, and to take out, in place of it, the double glass, which he presently spirits away with ease by the following process. The glass having been placed upon the table, he covers it with a square piece of strong paper, which he folds around it in such a way as to make it follow its contours and completely conceal it (Fig. 1). This paper, which must be very stiff, as well as strong, afterward preserves the form upon which, so to speak, it has been molded, although it is no longer supported by the glass, which has been allowed to fall behind the table into a sort of pocket of canvas, or into a box lined with silk waste, arranged to this effect (Fig. 2).

The prestidigitateur, having thus got rid of the glass, walks toward the spectators, delicately pressing the top of the paper between the thumb and forefinger of the left hand, as if he still held the glass in the paper, and the foot of which seems to be supported by the right hand. A spectator is then invited to take the glass with the paper, and care is taken to advise him not to allow the wine to run up his sleeves.   He then stretches out his hands, but at the same instant the paper, suddenly crumpled into a ball, is thrown into the air, and the glass of wine has passed invisibly into the hat.

THE WINE CHANGED TO WATER.

After having done considerable talking, as required by his profession, a prestidigitateur is excusable for asking permission of his spectators to refresh himself in their presence, especially if he invites one of them to come to keep him company.

WATER CHANGED INTO WINE AND WINE INTO WATER.

An assistant then brings in upon a tray two claret glasses and two perfectly transparent decanters, one of which contains red wine and the other water. The prestidigitateur asks his guest to select one of the two decanters and leave the other for himself.   No hesitation is possible.   The guest hastens to seize the wine and each immediately fills his glass.   How astonishing!   Upon its contact with the glass the wine changes into water and the water becomes wine. Judge of the hilarity of the spectators and the amazement of the victim! The pretended wine was nothing but the following composition: one gram potassium permanganate and two grams sulphuric acid dissolved in one quart of water.   This liquid is instantaneously decolorized on entering the glass, at the bottom of which has been placed a few drops of water saturated with sodium hyposulphite. As for the water in the second decanter, that had had considerable alcohol added to it, and at the bottom of the glass that was to receive it had been placed a small pinch of aniline red, which, as well known, possesses strong tinctorial properties. The glasses must be carried away immediately, since in a few moments the wine changed into water loses its limpidity and assumes a milky appearance. The mixtures are, of course, poisonous.

THE ANIMATED MOUSE.

Street venders are often seen selling, at night, a little mouse which they place upon the back of their hand, and which keeps running as if, having been tamed, it wished to take refuge upon them. In order to prevent it from attaining its object, they interpose the other hand, and then the first one, which is now free, and so on. The mouse keeps on running until the vender has found a purchaser for it at the moderate price of two cents, including the instructions for manipulating it, for, as may have been divined, it is not a question here of a live mouse, but of a toy. This little toy is based upon two effects— first, an effect of optics; and second, the effect due to an invisible thread.

The mouse, which is flat beneath, is provided near the head with a small hook, and the operator has fixed to a but-

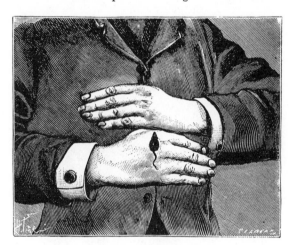

THE ANIMATED MOUSE.

tonhole a thread ten inches in length, terminating in a loop. He fixes this loop in the hook above mentioned, and, tautening the thread, places the mouse upon the back of his left hand (near the little finger, for example).

On moving the hand away from the body, the mouse, which does not stir, seems to slide over the back of the hand, and, at the moment that it is about to fall on reaching the thumb, the right hand, passed beneath, arrives just in time to catch it near the little finger, whence, by the same movement as before, it seems to go toward the thumb.

In order to perform the experiment off-hand, it suffices to take a cork and carve it into the form of a mouse, then cut away the under part of the animal thus rough-shaped, so that it may lie perfectly flat, then make two ears out of cardboard, and a tail out of a piece of twine, and finally blacken the whole in the flame of a candle.   After this, the black thread, terminating in a ball of soft wax or a pin hook, having been fixed to a button-hole, allow the spectators to examine the mouse, and, after is returned to you, fix the thread, either by its ball of wax or its hook, to the front of the flat part of the rodent, which you may then cause to run as above described.

THE SAND FRAME TRICK.

The sand frame is a very ingeniously constructed little apparatus which is employed in different tricks of prestidigitation for causing the disappearance of a card, a photograph, a sealed letter, an answer written upon a sheet of paper, etc.

In appearance it is a simple, plush-covered frame, the back of which opens with a hinge behind a glass, which, at first sight, presents nothing peculiar.

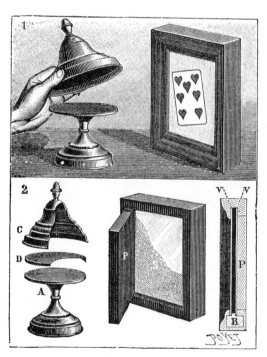

THE SAND FRAME.

In reality, there are two glasses separated from each other by an interval of three millimeters. The lower side of the frame is hollow and forms a reservoir filled with very fine blue sand. In the interior the door is covered with blue paper of the same shade as the sand. The card, portrait, or letter that is sub-sequently to appear is placed in the frame in advance, but, in order to render it invisible, the latter is held vertically, the reservoir at the top. The sand then falls, and fills the space that separates the two glasses, and the blue surface thus formed behind the first glass seems to be the back of the frame. In order to cause the appearance of the con-cealed object, the frame is placed vertically, with the reservoir at the bottom, and covered with a silk handkerchief. In a few seconds the sand will have disappeared. The door that closes the back may be opened by a spectator and the frame shown close by, provided that it be held vertically in order to prevent the sand from appearing between the two glasses.

Fig. 2 shows the frame as seen from behind. The door, P, is seen open, and at S is seen the sand falling between the two glasses. In the section at the side, V and V are the two glasses, P, the door, and R, the reservoir.

Another experiment may be made by means of a small standard on a foot, A, upon which a spectator has placed the seven of hearts. The card passes into the frame. To tell the truth, it is removed by the cover, C, along with the thin disk, D, that covered the foot, A, and upon which it was placed. It will be said that we have here to do with a double bottom. Allow the cover, C, before covering the card, and the foot, A, after the experiment is finished, to be examined. Is the cover asked for again? One will hasten to show it without saying that the back edge of the table has just been struck with it in order to cause the disk, D, and the card to fall on to the shelf.

HOUDIN'S MAGIC BALL.

This ball, which was recently seen in a toy shop, has the aspect, externally, of the one used in the familiar toy known as the " cup and ball." Extending through its center there is a straight cylindrical aperture, and when a cord is passed through the latter, the ball easily slides along it.

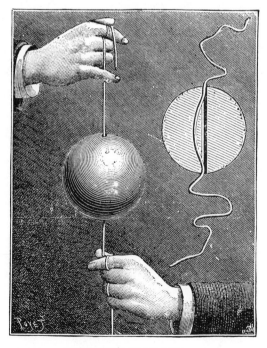

HOUDIN'S MAGIC BALL.

If a person who is in the secret holds the cord by its two extremities, things change, since the ball, far from falling, descends very slowly along the string, or even remains stationary, and does not move again until the operator allows it to.   This trick, which was formerly performed by Robert-Houdin with a ball of large size, very much surprised spectators.

How does the affair work?   That is explained in the section of the magic ball shown in the figure.   In addition to the central aperture, there is another and curved one, which ends near the extremities of the axial perforation, and a person in the secret, while making believe pass the cord through the straight aperture, actually passes it through the curved one.   It will now be apparent that it is only necessary to tighten the cord more or less in order to retard or stop the descent of the ball.   To the left of the engraving is seen the magic ball thus suspended between the operator's hands.

CHAPTER V.

JUGGLERS AND ACROBATIC PERFORMANCES.

JUGGLERS.

The tricks performed by jugglers afford a most wonderful example of the perfection that our senses and organs are capable of attaining under the influence of exercise.

The juggler is obliged to give impetuses that vary infinitesimally. He must know the exact spot whither his ball will go, calculate the parabola that it will describe, and know the exact time that it will take to describe it. His eye must take in the position of three, four, or five balls that are sometimes several yards apart, and he must solve these different problems in optics, mechanics, and mathematics instantaneously, ten, fifteen, twenty times per minute, and that, too, in the least convenient position—upon the back of a running horse, upon a tight-rope, upon a ball, or upon a barrel that he causes to revolve. His dexterity is wonderful. Many jugglers are content to perform their feats of skill with their hands, and, in addition, do balancing worthy of remark.

FIG. 1.

We can obtain experimentally some idea of the dexterity shown by a juggler by trying for ourselves the simplest of his tricks. Whoever is capable of throwing two balls into the air at once, and catching them in succession while standing steadily in the same spot, and without being obliged to step to the right or left, or undergoing contortions, is endowed with an undoubted aptitude for juggling. On the other hand, whoever can stand upright upon a rickety chair without any feeling of fear, or cross a country brook, not upon a tight-rope or wire (which would be too much to ask for a *début*), but upon a plank of two hands' width, and do this without a quick palpitation of the heart, has an aptitude for tight-rope walking.

FIG. 2.

To perform with a couple of balls, however, is quite simple, and many children succeed in it after a few days' practice. They proceed as follows: Having a ball in each hand, they throw the one in the right vertically into the air, pass into the right the one that is in the left and throw this up too, receive the first ball in the left hand, and pass it into the right, throw it up again, and so on; so that the two balls are almost constantly in the air, save during the time it takes to receive the ball with one hand and pass it into the other. If, instead of using both hands, the child employs but one, receiving and throwing one ball while the other is in the air, the difficulty is greater, and the young man who can perform this operation twenty times without dropping one of the balls can treat the artist of the circus as a *confrère*. To perform with three balls it is necessary to have been taught by a professor. Moreover, it should be remarked that the art of juggling has sufficient advantages as regards the development of the touch, the quick calculation of distances, the nimbleness of the fingers, and the accuracy of the eye and of motion, to cause it to be added to those gymnastic exercises which children are taught at school. It is to this art that the celebrated prestidigitateur Robert-Houdin attributed the dexterity and accuracy that he displayed in his tricks. In his memoirs, he relates that, while taking some lessons from an old juggler, he applied himself so closely to the exercises that at the end of a month he could learn nothing further from his instructor. "I succeeded," says he, "in performing with four balls, but that did not satisfy my ambition. I wished, if it were possible, to surpass that faculty of reading by appreciation, which I had so much admired in pianists; so I placed a book in front of me, and, while the four balls were flying in the air, accustomed myself to read without hesitation. It could not be believed how much delicacy and certainty of execution this exercise communicated to my fingers, and what quickness of perception it gave my eye. After in this way rendering my hands supple and obedient, I no longer hesitated to directly practice prestidigitation.''

In order to keep their hand in, professional jugglers have to exercise daily, since a few days of voluntary or forced rest would necessitate double work in order to give the hands their former suppleness and dexterity. As is well known, the same is the case with the agility of the *danseuse*, with whom one day of rest often means more than eight days of double work.

FIG. 3.

Some jugglers perform with objects of the most diverse nature, throwing up, for example, at the same time, a large ball, an orange, and a piece of paper, and giving these articles of different size and weight such an impulsion that each falls and is thrown again at the moment desired. Some jugglers, as a support, use merely a simple wooden bar held vertically, and upon the top of which they perform their various feats of dexterity or contortion. It is the same apparatus formerly used by Greek acrobats, and, by reason of its form, called πεταυρον (perch for fowls). Some acrobats even balance themselves on the head at the top of this perch, with their legs extended in lieu of a balancing pole. Their arms are free, and they eat, drink, smoke, shoot off a pistol, perform with balls and daggers, and, in a word, perform the most diverse feats (Fig. 2).

Some jugglers are capable of performing extremely curious feats of dexterity with the most diverse objects; for example, with rings that they throw into the air, with hats that they revolve by striking the rim, or with a flag or napkin that they revolve. These hats and napkins no longer seem to obey the laws of gravity. Others, by means of a streamer, form helices and graceful curves; and others, again, by means of a simple bit of paper, succeed in reproducing the Japanese butterfly trick. Japanese maidens are noted for performing this with extraordinary grace and skill.

THE LEAMY REVOLVING TRAPEZE.

The application of mechanics to scenic and gymnastic displays has an interesting exponent in the revolving trapeze, an exhibition which, after attracting much attention in England, has come back to the United States.

In the smaller cut we illustrate the mechanism of the apparatus, while the performance executed upon the apparatus is shown in the larger cut. From the ceiling of the great auditorium is suspended a vertical three sided rectangular frame open at the bottom.   In its lower extremity is journaled at

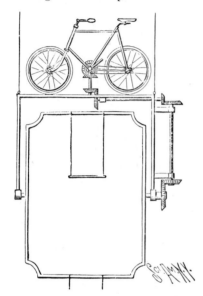

the center a four-sided rectangular frame, from whose extremities two trapezes hang. To the upper side of the vertical frame is secured a bicycle, which, by gearing shown in the small cut, connects with the axle of the lower frame, so that when the cranks of the bicycle are worked the lower frame is turned round and round.   It can be brought into accurate balance by means of shot.   The whole apparatus, including the bicycle, is studded with incandescent electric lamps, and the performer who rides the bicycle wears a helmet carrying electric lights. The very striking performance is explained in great measure by the cut.

One of the performers sits on the bicycle and, turning the cranks, as if riding, keeps the lower frame in rotation, while two performers go through different evolutions on the trapezes thus carried

DIAGRAM OF THE REVOLVING TRAPEZE.

around through the air. A switch board is placed at the head of the bicycle, and by manipulating switches the vari-colored electric lights are turned on and off so as to produce any desired effect. Independent of the high merit of the performance simply as gymnastics, the mechanical points are of value; for ease and safety of manipulation and security from any failure is an absolute essential.   No one has anything to do with its operation except the three performers, so that it is constantly under their control. Where any attempt is made to operate such mechanism from behind the scenes, there is always a great liability of trouble or partial failure; but here the performer on the bicycle does all the work of actuating the mechanical portion and has every part under constant supervision and control, while the illuminated bicycle, located as it is at great height from the floor, is an added attraction. The length of the trapeze ropes, it will be observed, is so adjusted as to allow the performer to pass through the frame without touching it, and the absence of a center bar in the frame is necessary to the same end.

THE LEAMY REVOLVING TRAPEZE.

WALKING ON THE CEILING HEAD DOWN.

A performance of considerable scientific interest has been produced in this and other cities which is presented in the accompanying illustration.* In order to procure a perfectly smooth surface to walk on, a board twenty-four and one-half feet long is suspended from the ceiling, and near one end of this is a trapeze. The lower surface of the board is painted, and is smooth and polished. The performer, who is known as Aimée, the human fly, is equipped with pneumatic attachments to the soles of her shoes. Sitting in the trapeze with her face to the audience, she draws herself upward by the arms, and raises her feet until they press against the board. They adhere by atmospheric pressure. She leaves the trapeze, and hangs head downward, as shown. Taking very short steps, not over eight inches in length, she gradually walks the length of the board backward. She then slowly turns round, taking very short steps while turning, and eventually returns, still walking backward. This closes the performance.

To provide against accident a net is stretched under the board. The performer has frequently fallen, but so far no serious accident has happened. There is a certain art in managing the fall, as, if the shock were received directly by the spinal column, it might be very severe.

The attachment to the shoe is, in general terms, an india-rubber sucker with cup-shaped adhering surface. It is a disk four and one-half inches in diameter and five-eighths of an inch thick. To its center a stud is attached, which is perforated near the end. This stud enters a socket fastened to the sole of the shoe. The socket is also perforated transversely. A pin is passed through the apertures, securing the hold between socket and disk. The socket is under the instep and is attached to the shank of the shoe sole.

A wire loop that extends forward under the toe of the shoe is pivoted on two studs which are secured on each end of the transverse central diameter of the disk. This loop is normally held away from the disk and pressing against the shoe sole by a spring. One end of the loop projects back toward and over the rear edge of the disk. A short piece of string is secured to the india rubber and passes through a hole in the extension, or rearwardly projecting arm, of the loop. The disk when pressed against a smooth surface is held fast by the pressure of the atmosphere. If now the loop is pressed toward the surface to which it adheres, the string will be drawn tight and will pull the edge of the india rubber away from the board. Air will rush in, and the adhesion will cease. As each new step is taken, one disk is made to adhere by pressure, and the other is detached by the action just described.

The power of the disk to sustain the weight of a performer may be easily calculated.

---

* The performer ascends to the top of the audience hall and walks on the ceiling, head down. The ease with which it is apparently done is marvelous.

"AIMÉE," THE HUMAN FLY.

Each sucker is 4½ inches in diameter, and contains therefore 16 square inches of surface. The full atmospheric pressure for the area would amount to 240 pounds. The stud and socket attachment provides a central bearing, so that the full advantage of this and the disk is obtained, and a fairly perfect vacuum procured. As the performer only weighs about 125 pounds, there is about 115 pounds to spare with a perfect vacuum.

THE MYSTERIOUS BALL.

At the circus of the Champs Elysées, at Paris, a performance was given a few years ago that would really put the sagacity of the spectators to the test, did not the performer explain it after his exhibition.

A ball, thirty inches in diameter, is brought into the ring and placed on top of a sloping bridge formed of two planks with an intervening platform (Fig. 1). All at once the ball begins to rock a little, and then moves to the edge of the platform, whence one might expect to see it roll immediately to the base of the inclined plane; but it does nothing of the sort. It stops at the edge and begins to descend with precaution. It seems to hesitate, passes over but a small space, then ascends a little, stops again, and then starts off again in fine style. When it has reached the base of the inclined plane, the lower extremity of which is about twenty inches from the ground, it stops, and then rapidly ascends to the top again. Here the mystery begins to be explained. All at once a flag is seen to make its exit through a small aperture, then a shot is fired from the interior; the ball is certainly inhabited. This we soon have proof of, for, after rolling rapidly to the base of the second inclined plane, it falls upon a cushion placed upon the ground, where a man steps forth from it. It is the clown Lepère. It is very surprising to see a man of such a stature (five feet) make his exit from so small a ball.

Although we have seen "india-rubber men" who could place themselves in so confined a space, we cannot compare their performance to that of M. Lepère, who not only places himself within his ball, but moves therein with a skill that is truly wonderful. It is necessary, in fact, to have a remarkable sense of equilibrium and remarkable suppleness to be able, in such a position, to continually displace the center of gravity of the ball and keep it always in the vertical plane passing through the axis of the bridge. Our second engraving shows how M. Lepère places himself. After the ball is closed, an equilibrium exists only when he is seated.

When he wishes to make his ball move forward, he must bend over and walk upon his hands and knees, after the manner of a squirrel in his wheel. But how many precautions have to be taken to make the axis of the body coincide with that of the bridge, so that the ball shall not fall from the inclined plane, which is but twelve inches wide! And what agility does it not require to react immediately against the velocity acquired after the ball, in conse-

FIG. 1.—THE MYSTERIOUS BALL.

quence of a displacement, has begun to roll! Center of gravity, velocity, and inertia are principles of mechanics that exhibitions of strength and dexterity often put under contribution.   Although clowns do not bother themselves much with learning the principles of mechanics upon which their performances are based, they apply them with wonderful dexterity and have a sort of instinct, a special aptitude, which permits them quickly to find the position of equilibrium.   The performance that M. Lepère presents in so ingenious and new a fashion is an evident proof of this.

FIG. 2.—THE CLOWN IN THE MYSTERIOUS BALL.

CHAPTER VI.

FIRE EATERS AND SWORD TRICKS.

FIRE EATERS—TRICKS WITH FIRE.

Burning is undoubtedly that kind of pain against which the human being most strongly revolts, and the fear of being burned is not confined to man alone, but exists also as an instinct in the entire animal kingdom. This fear, the horror of being burned, which is so powerful in men, accounts for the fact that in all times the wonder and curiosity of the public have been excited by those who are capable of handling burning coals or red-hot iron with impunity, or of touching molten metal, and by those who are proof against flames or burning water or oil. There are many examples in history of individuals who are more or less fireproof, and the trials by fire in ancient and mediæval times do not need to be cited here. It was not until about 1677 that the ques-

tion of the proof of man against fire was looked at from a scientific standpoint. This was done by the physician Dodart, a member of the Academy of Sciences. These studies were provoked by the wonderful tricks which were being performed at that time in Paris by an English chemist named Richardson. Dodart explained that these experiments could be performed without the aid of any chemical preparation, by taking a few precautions, and also that the success of them depended upon the hardening that the epidermis may acquire under the influence of an oft-repeated action.

A MOUNTEBANK LICKING A RED-HOT BAR OF IRON.

This hardening of the skin among laborers results in their frequently being able to handle red-hot iron and lighted coals with impunity.   This, however, does not suffice to explain the tricks of those individuals who exhibit in public as fireproof.   The experiments of the Italian physician and chemist, Sementini, have shown that there are preparations which, when put upon the skin, render the latter absolutely insensible to contact with fire or incandescent materials. His first experiments had no result; finally, after submitting himself to repeated friction with sulphurous acid, he was enabled to apply a red-hot iron to his

FIRE EATERS AT THE OLYMPIA THEATER, PARIS.

skin with impunity.   Continuing his experiments, he found that a solution of alum had the same property.   One day, having accidentally rubbed soap upon the surface of a hand that had previously been impregnated with alum, he found that the hand was still further proof against fire.   He then discovered that a layer of powdered sugar covered with soap sufficed to render his tongue entirely insensible to heat.   After all these experiments Sementini succeeded in making himself much better proof against fire than was the charlatan who first suggested the experiment to him.

Fire eaters have always been very popular on the vaudeville stage, and we present an engraving showing two fire eaters at the Olympia Theater, Paris.

When the performers appear upon the stage, they are clad in a tight-fitting costume of a red color which represents that of the devils of fairy scenes. The stage upon which they appear is but dimly lighted during their presence upon it. The devils, after making their bow, go to the rear of the stage, and put some preparations upon their hands; they come to the front of the stage and cause very thin but brilliant flames to dart from their fingers; bringing these flames near to their mouths, they seem to swallow them and then extinguish them between their teeth. When the two devils touch each other's hands a crackling sound is heard, and long flames dart forth for a few seconds from the tips of their fingers, which they continuously move. They subsequently experiment without putting anything in their mouths; they blow with energy, and a brilliant flame makes its exit from between their lips. They shoot forth a bed of flame for a considerable length of time, which certainly exceeds half a minute. The combustion is due to a very volatile essence.

Certain eaters of burning tow proceed as follows: They form a little ball of material which they tightly compress and then light, and allow to burn up almost entirely. Then rolling this in new tow in order to guard the mucous membrane in the mouth against contact with the incandescent ball, they breathe gently, taking care while doing so to inhale only through the nose, and thus project smoke and sparks.

MOUNTEBANK SWALLOWING BURNING TOW.

Another trick of the fire eaters is when they pretend to drink burning oil. A little kerosene oil is poured into an iron ladle. The oil is now lighted, and while the ladle is held in the left hand, an iron spoon is dipped into the oil as though to take a spoonful; but in reality the spoon is only wet, and when it is brought blazing to the mouth the operator throws back his head as though to swallow it, and at the same time a slight puff is given by the breath, which blows it out. This trick is very effective if well done, but the reader is especially cautioned against trying any experiments in tricks of this kind, as the results are apt to be dangerous except in the hands of experts. This will be seen by what is called the sponge trick. Two or three small sponges are placed in an iron ladle, gasolene is poured over them, only a sufficient quantity being used to wet them; they must in no case drip.   The sponges are now set on fire, and the experimenter takes up one of them with his tongs, and, throwing his head back, drops the blazing sponge into his mouth.   He expels his breath quickly all the time.   Suddenly he closes his mouth; this cuts off the oxygen necessary for combustion, and the flame immediately goes out.   Performers who present fire tricks for the amusement of a company frequently try experiments which give a ghastly appearance to the audience.   This is done by pouring a few ounces of alcohol into a basin containing a handful of salt. When this is lighted the complexion of everyone is hideous.   A slightly different effect is used by infusing saffron in alcohol for a number of hours, and then adding salt as before; it is usually poured upon tow which is lighted.   There are 'some liquids that have the property of taking fire and burning without injuring the object upon which they are poured and without producing any painful sensation upon the skin.   As a usual thing such liquids are very volatile and consist of essential oils, ether, etc.   The reason that some substances can be burned without injuring them, or upon the skin without burning, are explained as follows: These substances are very volatile, and their tension is considerable, and, in reality, when they are burning, it is merely their vapor which is on fire.   This vapor then tends to borrow heat from the liquid, whence the latter may remain at a relatively low temperature while the surface is on fire.   This is a reasonable explanation of the curious phenomenon of the burning liquid.

SWORD TRICK—A STAB THROUGH THE ABDOMEN.

The sword employed is a simple, thin, flexible blade of steel, not at all sharp, and the plan of which is seen at A in the accompanying cut.   The point is sufficiently blunt to prevent it from doing any harm.

As for the prestidigitateur, whose body the sword will simply pass around, but not pierce, he carries concealed beneath his vest a sort of sheath that consists of a tube of rectangular section, and semicircular in shape, and the two extremities of which are bent in contrary directions in such a way that they are situated in the same straight line, the two orifices opening in front and behind at right angles with the abdomen.   This apparatus, B, is held in place by cords attached to two small rings at the two extremities of the tube.

It is the prestidigitateur himself who, appearing instinctively to grasp the point of the sword as if to protect himself, directs it into the metallic tube. It makes its exit between the tails of the coat.   It might be made to come out at the center of the back, but in this case it would be necessary to have an aperture formed in the seam of the coat.   The illusion produced is complete, seeing that the flexible blade straightens out on making its exit from the tube, on account of the form of the latter's extremity.   It is necessary to operate rapidly, so that the spectators shall not have time to see that the length of the sword has diminished at this moment, the curved line that it follows not being the shortest passage from one point to another.

A SWORD TRICK.

The figure represents a variant of the trick in which the sword is provided with an eye through which a long red ribbon is passed, and which follows the blade when the latter is pulled out at the opposite side of the body.

THE HUMAN TARGET.

Japanese jugglers, as well known, are possessed of very extraordinary skill. A few years ago two of them performed the following feat, which required a wonderful dexterity. One of them stood, with arms extended, in front of a thick board placed vertically; and the other, armed with a number of wide-bladed knives, stationed himself at a distance of about six yards from the board, and from thence threw the knives with a sure hand and stuck one of them in the board just above the head of the target, two of them very close to the right and left of the neck, and others around the arms; in a word, he outlined the form of his companion with the knives stuck very deeply into the board. This performance met with extraordinary success, and an effort was at once made to reproduce it; but as such dexterity is not possessed by everybody, and as, in addition, the operation is dangerous, the following substitute was devised by M. Voisin for the use of prestidigitateurs.

JAPANESE KNIFE-THROWING EXECUTED BY MEANS OF A MECHANICAL DEVICE.
FIG. 2.—DETAILS OF THE MECHANISM THAT CAUSES THE KNIFE TO APPEAR.

The board that is employed in this case, instead of being, as in the genuine performance, a simple one, is a piece of cabinet work containing an ingenious mechanism. The place which the human target will occupy on this board is carefully marked, and the knives that are to be stuck into the board in succession around such place are contained in the cabinet work, which, at first sight and at a short distance, seems to be absolutely without preparation.

Each of these knives is fixed by its point upon a pivot. In addition, it is controlled by a spring, and is concealed within the board by a very finely adjusted double-valved window, which, at the proper moment, opens and allows it to appear, and then closes. The spring causes the knife to fall or rise according to the place that the latter is to occupy. No. 2 of the engraving shows the window opening to allow of the fall of the knife, which will appear as if stuck into the board just above the instep. In each of the valves the angles that meet each other are cut slopingly either at the top or bottom, according as the knife is to fall or rise, in order to make space for the blade when the valves are closed. Before the exit of the knife, the incision is closed with modeling wax the color of the wood. In our engraving the incision is at the bottom.

Naturally the knives are concealed in the board in such a way that on making their exit the field shall be free, and that they shall not come into conact with the limbs of the target. Each of these knives, with its window, forms a distinct apparatus, which is controlled by a rod that ends at the edge of the board just at the place where the fingers of the human target can reach them. It is he who, by pressing upon the ends of the rods as if upon the keys of a piano, causes the blades to come out of their place of concealment, one after another, and appear as if they had just stuck into the board. The sound made by the spring in expanding and the sudden appearance of the knife, combined with the motion of the person throwing it, affords a complete illusion. Let us add that each knife mounted on a pivot at its point, as we have explained, may be easily disengaged from its axis when, after the operation, the person who threw the knives makes believe to pull them out by force from the wood in which they seem to be inserted.

The board having been invented, it became necessary to find a method of throwing the knives in such a way as to cause them to disappear. To this effect the board is placed on one side of the stage, near the side scenes, and the person who throws the knives stations himself on the other side of the stage, near the opposite side scenes, and he can therefore act in two ways, viz., first, in poising his arms to take aim, he can, at the last moment, throw the knife between the side scenes back of him while he takes a step forward. The knife supposed to be thrown thus disappears completely at the desired moment, but, since the spectators do not see the flash of the blade traversing the stage, it is preferable to employ the second method. This consists in a genuine throwing of the knife, but in such a way as to cause it to pass by the board and fall between the side scenes, where the sound of its fall is deadened by some such material as a piece of carpet. In both of these two methods, it is for the human target to press the spring of the knife that he wishes to make appear at just the precise moment, in order that the click of the expanding spring may be taken by the spectators for the sound of the knife sticking into the wood.

This trick, when well executed, has often deceived the shrewdest spectators, and that, too, with so much the more facility in that many had seen the Japanese perform in the middle of a circus, where it was impossible to conceal the knife, since it could be followed by the eye in its travel from the hand of the Japanese to the point where it penetrated the board.

To be precise, and to omit no information, let us say in conclusion, that there exist boards in which the freeing of the knives is effected by the pulling of a thread held in the side scenes by a third party. This process has the advantage that there is no danger of the spectators seeing the manipulation of the rods ; but, on the other hand, it has its inconveniences, viz., in a place where a communication cannot be established between the invisible confederate and the mechanical board, the use of it is impossible, and it is necessary to employ the other method.

SWORD SWALLOWERS.

When a physician introduces his finger, the handle of a spoon, or a pencil into the throat of a patient, the latter experiences an extremely disagreeable sensation. Any touching of the pharynx, however slight it be, causes strangling, pain, and nausea, and the organ reacts with violence against the obstacle that presents itself to free respiration. There is no one who has not more than once experienced this disagreeable impression, and for this reason we are justly surprised when we meet with people who seem to be proof against it, and who, for example, introduce into their pharynx large, solid, and stiff objects like sword blades, and cause these to penetrate to a depth that appears incredible. It is experiments of this kind that constitute the tricks of sword swallowers.

These experiments are nearly always the same. The individual comes out dressed in a brilliant costume. At one side of him there are flags of different nationalities surrounding a panoply of sabers, swords, and yatagans, and at the other, a stack of guns provided with bayonets. Taking a flat saber, whose blade and hilt have been cut out of the same sheet of metal, the blade being from fifty-five to sixty centimeters in length, he introduces its extremity into his throat, taps the hilt gently, and the blade at length entirely disappears. He then repeats the experiment in swallowing the blade at a single gulp. Subsequently, after swallowing and disgorging two of these same swords, he causes one to penetrate up to its guard, a second not quite so far, a third a little less still, and a fourth up to about half its length, the hilts being then arranged as shown in our third illustration (C).

A SWORD SWALLOWER.

Pressing now on the hilts, he swallows the four blades at a gulp, and then he takes them out leisurely one by one. The effect is quite surprising. After swallowing several different swords and sabers, he takes an old musket armed with a triangular bayonet, and swallows the latter, the gun remaining vertical over his head. Finally he borrows a large saber from a dragoon who is present for the purpose, and causes two-thirds of it to disappear. As a trick, on being encored, the sword swallower borrows a cane from a person in the audience, and swallows it almost entirely.

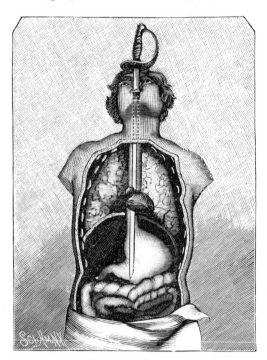

POSITION OCCUPIED BY THE SWORD BLADE IN THE BODY.

A certain number of spectators usually think that the performer produces an illusion through the aid of some trick, and that it is impossible to swallow a sword blade. But this is a mistake, for sword swallowers who employ artifices are few in number and their experiments but slightly varied, while the majority really do introduce into their mouths and food passages the blades that they cause to disappear. They attain this result as follows:

The back parts of the mouth, despite their sensitiveness and their rebellion against contact with solid bodies, are capable of becoming so changed through habit that they gradually get used to abnormal contacts. This fact is taken advantage of in medicine. It daily happens that persons afflicted with disorders of the throat or stomach can no longer swallow or take nourishment, and would die of exhaustion were they not fed artificially by means of the œsophageal tube. This latter is a vulcanized rubber tube which the patient swallows, after the manner of sword swallowers, and through the extremity of which milk or *bouillon* is introduced. But the patient, before being able to make daily use of this apparatus, must serve a genuine apprenticeship. The first introduction of the end of the tube into the pharynx is extremely painful, the second is a little less so, and it is only after a large number of trials, more or less prolonged, that the patient succeeds in swallowing ten or twelve inches of the tubing without a disagreeable sensation.

The washing out of the stomach, performed by means of a long, flexible tube which the patient partially swallows, and with which he injects into and removes from his stomach a quantity of tepid water by raising the tube or letting it hang down to form a siphon, likewise necessitates an apprenticeship of some days; but the patient succeeds in accustoming his organs to contact with the tube, and is finally able, after a short time, to swallow the latter with indifference, at least.

With these sword swallowers it is absolutely the same; for with them it is only as a consequence of repeated trials that the pharynx becomes sufficiently accustomed to it to permit them to finally swallow objects as large and rigid as swords, sabers, canes, and even billiard cues.

Swallowers of forks and spoons serve an analogous apprenticeship. As known, the talent of these consists in their ability to introduce into the throat a long spoon or fork while holding it suspended by its extremity between two fingers. This trick is extremely dangerous, since the œsophagus exerts a sort of suction on all bodies that are introduced into it. The spoon or fork is, then, strongly attracted, and if the individual cannot hold it, it will drop into his stomach, whence it can only be extracted by a very dangerous surgical operation—gastrotomy. It was accidents of this kind that made the "forkman" and the "knifeman" celebrated, and, more recently, the "spoonman" who died from the effects of the extraction from his stomach of a sirup spoon.

All sword swallowers do not proceed in the same way. Some swallow the blade directly, without any intermediate apparatus; but in this case, their sabers are provided at the extremity, near the point, with a small bayonet-shaped appendage over which they slip a gutta-percha tip without the spectators perceiving it (F and G). Others do not even take such a precaution, but swallow the saber or sword just as it is.

This is the mode of procedure of an old zouave, especially, who has become a poor juggler, and who, in his experiments, allows the spectators to touch, below his sternum, the projection that the point of the saber in his stomach makes on his skin.

But the majority of sword swallowers who exhibit upon the stage employ a guiding tube which they have previously swallowed, so that the experiments they are enabled to perform become less dangerous and can be varied more. This tube, which is from forty-five to fifty centimeters long, is made of very thin metal. Its width is twenty-five millimeters, and its thickness fifteen (B). These dimensions permit of the easy introduction of flat-bladed sabers, among other things, and of the performance of the four-sabers experiment, and of the introduction of sabers and swords of all kinds.

To explain the latter from a physiological standpoint, the saber swallowed by the performer enters the mouth and pharynx first, then the œsophagus, traverses the cardiac opening of the stomach, and enters the latter as far as the antrum of the pylorus—the small cul-de-sac of the stomach. In their normal state these organs are not in a straight line, but are placed so by the passage of the sword. In the first place, the head is thrown back so that the mouth is in the direction of the œsophagus, the curves of which disappear or become less; the angle that the œsophagus makes with the stomach becomes null; and, finally, the last-named organ distends in a vertical direction and its internal curve disappears, thus permitting the blade to traverse the stomach through its greater diameter; that is to say, to reach the small cul-de-sac. It should be understood that before such a result can be attained the stomach must have been emptied through fasting on the part of the operator.

The depth of fifty-five to sixty centimeters to which these men cause their instruments to penetrate, and which seems extraordinary to spectators, is

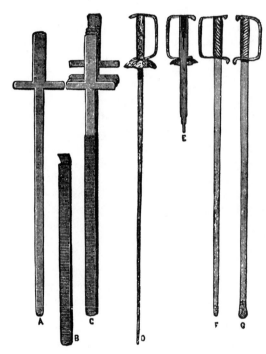

explained by the dimensions of the organs traversed. Such lengths may be divided thus:

Mouth and pharynx, 10 to 12; œsophagus, 25 to 28; distended stomach, 20 to 22—55 to 62 centimeters.

According to the stature of the individual, a length of organs of from 55 to 62 centimeters may give passage to swallowed swords without inconvenience.

Sword swallowing exhibitors have rendered important services to medicine. It was due to one of them—a swallower of both swords and pebbles—that, in 1777, a Scotch physician, Stevens, was enabled to make the first studies upon the gastric juice of human beings. In order to do this, he caused this individual to swallow small metallic tubes pierced with holes and filled

VARIOUS APPARATUS FOR SWORD SWALLOWERS.

with meat according to Reaumur's method, and got him to disgorge them again after a certain length of time. It was also sword swallowers who showed physicians to what extent the pharynx could become habituated to contact; and from this resulted the invention of the Foucher tube, the œsophageal tube, the washing out of the stomach, and the illumination of the latter organ by the electric light.

It sometimes happens that sword swallowers who exhibit in public squares and at street corners are, at the same time, swallowers of pebbles, like him whose talents were utilized by Stevens; that is to say, they have the faculty of swallowing pebbles of various sizes, sometimes even stones larger than a hen's egg, and that, too, to the number of four, five, or six, sometimes more, and of afterward disgorging them one by one through a simple contraction of the stomach. Here we have a new example of the modification of sensitiveness and function that an individual may secure in his organs by determination and constant practice.

In conclusion, let us say a word in regard to the tricks that produce the illusion of swallowed swords or sabers. One of these, which deceives only at a certain distance, consists in plunging the saber into a tube that descends along the neck and chest, under the garments, and the opening of which, placed near the mouth, is hidden by means of a false beard. Another and much more ingenious one, which has been employed in several enchantment scenes, is that of the sword whose blade enters its hilt, and which is due to M. Voisin, the skillful manufacturer of physical apparatus. In its ordinary state this sword has a stiff blade, eighty centimeters in length, which, when looked at from a distance of a few meters, presents no peculiarity (see D in our engraving); but when the exhibitor plunges it into his mouth, the spectator sees it descend by degrees, and finally so nearly disappear that but a few centimeters of the blade protrude. In reality, the blade has entered into the hilt, for it possesses a solid tip that enters the middle part, which is hollow, and these two parts enter into the one that forms the base of the sword. The blade is thus reduced to about twenty-five centimeters, a half of which length enters the hilt. There then remain but a few centimeters outside the exhibitor's mouth, so that he seems to have swallowed the sword see (G and E). This is a very neat trick.

THE SWORD WALKER.

Of all the daring tricks that have been introduced in the circus, none have caused more comment than the one in which a person, generally a lady, walks with bare feet up a ladder of sharp swords, treading directly on the sharp edges without any injury to the feet.

It is amusing to a person who is acquainted with the secret to hear the many explanations of "how it is done" offered by the spectators, yet none of them ever come near guessing the truth. This secret has been so jealously and successfully guarded that very few, even among the best informed experts, know how it is performed.

From the illustration it will be seen how the swords are arranged in a rack with the cutting edges on top. The rack is usually about seven feet high, and eight swords are used. One of the most necessary points in the preparation for the trick is that the rack should stand firm, and the swords fit snug and tight in the slots made to receive them.

Usually the inspectors are invited to examine the rack as well as the swords, and paper is cut with the swords to show that they are really sharp. The secret is not in the swords or rack, but in the preparation of the performer's feet. In a pint of water as much alum is dissolved as the water will readily take up. To the alum water is added as much zinc sulphate, thoroughly dissolved, as will lie on a silver dime.

A few minutes before doing the act the performer bathes the feet in this solution and allows them to dry without wiping. Just before leaving the dressing-room the feet are dipped for a moment in as cold water as can be secured, and at once wiped dry without rubbing.

By placing the feet squarely on the swords there is no danger, but great care must be used not to allow the foot to slide or slip on the sword, or the result would be a very bad accident.

SWORD WALKER.

On leaving the circus in which one has seen the above act, visitors are almost sure to see before the ever-present side show a large painting on which is the representation of a Mexican dancing with bare feet in a shallow box filled with broken glass.

If you are of an inquisitive nature, and have seen a lady walk with bare feet up a ladder of sharp swords, you enter the side show to see this new wonder.

On a raised platform is found a box about four feet long, three feet wide, and six inches deep, the bottom of which is covered with broken glass. In a few moments a man dressed in the Mexican costume appears on the platform and proceeds to break a few old bottles and throw the broken glass in the box, then removes his shoes, shows his feet to be free from any covering, steps in the box, and dances among the glass. After he has finished dancing he shows his feet to be uninjured, and retires. The trick is performed in the following manner:

Secure a number of thick glass bottles, break them in rather small pieces and file or grind all the sharp edges round. This stock of glass you place in the center of a box made according to above measurement. Now soak your feet in

GLASS DANCER.

strong alum water and wipe dry, and give them a thorough rubbing with pulverized rosin. Dust the inside of your shoes with rosin, put them on, and go upon the platform. Take some old lamp chimneys and bottles, break them in bits, and throw this fresh broken glass in the box, around the edges and in the corners, not in the center. Remove your shoes, step in the center of the box, among the prepared glass, and do your dancing. Avoid the sides or corners of the box, where you have thrown the glass, and you run no risk of cutting your feet, especially if you use plenty of rosin. The amateur hardly needs to be informed that such tricks should be left entirely to professionals.

CHAPTER VII.

VENTRILOQUISM AND ANIMATED PUPPETS.

Ventriloquists may, according to their specialties, be divided into various categories. Some devote their talent to the imitation of the cries of animals, the songs of birds, the noise of tools, etc.; others imitate the sound of musical instruments; some mock the noise produced by a crowd, a regiment, or a procession; while others, again, make dolls or dummies speak.

Certain ventriloquists imitate the sound of musical instruments, from that of the violin up to that of brass instruments with the most piercing notes. Others excel in imitating the noise of the plane, saw, etc.

Certain ventriloquists, while hidden by a screen simply, have the faculty of making their audience believe that several persons, or even a crowd, are in the vicinity.

At Egyptian Hall, London, a magician recently made his appearance upon the stage, carrying a doll, with which he held a somewhat uncouth conversation. The lips of the doll were observed to move, and the illusion was complete, when all at once the doll's head was strangely transformed. The magician had just opened his hand, showing that it was the latter alone that— inclosed in a white glove upon which were a few colored marks—formed the doll's head.

In our engraving may be seen two methods of arranging the fingers for forming a doll's head with the hand. The illusion is produced by making a few simple lines with charcoal, and wrapping a handkerchief or napkin around the hand; then, if one has a little aptness for ventriloquism, he may hold a conversation with the head.

In our time, most ventriloquists who exhibit in public considerably facilitate the illusion that they desire to produce by using large articulated dummies, which they make speak and sing, and talk to one another—each in a different voice. These figures are so constructed that the ventriloquist's hands can move their arms and legs, turn their heads to the right or left, give their shoulders a shrug, open or close their eyes, and move their lower jaws in such a way that their mouths seem to utter the words that the spectator hears.

We may say, in a general way, that these ventriloquists, thanks to the use of their dummies, succeed in producing so complete an illusion that people are frequently persuaded that the voice heard actually comes from the mouth of the figure, and that it does not proceed from the ventriloquist standing near the latter, but from a confederate hidden somewhere about, whose voice is heard through the intermedium of a speaking-tube.

There is one trick that always tends to confirm the spectator's illusion, and that is this: in the little prefatory speech that the ventriloquist makes, he gives out that he is a foreigner, and does not speak the language of his audi-

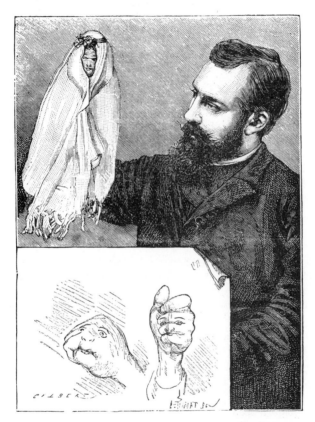

METHOD OF MAKING FACES WITH THE HAND.

ence well; in fact, he expresses himself with difficulty and with a strong accent. His dummies, on the contrary, answer in very good French or English, as the case may be; and when the auditors hear them, they are led to believe that ventriloquism counts for nothing in their answers or conversation.

Explanation of Ventriloquism.—The art of ventriloquism is primarily based upon an acoustic phenomenon—the difficulty that the ear experiences in determining the exact point whence comes the sound that it hears. That there is such an incertitude as to the direction of sounds is easily verified, and the following are a few cases in proof of it. Mr. Stuart Cumberland, a mind reader, who exhibited at Paris a few years ago, performed a little experiment in the drawing-room, after his " second-sight " séances, which usually resulted in surprising and amusing his auditors. In this experiment, a willingly disposed person, being seated in the middle of the room, allowed his eyes to be bandaged. Then Mr. Cumberland took a five-franc piece and made it jingle by striking it with a hard object, say a key or another coin. The person submitted to the experiment then had to tell the direction from whence the sound emanated, and to give the distance at which it seemed to him to have been made. In almost all cases the individual guessed a direction and distance very different from the real one, and the error, which was ofttimes great, naturally provoked great hilarity from the spectators. Moreover, Mr. Cumberland, by varying the position of his hand in such a way that the latter formed a screen between the coin and the ear of the blindfolded person, caused the latter's perception as to the direction of the sound to vary, although, as a matter of fact, the experimenter had not budged from his first position.

At a *soirée*, we have seen a member of the Institute, who had cheerfully submitted himself to the experiment, extremely surprised, when his bandage was removed, at the gross errors in auditory perception that he had just committed. The illusion that it is thus possible to produce by varying the positions of the hand in which a coin is jingled is, in the main, analogous to that obtained through ventriloquism. Another example: If several persons be standing in the same line, at a few feet from a spectator, and one of them emits a prolonged sound—a vowel, for example, say *a a a*—that requires no motion of the lips, the spectator will be unable to determine from which of the persons the sound proceeds; or if, moreover, he tries to point the one out, he will be almost certain to commit an error, the person designated by him being the third or fourth to the right or left of the one who actually produced the sound.

In the choruses of operas, an endeavor is made to have an agreeable aspect in addition to vocal qualities; and, as a beautiful voice is not always accompanied with a pretty face, it often happens that in the first row of a chorus they will place pretty supernumeraries, who, although not obliged to sing, open their mouths and make believe pronounce words, while in reality the singing is being done only by their companions in the rear. This fraud is very rarely detected by the audience.

If a man standing near a child should, without moving his lips, speak with a squeaking voice, while the child was making believe pronounce words, it might easily be believed that the words heard were being spoken by the child. It is possible to teach a dog to open his mouth and follow the motions of his master's hand; and if the master be any sort of a ventriloquist, he can easily make believe that he has an animal endowed with speech.

The ventriloquist who, standing near his dummies, succeeds in keeping his facial muscles absolutely immovable, while his figures become animate and move their lips and seem to speak, produces such an illusion among the spectators by virtue of the acoustic principle that we have just noted; that is, the difficulty that the ear experiences in determining the precise point whence emanates the sound that it hears.

It is to be remarked that the chief difficulty in the art of ventriloquism is to keep the countenance immovable, and to speak without causing any of the facial muscles to act.

The ventriloquist who talks with a dummy that is interrogating him, addresses his questions in an ordinary voice, articulates distinctly, and plainly moves his lips; but when the dummy answers, the ventriloquist's face no longer contracts, and his lips scarcely part except to smile. The facial immobility preserved by him while he is really speaking, then, can be explained by recalling a few principles of grammar, which are merely applications of the physiology of the voice.

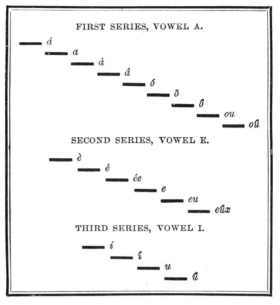

FIG. 2.—CLASSIFICATION OF THE VOWELS.

Articulate speech, which separates the language of man from that of the lower animals, is divided, as grammar teaches, into sounds and articulations. The sounds or vowels are made up of all the continuous and uniform noises that the vocal organs can emit. Thus *a*, *e*, *i*, *o*, and *u* are vowels, because they may be infinitely prolonged; *a a a a a a*, for example. There are a greater number of vowels than is usually admitted in writing; it is possible, in fact, to modify them to infinity, so to speak, by a slightly more open or more closed sound. They may be classified in the form of gamuts, each having a typical vowel, the entire corresponding series of which is but the result of a more and more pronounced contraction of the lips, without the tongue and other vocal organs having to undergo the slightest modification.

These type-vowels and their descending gamuts are shown in Fig. 2.

If, in pronouncing each of these vowels, we draw the base of the tongue toward the back of the throat, without changing the position of the lips or tongue, we shall obtain the *nasal* sound thereof. The chief of such sounds are:

an, nasal sound of *a* ;
on, nasal sound of *o* ;

then,

en, *in*, nasal sound of *é* ;
eun, *un*, nasal sound of *eu*.

The vowels *i* and *u* have no nasal sounds, because of the back position that the base of the tongue naturally occupies in pronouncing them, and which is but slightly modified when we endeavor to give them a nasal sound.

What precedes may be called the theory of the vowels. From the standpoint of ventriloquism, we must remark that, in order to pronounce the vowels, no motion of the lips is necessary; but it will suffice to allow the latter to remain slightly parted in order to give passage to the sound—this being generally done by the ventriloquist through the aid of a smile, that seems to be provoked by the interest that he takes in the talk of his dummies.

All the modifications in the organs necessary for passing from one vowel to another, as in the diphthongs *oa* and *aé*, or when they suppress certain intermediate articulations, are easily obtained by the ventriloquist by the aid of the tongue and the interior organs of the mouth, without causing the lips and facial muscles to undergo the slightest motion or the least contraction; or, in other words, without any visible sign exhibiting itself to the eyes of the spectators. The pronunciation of the vowels, then, constitutes no difficulty for the ventriloquist. The same is not the case with the articulations or consonants, the pronunciation of some of which is a difficulty that the ventriloquist can overcome only by virtue of practice and skill, or again by an approximate pronunciation—the articulation difficult to pronounce without moving the facial muscles being replaced by another which gives nearly the same sound, but which is obtained with the internal vocal organs of the mouth.

The consonants may be classed by categories, according to the vocal organs employed for pronouncing them. In each category they are divided into strong and weak, and, as regards ventriloquism, they comprise two series. A classification of them is given in Fig. 3.

Upon examining this table, it will be seen that, in the entire first series of these consonants, the tongue, acting upon the pharynx, bearing against the teeth, or taking different shapes, can act and articulate without the aid of the lips, and without the necessity of the facial muscles contracting. The ventriloquist, then, will be able to pronounce any word in which none but these vowels and consonants enter, without moving his facial muscles.

The same is not the case with the consonants of the second series, that is to say, with the five labials, *f, v, p, b, m.* The ventriloquist's art consists in pronouncing these without moving the lips or facial muscles. With a little practice it is easy to reach such a result with *f* and *v*, which may be pronounced by causing only the interior muscles of the lips to act; *p* and *b*, and *m* especially, present a greater difficulty, and we may say that, in most cases, ventriloquists who wish to keep their lips perfectly motionless pronounce none of these three consonants distinctly, but usually substitute for them a sound bordering on that of the letter *n.*

It is partly for this reason that ventriloquists succeed much better in imitating the language of children, or that of persons of slight education.

So, upon the whole, the illusion produced by ventriloquists is the result, primarily, of an acoustic phenomenon, the uncertainty of the sound's direction, and, secondarily, of a habit acquired of speaking without moving the facial muscles.

Those ventriloquists who, without accessories, have the power of throwing their voices almost anywhere, succeed therein by utilizing the same principle of acoustics that we have explained above. As for the exact point whence the sound proceeds, the ventriloquist usually takes care to show that by an expressive motion and by looking in that direction, and by designating it, too, with his finger, while his face expresses great fear, interest, or surprise. So the spectator easily persuades himself that the sound does really come from the exact spot that is thus pointed out to him in a seemingly unintentional manner.

The words are often pronounced very indistinctly by the mysterious voice, but the ventriloquist takes care, as a general thing, to render them intelligible by repeating them in his ordinary voice, by accenting them, and by commenting upon them. He thus persuades his auditors that these are the very words that they heard.

FIRST SERIES.—CONSONANTS FORMED BY THE INTERNAL VOCAL ORGANS.		
	Strong.	Weak.
Gutturals	c	g
Palatal linguals	l	ill
Dental linguals................. ...	r	
Dentals	t	d
Palatal dentals	n	gn
Dental sibillants...................	s	z
Guttural sibillants............. .. .	ch	j
SECOND SERIES.—LABIAL CONSONANTS.		
	Strong.	Weak.
Sibillant labials	f	v
Simple labials	p	b
Aspirated labials	m	

FIG. 3.—CLASSIFICATION OF THE CONSONANTS.

In order to produce a muffled sound that seems to come from afar or from an inclosed place, the ventriloquist arranges his tongue in such a way that its base, upon bearing against the soft palate, shall form a sort of diaphragm that allows but very little of the voice to pass. If, then, the ventriloquist articulates his words with a strong guttural voice, the sound will appear to come from the earth, from a grotto or cavern, or from a box, or cask, or closet. If, on the contrary, the tongue being in the same position, the ventriloquist speaks with a sharp voice, he will produce the illusion of a voice coming from the ceiling, or from some high place, such as the top of a tree or the roof of a neighboring house. But, in both cases, in order to effect the emission of this muffled, somewhat indistinct, voice, the ventriloquist keeps his lungs distended, and emits as little breath as possible in pronouncing.

Richerand, the celebrated physiologist, who had an opportunity of examining the ventriloquist Fitz-James, says: "His entire mechanism consists in a slow and graduated expiration, which is, after a manner, protracted, and which is always preceded by a strong inspiration, by means of which he introduces into his lungs a great volume of air, which he carefully husbands."

As for the modifications to be introduced into the usual position of the organs in order to obtain the voices of aged people or children, hoarse or nasal voices, the cries of animals, sounds of musical instruments, the noises of tools, and so forth, they are easily effected, owing to the mobility, perfection, and resources of such organs; and it is by practice and feeling his way that the ventriloquist comes to know them and repeat them, so as to obtain the voice that he desires, with certainty. Moreover, in order to get a good idea of the modifications that may be introduced in the voice by regulating the breathing, the opening of the pharynx, and the position and curvature of the tongue, it is only necessary to devote ourselves to this exercise for a few minutes, when the processes used by ventriloquists, and the illusions that it is possible for them to produce, will be easily understood. Perhaps, indeed, such an exercise will reveal to the experimenter that he has an aptness for ventriloquism that he was far from suspecting.

ANIMATED PUPPETS.

Puppets have been in use since antiquity, and when skillfully constructed and operated the effect is very amusing. The French painter M. G. Bertrand devised some very ingenious puppets, which he calls "animated models," which he exhibited for a long time in Paris. When the characters make their appearance and walk and approach each other, they appear to be real. One of the most charming of the puppets was a violoncellist who bows, rubs resin on his bow, and plays a march. After the player has finished, he bows and repeats the piece for an *encore*. M. Bertrand's *danseuses* are no less wonderful. Fig. 3 shows one of them while she is executing a difficult scene. The little puppets are about half life size, being twenty-two inches in height. They are suspended from the upper part of the theater by very fine wires fixed to a rubber spring. Left to itself the puppet is suspended about three feet from

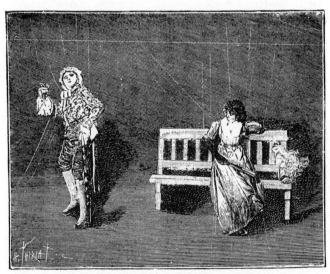

FIG. 1.—BERTRAND'S ANIMATED PUPPETS.

the floor of the stage. It is from beneath that the operator holds it by means of wires attached to its feet, which keep it on the floor and make it walk, jump,

FIG. 2.—LA RENCONTRE (SECOND SCENE).

or dance. Lateral wires are attached to the hands, and are manipulated from the side scenes. Each figure is built up on a skillfully wrought skeleton.

FIG. 3.—AUTOMATIC DANSEUSE.

The fifth figure shows that the fundamental osseous framework is made of hard wood, and the articulations formed of steel springs. When this wooden skeleton is made to dance upon the stage, it has the attitude of an animated being; all of the articulations operate of themselves, with perfect suppleness.

FIG. 4.—THE TOILET OF A DANSEUSE.

The covering of tow and dress materials give the external human form.   Our last engraving shows the clown, who, at the rising of the curtain, recites the

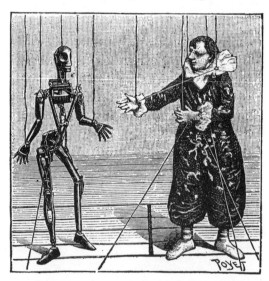

FIG. 5.—TOM MINOR THE CLOWN AND HIS SKELETON.

prologue.   He is capable of showing his own skeleton to the spectators and of saying, "This is the way I am made.   Look at my framework!"

CHAPTER VIII.

SHADOWGRAPHY.

By Henry Ridgely Evans.

Paris is the home of the fantaisiste. These rare exotics flourish in the genial atmosphere of the great French capital, and cater to the most critical, as well as the most appreciative, public in the world. No matter how trivial your profession may be, if you are an artist in your particular line, you may be sure of an admiring audience. To-day you are a performer in the *cafés*; to-morrow you tread the boards of some minor theater, and the journals duly chronicle your *début*, sometimes with as much elaborateness as they would "write up" that of a new singer at the Grand Opera. Two of the greatest entertainers in Paris to-day are Yvette Guilbert, *chanteuse eccentrique*, and M. Félicien Trewey—fantaisiste, mimic, shadowgraphist, and juggler. It is M. Trewey and his wonderful art I wish to introduce to the American reader. The clever Frenchman is one of the best sleight-of-hand artists in France, but his lasting fame has been made through his ombromanie, or shadowgraphy, the art of casting silhouettes with his hands, on an illuminated screen. These silhouettes are projected with marvelous dexterity of manipulation.

The idea of projecting the shadows of different objects (among others the hands) upon a plane surface is very ancient, and it would be idle to attempt to assign a date to the creation of these animals and classic figures, such as the rabbit, swan, negro, etc., that have served to amuse children in the evening since time immemorial.

Within a few years these rude figures have been improved, and the play of shadows has now become a true art instead of a simple diversion. The Italian painter Campi was one of the first who thought of adding new types to the collection of figures capable of being made with the shadow of the hands. He devised amusing forms of animals that delighted the school-children before whom he loved to exhibit them. His imitator, Frizze, imported the nascent art into Belgium, and it was in this latter country that Trewey got his knowledge of it.

Trewey was not long in discovering that ombromanie was capable of improvement, and, after patient exercise of his fingers to render them supple, he succeeded in producing new silhouettes, which are, each in its kind, little masterpieces.

TREWEY EXHIBITING UPON A STAGE.

Trewey has made his hands so supple that he not only can form the most diverse figures upon a screen, but can also give them motion and life. The swan smoothing its plumage, the bird taking flight, the cat making its toilet, the tight-rope dancer, who, after saluting the public, rubs chalk on her feet before walking on the rope, are true wonders, and it is hard to believe that these perfectly accurate profiles are obtained solely by means of the shadow of the hands. The artist has thus far devised more than three hundred figures, and his inventive mind is leading him to get up new ones every day.

The better to initiate the reader into the art of ombromanie, let me take, for example, the dog's head represented in Fig. 1 (No. 1). The ears are erect, the snout is thrust forward, and we conjecture that the animal has just scented a choice bit; in fact, he is snapping at it (No. 2). No. 4 shows us the efforts that he is making to swallow his prey, which is represented by the angle of the bent forefinger that moves in the mouth. After strong efforts, the mouth is seen to close (No. 3), showing the act of swallowing. A progressive motion of the hand shows us the swelling of the throat caused by the descent of the food in the œsophagus. One would imagine that he had before him the shadow of a genuine dog, so wonderful, natural, and accurate are the motions. After this laborious repast, we finally see the animal yawning voluptuously, the middle finger representing the tongue, which cleaves to the palate, and the general profile of the head expressing the completest beatitude.

It is very evident that, in order to reach such a degree of perfection, the artist must be naturally endowed with great manual dexterity. There are signs by which such dexterity is recognized, and an attentive examination of Trewey's hand has enabled me to verify the laws laid down by M. Henri Étienne upon the native perfection of the senses. Thirty-five years of research have permitted M. Étienne, who has been continuously in contact, in shops, with Swiss watchmakers' apprentices, experienced workmen, and artists even, to find a certain criterion by which to judge of aptitudes in different trades and several professions.

One day M. Étienne was present in the shop of a skillful master watchmaker, when there entered a young Frenchman, an ex-law student, who was desirous of apprenticing himself to the watchmaking trade. The neophyte, who was very intelligent looking, received a cordial reception. While pressing the hand of the future workman, a cloud passed over the placid face of the master-watchmaker. "What did you feel, then, in pressing the hand of that young man who has just gone out?" asked M. Étienne. "With hands like his we don't make a watchmaker," was the reply, and the prediction came true. It was as a consequence of this conversation that M. Étienne sought and discovered the following rules:

The characteristic of dexterity is shown in the first place by the *curve of the thumb arched outwardly.* This is an indispensable condition for the handling of the hammer. The blacksmith, who wields with his arm the heavy striking mass that he lets fall perpendicularly, without deviation, repeatedly upon the same point; the file-cutter, who strikes such regular blows upon the

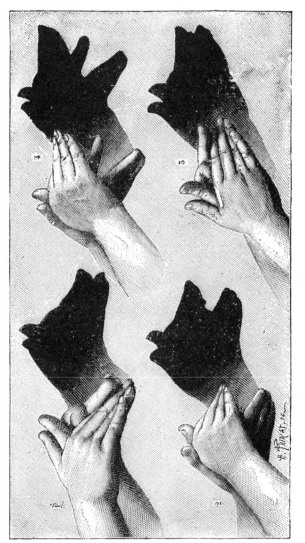

FIG. 1.—SHADOWS OF A DOG SWALLOWING A PIECE OF MEAT.

chisel that no flaw is visible in the cut, so equal everywhere is the imprint of the tool—these and all superb workmen, all artists who shape white-hot iron with the hammer, who chisel the precious metals, who sculpture marble and stone, owe the exact precision in the force and accuracy of the blows that they give with the hammer to the suppleness of the first joint of the thumb.

A second characteristic of skillfulness is indicated by the faculty of reversing the metacarpal phalanges of the fingers, so that when the hand is extended it is convex. On the greater or less flexibility of all the joints, either at the base or extremity of the fingers, depend the dexterity and skillfulness displayed in work executed with the file, plane, or lathe.

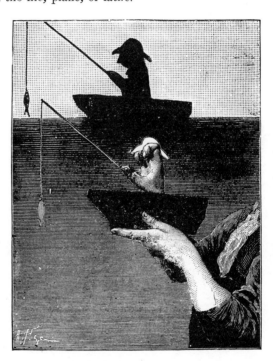

FIG. 2.—THE FISHERMAN.

The two characteristics mentioned above — the curved thumb and the peculiar suppleness of the fingers—are in most cases united in the same person. The more important of these is the first.

Trewey's hand, reproduced by molding, figures in several English museums. It possesses the faculty of reversal of the phalanges to the highest degree, and the thumb, which is of wonderful suppleness, renders Trewey, as we shall see, the greatest service in the formation of his shadows. Let me add that his fingers, which are long and slender, differ very perceptibly in length, the middle finger, for example, exceeding the ring finger by nearly an inch.

In addition to the profiles of men and animals, the artist, by means of a few accessories, exhibits to us living persons playing amusing pantomimes. Here, for example (Fig. 2), we have a fisherman. A piece of cardboard, properly shaped and held between two fingers, forms the hat; the boat is a piece of wood held in one of the artist's hands; a metallic ring holds the fish-pole against the thumb of the other hand, and it is opposite this latter, bent as shown in the figure, that we observe all the emotions of the fortunate fisherman, who, phlegmatic at first, and livening up when the fish bites, finally is triumphant when he has it at the end of his line. It is necessary to have witnessed all these little scenes in order to understand how, by means of his fingers alone, the artist can evoke the laughter and applause of hundreds of spectators. Here, now (Fig. 3), we have a scene with two persons. It is a fight between a janitress and one of her tenants. As may be seen, the accessories are here very simple again.

To make the shadows sharp, the following things are indispensable: The source of light must be a single lamp inclosed in a projecting apparatus, throwing very divergent rays. The lens must consequently be of very short focus. The electric light or oxyhydrogen lamp necessary in a theater may be replaced at the amateur's house by a lamp, or, better, by a wax candle, or, indeed, even by a common candle that gives very sharp shadows. The mirrors in the room

where the exhibition is given must be veiled in order to prevent reflections, and all brilliant objects must be removed. When the oxyhydrogen lamp is used, the screen is placed ten feet away from the light, and the artist's hands at three feet from the same, and consequently at seven from the screen. But it will be understood that there can be no absolute rule about this, all depending upon the scale of the figures. It suffices to recall the fact that the nearer the hand is brought to the light, the more the shadow enlarges and loses its intensity, while on bringing the hand nearer the screen, the shadow becomes sharper, but smaller and smaller. Fig. 4 shows Trewey exhibiting the scene

FIG. 3.—FIGHT BETWEEN A JANITRESS AND TENANT.

of the preacher in the pulpit. The canopy is formed by the arm and the first phalanges of the fingers bent at right angles, while a block of wood affixed to the arm near the wrist forms the pulpit. In order that the preacher may appear smaller than the pulpit, he must necessarily be nearer the screen, and this explains the distance apart of the artist's arms in the engraving, the screen being situated in front of the arm that forms the preacher. The necessary distances, however, are best determined by experiment.

Trewey's appearance on the stage is very prepossessing. He is a man of commanding physique, with a jovial countenance, indicative of the comedian. He always appears in full court costume—dress coat, silk stockings, and pumps.

On his first appearance on the stage he wears a long Spanish cloak, which he removes before beginning his entertainment of juggling and sleight-of-hand. He is the past grand master of balancing feats, the startling nature of which causes one to hold his breath with dismay at such boldness and audacity. His dexterity in throwing cards is really extraordinary. I have seen him project these little oblongs of glazed cardboard from the stage of the Alhambra, London (the largest hall in Europe) to the farthest part of the top gallery. He also possesses great skill in the unique art of writing backwards any word or sentence chosen by the audience, and he is a lightning sketch artist of no mean ability.

"Tabarin," or twenty-five heads under one hat, is a performance named after the inventor, a certain M. Tabarin, juggler, mountebank, and quack-salver, who used to frequent the quays of Paris during the early part of the eighteenth century. With the brim of an old felt sombrero, Trewey is able, by dexterous manipulation, to construct every variety of headgear, from the shovel hat of a snuffy-nosed French *abbé* to the headdress of a Norman peasant girl, to say nothing of the famous *chapeau* affected by the great Napoleon. It is not these varieties of headgear that astonish the audience, but Trewey's facial interpretations of the different types of character assumed. His mobile features are an international portrait gallery, and we see represented in the "Tabarin" Irishmen, Scotchmen, Englishmen, Chinamen, and other nationalities. It is a facial pantomime of exceeding skill.

The Paris *Figaro* has described the work of this fantaisiste as "Treweyism," and *Illustration* and *La Nature* never fail to send their staff artists behind the scenes to make sketches of the ombromanist's latest creations. Robert-Houdin, in his memoirs, says, the excellence of an artist's work must never flag, but continue to excite and stimulate public curiosity. Trewey realizes this to perfection. He has something unique and novel from week to week to present for the delectation of his audiences. He is the most tireless experimenter I have ever met on any stage, and gets up early and goes to bed late to think out new problems in the *art amusante*. I first became acquainted with this versatile artist in the summer of 1893, when he was playing a phenomenally long engagement in the music halls of London, and heard from his own lips the story of his early struggles and hardships before attaining eminence in his chosen profession. I quote the following, contributed by me to the pages of *Mahatma*, a very clever little periodical devoted to sleight-of-hand, jugglery, and natural magic:

"Trewey was born in Angoulême nearly forty-five years ago. His father was a machinist employed at one of the paper mills of the city, and desired the young Trewey to become engineer in the manufactory. An unexpected incident diverted Trewey's mind from mechanics to jugglery. He was taken one day to the circus at Marseilles, and saw the performance of a conjurer. He was so delighted with the entertainment of the mountebank that he forthwith determined to become a professional prestidigitateur. Finding that he could not enlist the interest of his son in machinery, Trewey *père* sent him to a

Jesuit seminary at Marseilles to study for the priesthood.   One day, after he had completed three years at the seminary, he returned home for a short holiday, and refused to return, whereupon his father sent him to work daily at the factory.   During his sojourn at the school, Trewey exhibited his skill as an amateur juggler, and took part in the dramatic exhibitions given by the students from time to time.   He kept up his practice while at work at the factory, and then one fine summer's day, at the age of fifteen, ran away from home with a professional acrobat not much older than himself.   The two boys gave performances in the *cafés* of the neighboring towns, and eventually Trewey succeeded in getting an engagement in one of the Marseilles music

FIG. 4.—THE PREACHER IN THE PULPIT.

halls at the munificent salary of a franc a day.   He had to give his own juggling entertainment several times a day, and appear in a pantomimic performance every night.   In this same company was Plessis, afterwards one of the greatest of the French comedians.   Speaking of this period of his interesting career, Trewey said to me: 'It was the custom in French places of amusement, when I was a young and struggling entertainer, for the spectators to throw money on the stage to a successful actor.   I carefully saved the coin obtained in this way until I was able to purchase two grand new costumes.   These costumes and the popularity acquired enabled me to obtain an engagement at the Alcazar, the principal place of amusement in Marseilles.

   "'Other engagements offered themselves in quick succession after that, and I became a favorite performer in all the principal towns in the south of France, where I remained for three or four years.   After a while I returned to the strolling branch of the profession, and started anew as the proprietor of a traveling pantomime and vaudeville company.

"'I traveled from one little town to another, playing various *rôles* including Pierrot and Cassandre, the clown and pantaloon of French pantomime; danced in the *Clodoche*, a grotesque quadrille; and took part in a comedy, in addition to giving my own entertainment. It was a bare living only that was gained in this manner for two years, after which an offer of an engagement came to me from Bordeaux. Here I was most successful, and made a hit with a number of new feats of balancing with bottles, etc., with which I had been busy for a long time perfecting myself. It was at this period I invented the ombromanie. An offer quickly came for an engagement at the *Concert des Ambassadeurs*, in Paris, and my success was complete. I stayed in Paris nine years, and since then traveled all over Europe—in Spain, Germany, Belgium, Austria, Russia, Great Britain, and, as you know, introduced shadowgraphy to the American public in 1893.'

"Trewey's home in the Rue Rochechouart, Paris, is an interesting place to visit; it is crowded with apparatus and all sorts of new inventions intended for use in his conjuring entertainments. His scrap and memorandum books are unique in themselves and contain hundreds of sketches in water colors of juggling feats either performed by himself or by other artists. Under each drawing is a carefully written description of the particular act.

"'What are you going to do with all this material?' I once asked him. 'I may publish a book one of these days,' he replied, with a merry twinkle of the eye; 'who knows? I've done worse things.'"

FRENCH SHADOWS.

M. Caran d'Ache, the cartoonist and illustrator, got up a few years ago, at the Theater d'Application, at Paris, a special representation of Chinese shadows which were devised by him, and are so superior to anything that has previously been done in this line that he has been able to call them "French shadows," in order to distinguish them from similar productions.

M. d'Ache takes pleasure in representing the military scenes of the first republic and first empire. He projects upon the screen an entire army, wherein we see the emperor with his staff at different distances amid the ranks. The defiling of the troops is astonishing, and one would think that he was present at a genuine review. A "Vision in the Steppes" is another series of pictures that represent the advent of the Russian army. The shadows entitled the "Return from the Woods" form a masterpiece as a whole, and the figures are so skillfully cut that the celebrities of the day who are passing in the Avenue des Acacias can be recognized. Two amusing specimens of this part of the representation are given in Figs. 2 and 3. These reproductions are much reduced, the real height of the figures being about eighteen inches.

Says a writer in *La Nature*, "We were not content to remain in the body of the theater to witness the shadows, but requested M. d'Ache to admit us to his side scenes for the sake of our readers, and to initiate us into the processes of actuating his figures; for, aside from the artistic aspect, there is here a very interesting application of physics.

"The silhouettes, after being composed and drawn, are cut out of sheet zinc, which gives them great rigidity. The cutting is a very delicate operation and requires great accuracy. Some figures, such as those of cavalrymen, hussars,

FIG. 1.—FRENCH SHADOWS.

and dragoons of the grand army, have apertures in certain parts, and behind these is pasted colored transparent paper. In this way, the black shadows that move along the screen have certain parts in color, such as the plumes of the helmets and the horses' saddles.

"A large number of the zinc silhouettes act through mechanism. At a grand review, to the order ' Carry arms,' all the guns are seen to rise in unison. The silhouette is provided with a series of guns properly arranged and mounted upon a rod which is lowered or raised by the action of a lever.

"Fig. 1 represents the back of M. d'Ache's theater. The screen being brilliantly illuminated by an oxyhydrogen lamp, and the light in the body of the theater being turned down, the silhouettes, in passing, project upon the screen a very strong shadow which the spectators perceive, but which is not visible from the side scenes. Each silhouette is taken from a large box by a man who places it in a groove at the bottom of the screen. Four or five operators suffice to keep the shadows succeeding one another without interruption.

FIGS. 2 AND 3.—FACSIMILES OF TWO SILHOUETTES.

During the *Epopée* we witness great combats, the capture of redoubts, and terrible cannonading. Nothing is more amusing than the method of producing the effects of these epic contests. The cannons are provided with little fuses that an operator fires, and, at the same moment, the big drum of the orchestra imitates the noise of the cannonading, and a rattle of large size simulates the sound of the discharge of musketry. As for the smoke that the spectators perceive upon the screen, that is produced by the cigarette of one of the operators, who projects it at the desired place. The light of the shells is obtained by means of a wad of gun cotton lighted and properly projected.''

CHAPTER IX.

MENTAL MAGIC.

By Henry Ridgely Evans.

The most sphinx-like problem ever presented to the public for solution was the "second-sight" mystery. As has been stated in the Introduction, the idea was an old one, having originated with the Chevalier Pinetti, a conjurer of the eighteenth century. On this subject the "Encyclopædia Britannica" says:

"In 1783 Pinetti had an automatic figure about eighteen inches in height, named the Grand Sultan or Wise Little Turk, which answered questions as to chosen cards and many other things by striking upon a bell, intelligence being communicated to a confederate by an ingenious ordering of the words, syllables, or vowels in the questions put. The teaching of Mesmer and feats of alleged clairvoyance suggested to Pinetti a more remarkable performance in 1785, when Signora Pinetti, sitting blindfold in a front box of a theater, replied to questions and displayed her knowledge of articles in the possession of the audience."

Robert-Houdin invented a "second-sight" system under the following circumstances:

"My two children," he says, in his memoirs, "were playing one day in the drawing-room at a game they had invented for their own amusement. The younger had bandaged his elder brother's eyes, and made him guess the objects he touched, and when the latter happened to guess right, they changed places. This simple game suggested to me the most complicated idea that ever crossed my mind—'second sight.'

"On the 12th of February, 1846, I printed in the center of my bill the following singular announcement:

"*In this programme M. Robert-Houdin's son, who is gifted with a marvelous second sight, after his eyes have been covered with a thick bandage, will designate every object presented to him by the audience.*"

Houdin never revealed the secret of this remarkable trick, but plainly indicated in his autobiography that it was the result of an ingenious combination of questions that gave the clue to the supposed clairvoyant on the stage. One of the first to come forward with an *exposé* was F. A. Gandon, who wrote a work entitled *La Seconde vue dévoilée*, Paris, 1849. Robert Heller saw

Houdin give an exhibition of "second sight" in London. It was the idea of people at the time that the experiment was the result of animal magnetism, but the acute Heller thought otherwise, and he went to work to perfect a system that far exceeded any of his predecessors in the art, adding certain subtle improvements that made the trick all but supernatural.

Briefly stated, the effect is as follows: A lady is introduced to the audience as possessed of clairvoyant powers. She is blindfolded and seated on the stage. The magician, going down among the spectators, receives from them various articles which the supposed seeress accurately describes; for example, in the case of a coin, not only telling what the object is, but the country where it was coined, its denomination and date. In the case of a watch, she gives the metal, maker's name, what kind and how many jewels in the works, and, lastly, the time to a dot. And the same with other objects, no matter what they may be. Nothing offered by a spectator seemed to baffle Houdin and Heller. Half-obliterated Roman, Grecian, and Oriental coins were described with wonderful ease and accuracy by the assistant on the stage; also secret society emblems and inscriptions thereon, numbers on bank-notes, surgical instruments, etc.

ROBERT HELLER.

At a performance in Boston, described by Henry Hermon in his work, "Hellerism," a coin was handed to Heller. He glanced at it for a moment and asked his assistant to name the object.

"A coin," she quickly replied.

"Here, see if you can tell the name of the country, and all about it," he next inquired.

Without a second's hesitation she answered, "It is a large copper coin—a coin of Africa, I think. Yes, it is of Tripoli. The inscriptions on it are in Arabic; one side reads, 'Coined at Tripoli;' the other side, 'Sultan of two lands, Sultan of two seas, Sultan by inheritance, and the Son of a Sultan.'"

"Very well," said Heller, "that is correct. But look, what is the date, now?"

"The date is 1-2-2-0, one thousand two hundred and twenty of the Hegira, or Mohammedan year, which corresponds to 1805 of the Christian era."

Salvos of applause greeted the performers at the conclusion of the scene.

Mr. Fred Hunt, Jr., who was Robert Heller's assistant for many years, wrote the following *exposé* of the trick for the London *Times*, soon after Heller's death:

"In the years we were together, Heller was constantly enlarging and perfecting his system. He is now gone and has solved a greater mystery than that which puzzled so many thousands while he was on earth, and I believe that his sister, Haidee Heller, and myself are the only living persons in whom Robert Heller's second sight is vested. Heller had so simplified this system as to embrace every variety of article classified in sets; one question, with a word or two added, sufficing to elicit a correct answer for ten different articles.

"The student must be first posted in a new alphabetical arrangement, with which he must familiarize himself as thoroughly as a boy in learning his primer. This is the most difficult part of the business, but when mastered thoroughly, it comes as easy as if the question were plainly propounded.

"This alphabet is as follows:

A is H	J is L	S is N
B is T	K is Pray	T is P
C is S	L is C	U is Look
D is G	M is O	V is Y
E is F	N is D	W is R
F is E	O is V	X is See this
G is A	P is J	Y is Q
H is I	Q is W	Z is Hurry.
I is B	R is M	

Hurry up—repeat last letter.

"For example, you want the initials or name in a ring. Say it is 'Anna.' By the alphabetical arrangement H stands for A, D for N. The explanation 'Hurry up' always means a repetition of the last letter, and again H will give the answer when put as follows:

"'Here is a name? Do you see it? Hurry up. Have you got it?'

"Attention is paid only to the first letter of every sentence, and it will be perceived that the name of Anna is spelled.

"Again, take 'Gazette,' which is abbreviated in a phonographic manner in order to simplify the question. G is A, A is H, Z is 'Hurry' (not 'Hurry up'), E is F, T is P. The question would be:

"'Are you able to tell the name? Here it is. Hurry. Find the name. Please be quick.'

"Here you have 'Gazet' in short meter. The letters K, U, X, and Z being difficult wherewith to commence an interrogative sentence, the words 'pray,' 'look,' 'see this,' and 'hurry,' are used, as will be seen in the table.

Care must be taken not to begin a sentence with either of these words unless applicable to the word to be spelled. For instance, if 'Xenia' is required, X is 'See this,' E is F, N is D, I is B, and A is H. Thus the question:

"'See this? Find it quick. Do hurry. Be quick. How is it spelled?'

"Again, for the initials U. S. you will say:

"'Look. Now, then.'

"U is 'Look,' and S is N.

"If you want Kentucky named, thus the question:

"'Pray name the State. Quick.'

"Pray is K, and Q is Y.

"After the alphabet we have the numbers, which, it will be seen, are easily understood after a little practice.

NUMBERS.

1 is Say or Speak.	7 is Please or Pray.
2 is Be, Look, or Let.	8 is Are or Ain't.
3 is Can or Can't.	9 is Now.
4 is Do or Don't.	10 is Tell.
5 is Will or Won't.	0 is Hurry or Come.
6 is What.	

"'Well' is to repeat the last figure.

"Example: The number 1,234 is required; attention must only be paid to the first word of a sentence, thus:

"'Say the number. Look at it. Can you see it? Do you know?'

"Or say the number is 100:

"'Tell me the number. Hurry!'

"A rather difficult number would be 1,111. The question would be put in this wise:

"'Say the number. Well? Speak out. Say what it is.'

"On a watch or greenback there are sometimes eight or nine numbers, which can be followed as easily as the above.

"The table of colors is as follows:

COLORS

1 is White.	5 is Red.
2 is Black.	6 is Green.
3 is Blue.	7 is Yellow.
4 is Brown.	8 is Gray.

"The solution of the numbers, as I have explained, will furnish the key. For example, the article presented is green; the question will be:

"'What is the color?' green being the sixth color in the list.

"Blue is wanted, and, as it stands third in the list, the word would be:

"'Can you tell the color?'

"White is wanted, and, as it stands first in the list, the question is:

"'Say the color.'

"Understand that the words explaining the numbers, as given in the list, are applied to the articles enumerated in each of the subjoined tables.

The Metals.

1. Gold.
2. Silver.
3. Brass.
4. Copper.
5. Lead.
6. Iron.
7. Tin.
8. Platina.
9. Steel.

The Setting.

1. Diamond.
2. Ruby.
3. Pearl.
4. Amethyst.
5. Onyx.
6. Garnet.
7. Emerald.
8. Turquoise.
9. Carbuncle.
10. Topaz.

The stone—opal.

"Take the metals, for instance. The metal presented is <u>copper</u>, which is fourth in the list. The question would be:

" ' <u>Do</u> you know the metal ? '

" If <u>steel</u>, which is ninth in the list:

" ' <u>Now</u>, what is the metal ? '

" Sex, countries, materials, fabrics, watches, are as follows:

Of What.

[This set to describe the sex, etc., of the pictures.]

1. Lady.
2. Gentleman.
3. Boy.
4. Girl.
5. Child.
6. Group.
7. Animal.
8. Drawing.
9. Sketch.

Countries.

1. America.
2. England.
3. France.
4. Germany.
5. Russia.
6. Italy.
7. Spain.
8. Canada.
9. Foreign.
10. Mexico.

The Material.

1. Wood.
2. Stone.
3. Marble.
4. Bronze.
5. Lava.
6. Rubber.
7. Glass.
8. Bone.
9. Ivory.
10. China.

The Fabric.

1. Silk.
2. Wool.
3. Cotton.
4. Linen.
5. Leather.
6. Kid.
7. Buckskin.
8. Lace.

WATCHES.

The maker's name?

Of what company's make?

[This is to tell the maker's name of watches.]

1. American Watch Co.
2. Waltham Watch Co.
3. Elgin Watch Co.
4. Dueber Watch Co.
5. Tobias.
6. Johnson.
7. Swiss.
8.
9.
10.

" Miscellaneous articles are divided into nineteen sets, thus:

FIRST SET.

What article is this?

1. Handkerchief.
2. Neckerchief.
3. Bag.
4. Glove.
5. Purse.
6. Basket.
7. Beet.
8. Comforter.
9. Headdress.
10. Fan.

SECOND SET.

What is this?

1. Watch.
2. Bracelet.
3. Guard.
4. Chain.
5. Breastpin.
6. Necklace.
7. Ring.
8. Rosary.
9. Cross.
10. Charm.

THIRD SET.

What may this be?

1. Hat.
2. Cap.
3. Bonnet.
4. Cuff.
5. Collar.
6. Muff.
7. Cape.
8. Boa.
9. Inkstand.
10. Mucilage.

FOURTH SET.

What is here?

1. Pipe.
2. Cigar.
3. Cigar-holder.
4. Cigarette.
5. Tobacco.
6. Tobacco box.
7. Tobacco pouch.
8. Match.
9. Matchbox.
10. Cigar-lighter.

FIFTH SET.

What have I here?

1. Spectacles.
2. Spectacle case.
3. Eyeglass.
4. Eyeglass case.
5. Opera glass.
6. Opera-glass case.
7. Magnifying glass.
8. Telescope.
9. Compass.
10. Corkscrew.

SIXTH SET.

Can you see this?

1. Knife.
2. Scissors.
3. Pin.
4. Needle.
5. Cushion.
6. Toothpick.
7. Comb.
8. Brush.
9. Thimble.
10. Looking-glass.

SEVENTH SET.

Do you know what this is?

1. Book.
2. Pocketbook.
3. Needlebook.
4. Paper.
5. Newspaper.
6. Pamphlet.
7. Programme.
8. Bill.
9. Letter.
10. Envelope.

EIGHTH SET.

Look at this.

1. Bank bill.
2. Treasury note.
3. Currency.
4. Coin.
5. Gold piece.
6. Piece of money.
7. Bank check.
8. Bond.
9. Silver dollar.
10. Postage stamp.

NINTH SET.

Now, what is this?

1. Stick.
2. Whip.
3. Parasol.
4. Umbrella.
5. Umbrella cover.
6. Picture.
7. Shoe.
8. Boot.
9. Button.
10. Stud.

TENTH SET.

Tell me this.

1. Earring.
2. Locket.
3. Sleeve button.
4. Hairpin.
5. Clothespin.
6. Fork.
7. Spoon.
8. Armlet.
9. Ornament.
10. Check.

Eleventh Set.

I want to know this.

1. Apple.
2. Nut.
3. Cake.
4. Orange.
5. Lemon.
6. Candy.
7. Popcorn.
8. Lozenge.
9. Grain.
10. Wax.

Twelfth Set.

Pray, what is this?

1. Screw.
2. Hinge.
3. Tool.
4. Nail.
5. Tack.
6. Knob.
7. Rule.
8. Lock.
9. Buckle.
10. Key.

Thirteenth Set.

You know what this is?

1. Shot.
2. Powder.
3. Bullet.
4. Gun.
5. Pistol.
6. Percussion cap.
7. Cartridge.
8. Surgical instrument.
9. Musical instrument.
10. Tuning fork.

Fourteenth Set.

Quick! This article.

1. Bouquet.
2. Bouquet holder.
3. Flower.
4. Wreath.
5. Leaf.
6. Toy.
7. Flag.
8. Bottle.
9. Game.
10. Doll.

Fifteenth Set.

Name this article.

1. Pen.
2. Penholder.
3. Pencil.
4. Eraser.
5. Rubber.
6. Case.
7. Spool.
8. Soap.
9. Perfumery.
10. Cup.

Sixteenth Set.

Say, what is this?

1. Card.
2. Cardcase.
3. Playing card.
4. Button-hook.
5. Key ring.
6. Bunch keys.
7. Tablet.
8. Cord.
9. Tweezers.
10. Cork.

SEVENTEENTH SET.

This article?

1. Bible.
2. Testament.
3. Tract.
4. Bookmark.
5. Prayer book.

6. Hymn-book.
7. Music.
8. Smelling bottle.
9. Vinaigrette.
10. Strap.

EIGHTEENTH SET.

Playing cards.

1. Diamonds.
2. Hearts.
3. Clubs.
4. Spades.

" Right "—Ace.
" That's right "—King.
" Good "—Queen.
" Very good "—Jack.

NINETEENTH SET.

Devices.

1. Masonic.
2. Odd Fellows.
3. Knights of Pythias.

4. Druids.
5. Musical.

ARTICLES IN SETS.

" It will be seen that the different articles are arranged in sets, numbering no more than ten. Each set has at the head a different question, worded very nearly alike, so as to make the audience believe that the same question is being constantly asked. The question at the head of the set, which is always asked first, is the clue to the set which contains the article to be described. Each set is numbered, as in the cases of the colors and metals, and the word conveys each particular article.

" For the first set the question is:

" ' What article is this? '

" This gives the clue to ten distinct articles. The next demand may be:

" ' Can you tell? '

" Which would be solution for ' bag,' it being the third in the list.

" ' Say the fabric.'

" The reply would be, ' Silk,' that being the first in the line of fabrics, and, as I have before stated, ' say ' representing No. 1. If a leather bag, it would be: ' Will you tell the fabric? ' ' will ' standing for No. 5.

" A handkerchief is presented, and the question is:

" ' What article is this? Say; ' which explains that it is a handkerchief, as that is the first article in the list.

" ' Can you tell the fabric? '

" ' Cotton,' cotton standing third in the list of fabrics.

"Then, again, if you want the color—say it is blue—

"'Can't you tell the color?'

"'Blue,' which stands third on the list of colors.

"A watch embodies a greater number of questions than almost any other article. If you want to describe it fully, it is first in the second set, the key of which is:

"'What is this?'

"We will say that it is a lady's watch, gold, double case, three hands, made by Tobias, No. 9,725, the initials 'From B. C. to C. H.' engraved on the case, the year '1860,' and blue enameled, set with five diamonds. This is a complex question, and must be put and answered as follows:

"*Question.* 'What is this? Say.'

"*Answer.* 'A watch.'

"*Q.* 'Say the metal.'

"*A.* 'Gold.'

"*Q.* 'Say to whom it belongs.'

"*A.* 'A lady.'

"*Q.* 'Yes.'

"*A.* 'A double case.'

"*Q.* 'Can you tell the number of hands?'

"*A.* 'Three.'

"*Q.* 'Will you tell the maker.'

"*A.* 'Tobias.'

"*Q.* 'Now the number. Please tell me. Be quick. Won't you?'

"*A.* '9,725.'

"*Q.* 'Can you tell me the color of this enamel?'

"*A.* 'Blue.'

"*Q.* 'Tell the initials. Say.'

"*A.* 'B. C.'

"*Q.* 'Say to whom. I want to know.'

"*A.* 'C. H.'

"*Q.* 'Say these stones.'

"*A.* 'Diamonds.'

"*Q.* 'Will you tell how many?'

"*A.* 'Five.'

"If it is a double case, the simple word 'yes' conveys the intelligence after 'to whom it belongs.' If an open case, the word 'well' is used.

PLAYING CARDS.

"These will be found in the sixteenth set, and the order of suits in the eighteenth. We will take the nine of spades as having been presented. The question will be:

"'Say, what is this? Can you tell?'

"'A playing card.'

" ' Do you know the suit ? Now, then.'

" ' Do ' is four, which means spades, and ' now ' is nine. The cards are told as follows: First, the ' playing card; ' second, the suit; third, the number or picture. If, after the preliminary question is put and answered, it is an ace, the interlocutor says ' Right; ' if a king, ' That's right; ' if a queen, ' Good; ' if a jack, ' Very good.'

MONEY.

" This will be found classed in the eighth set, the key to which is, ' Look at this.'

" No. 6 of the set is described as ' a piece of money,' and is always of a less value than a dollar. We will take a silver quarter of the date of 1820. The question is:

" ' Look at this. What is it ? '

" *A.* ' A piece of money.'

" *Q.* ' Let me know the amount. Will you ? '

" *A.* ' Twenty-five cents; ' as we know that ' let ' is 2 and ' will ' 5.

" If the coin is of this century, only the last two figures are asked; if of a prior date, the last three. The request therefore is:

" ' Look at the date. Hurry! ' which would bring the answer, ' 1820.'

" A foreign coin is furnished, say of Rome. The request would be:

" ' Look at this. Do you know what it is ? '

" The answer is, ' A coin.'

" ' What country ? '

" ' Italy; ' as Italy stands sixth in the list of countries, as will be seen by referring to the table.

" A Mexican dollar will elicit the remark:

" ' Look at this, now.'

" ' A silver dollar.'

" ' Tell me the country.'

" The reply will be, ' Mexico,' as that country stands tenth on the list.

" A treasury note is presented of the value of fifty dollars; the cue is:

" ' Look at this. Be quick.'

" *Answer.* ' A treasury note.'

" ' Will you tell me the amount? Come; ' which means 5 and 0, or $50; ' come ' being a substitute for ' hurry.'

" Again, a $2.50 gold piece is presented, and the question is as before:

" ' Look at this. Will you ? '

" *Answer.* ' A gold piece.'

" ' Let me know the amount. Won't you ? Come.' ' Let,' ' won't,' and ' come ' standing for ' 250.'

OTHER EXAMPLES.

" ' Pray, what is this ? Tell me.'

" The answer is, ' A key,' ' key ' being the tenth article of the set. Now, in order to tell what kind of a key, these simple words will explain:

" ' Yes,' a watch key; ' well,' a door key; ' good,' a safe key.

" ' What is here ?   Say.'

" The answer is ' pipe.'

" Now, to ascertain what kind of a pipe, the same words as above:

" ' Yes,' a meerschaum pipe; ' well,' a wooden pipe; ' good,' a clay pipe.

" ' Can you see this ?   Please say.'

" Answer is ' comb.'

" ' Yes,' a pocket comb; ' well,' a toilet comb; ' good,' a curry comb.

" ' Can you see this ?   Are you going to tell ? '

" The answer is ' brush.'

" ' Yes,' hair brush; ' well,' clothes brush; ' good,' paint brush.

" If an article is presented which is not down in the sets, the alphabet will have to be resorted to and the article spelled out.

" This concludes the ' second-sight ' mystery which so perplexed the world, and which I never would have exposed but for the death of my lamented friend, Robert Heller."

The perfect memorization of the preceding system will enable two ambitious amateurs or professionals to perform the " second-sight " mystery, but it will not enable them to produce *all* of the effects exhibited by Heller. Robert Heller had another system of conveying information to his blindfolded assistant on the stage—a system that permitted him to give a minute description of an object *without speaking a word*. It was this artistic effect that so puzzled every one. It was accomplished by means of electricity. A confederate sat among the spectators, near the center aisle of the theater, and the wires of an electric battery were connected with his chair, the electric push button being under the front part of the seat. Heller gave the cue to the set in which the article was, its number, etc., by some natural movement of his body or arms; and the confederate, rapidly interpreting the secret signals, telegraphed them to the clairvoyante on the stage. Mr. Hermon thus describes the receiving instrument in his clever little book, " Hellerism ":

" It will be remembered by all who ever witnessed Mr. and Miss Heller's ' second-sight ' act that when he came on the stage to begin this part of his performance, he rolled forward to the center of the stage a sofa. This sofa had no back to it, thus enabling Miss Heller to sit with her back to the audience. As the sofa was rolled forward it was so placed that one of the hind legs rested on a little brass plate screwed to the floor of the stage. On the foot of the leg there were two more, thus connecting and making a complete electric communication between his secret partner and Miss Heller.

" In the sofa there was a little machine so arranged that when the button was pressed a slight tap was the result. This tap could only be heard by Miss Heller, for it struck against a thin piece of board covered by the haircloth of the sofa, and sitting, as she was, directly on it, it could be easily felt."

The verbal system and the silent system were used interchangeably during Heller's performances, to the complete bewilderment of the spectators. Even magicians were mystified. When the former system was employed, Heller was enabled to go to any part of the theater; but in the latter, he was compelled, for obvious reasons, to confine himself to the center aisle, just below where the confederate was seated.   The connecting wires were concealed beneath the carpeting.

Other magicians, notably Kellar, have worked up the "second-sight" trick in an ingenious way, by the use of apparatus.   The clairvoyante sits on a chair placed upon a raised platform, and, after her eyes have been carefully bandaged, she tells the names of playing cards, the numbers on bank notes, and adds columns of figures writtten on a blackboard by people in the audience.   The explanation is as follows: A rubber tube runs from behind the scenes, under-neath the stage, and up through a hollow foot of the platform and the leg of the chair, terminating at the back of the chair.   In the back of the lady's dress is a small tube which reaches her ear, being cleverly concealed by the curly wig which she wears.   When she has taken her seat, the magician pre-tends to mesmerize her, and, under cover of the passes, connects the tubing in the chair with the tubing in her dress.   An assistant behind the scenes reads the numbers on the bank notes with a strong spyglass, and conveys the informa-tion to the lady through the speaking-tube.   To facilitate the assistant's work, the magician holds the bank note against the blackboard, which is turned slightly to one side.   The clairvoyante calls out the numbers in a loud voice, whereupon the magician proceeds to chalk them upon the board.   The squar-ing and the cubing of numbers are performed by the assistant behind the scenes, with the aid of logarithmic tables.   When the "second-sight" séance is con-cluded, the magician removes the bandage from the lady's eyes, and pretends to awaken her from the hypnotic state, taking advantage of the little comedy to disconnect the speaking tube.   She rises, bows herself off the stage, taking particular care not to show her back to the audience.

A very clever exhibition of "second sight" is given by Professor and Mrs. Baldwin.   Professor Baldwin calls himself the "White Mahatma," and his entertainment is a curious hodge-podge of pretended mediumship, clairvoy-ance, and vaudeville.   Slips of paper and pencils, and small pads of millboard to serve as writing desks, are distributed among the audience by assistants; the recipients of the writing materials are requested to write questions on the slips, fold them up, and secrete them in their pockets.   The "White Mahatma" disclaims any preparation about the millboards, remarking that they are given to the spectators to obviate the inconvenience of writing on the knee, and may be discarded if desired.   When the questions have been prepared, the assistants collect the pads and place them on the stage, near the footlights, in full view of the audience.   After this there is some dancing and singing by the vaudeville artists connected with the company, and then Mrs. Baldwin, the clairvoyante, makes her appearance; she is carefully blindfolded and "mesmerized" by the Professor.   Her communications to the audience are made after the following manner: "I see a lady in the orchestra, to the right.   She wants to know some-thing about a ring that was lost."   Professor Baldwin, who stands in the center aisle of the theater, near the stage, exclaims: "Will the lady who wrote that question kindly hold up the slip of paper and acknowledge the correctness of Mrs. Baldwin's statement?" The lady complies, and a thrill of astonishment pervades the audience. An assistant goes to the lady, takes the slip, and hands it to Professor Baldwin, who reads it, exclaiming: "Mrs. Baldwin is correct; but let us see if she cannot give us more detailed information concerning the ring which is lost." He mounts the stage, and, standing behind the clairvoyante, makes violent mesmeric passes over her head, the piano in the orchestra accompanying the operation with several loud chords and cadenzas. Then the "White Mahatma" advances to the footlights and commands his wife to speak. "The ring is of gold with a pearl setting," she says, "and has the initials 'M. B.' engraved within. It was lost about January 1, 18—," etc. The lady in the audience had only written: "I have lost my ring; can you describe it?" Consequently, when she hears this accurate description by Mrs. Baldwin, she is very much impressed.

The trick is an ingenious one. It is worked up with great dramatic effect by the Baldwins. The secret lies in the pads of millboard, some of which contain carbon sheets under two layers of brown paper. The writing of the spectators is thereby transferred by means of the carbon paper to sheets of writing paper placed under the carbon sheets. The genuine millboard pads which are distributed among the audience are laid on the stage, while the prepared pads are carried off behind the scenes to Mrs. Baldwin, who has ample time to post herself with the desired information before coming on the stage.

Of course, the spectators who get the genuine pads do not receive any clairvoyant communications, nor do those who discard the genuine pads. The surprising part of the feat is the extraneous information imparted by Mrs. Baldwin, which seems to preclude any possibility of trickery. This information is obtained from the spectators by the assistants when they go to collect the slips of paper, and is whispered by them to Professor Baldwin. Under cover of the pretended magnetizing, Professor Baldwin gives his wife this information, the chords from the piano preventing any one from hearing what he says. It is all done very rapidly, the spectators being completely deluded. The people who have been pumped by the assistants seem to forget the fact in their interest in the main part of the trick, viz., the reading of the slips by Mrs. Baldwin. One reason of this self-deception is, perhaps, the fact that they do not suspect the integrity of the innocent-looking ushers, or regard them as a part of the experiment.

Where numbers are to be conveyed, the Baldwins use a verbal code of signals. This obviates the necessity of Mr. Baldwin going upon the stage to remagnetize his wife.

Silent Thought Transference, No. 1.

In this ingenious trick the clairvoyante, while blindfolded, tells "the suit and value of any number of selected cards, solves arithmetical problems, gives numbers on borrowed bank notes, indicates time by any watch, describes borrowed coins, and many other tests." All this is accomplished in silence, the medium being surrounded by a committee from the audience, if desired. The trick can be given in a private parlor, and requires no electrical apparatus, speaking tubes, etc. I am indebted for an explanation of "silent thought transference" to Mr. H. J. Burlingame. In his little *brochure*, "Tricks in Magic, Illusions, and Mental Phenomena," he writes as follows: "By means of the silent code all the usual effects generally exhibited at thought-reading séances can be reproduced. It consists in both medium and performer counting mentally and together. It is a known fact that the beats for 'common time' are always the same in music; therefore, with little practice, it is easy for two persons, starting on a given signal, to count at the same time and rate, and when another signal is given, to stop. Of course both will have arrived at the same number. This then is the actual method employed in this code, and from it you will see that any number from 0 to 9 can be transmitted by the performer to the medium. It is best to experiment and find out what rate of counting best suits the two persons employing this code, but the following suggestions are offered: It may, perhaps, be best to begin counting at a slow rate, gradually increasing until you find it advisable to go no faster. Say you have in the room, when first practicing, a loud-ticking clock, with a fairly slow beat. On the given beat or signal you both start counting at the same rate as the clock. Of course the clock must be removed when the rate has been well learned. If preferred, count at the rate of 'common time,' viz.: 1 and 2 and 3 and 4, and so on, or practice with a 'metronome,' such as is used during piano practice for the purpose of setting time. A very good rate to finally adopt is about 70 to 75 per minute. Whatever rate is found to suit best must be adhered to. You will find at the rate mentioned that any number up to 9 can be transmitted with absolute certainty, after an hour or so of practice.

"Now that the principle has been explained, the next items are the signals to give the medium the cue when to start and when to stop counting mentally.

"Say the performer has borrowed a coin, the date of which is 1862. The first figure of the coin 1 and 8 are generally understood, as most coins in use are 18 something or other; if of date 18, in the hundreds. The performer must advise the medium of this by his manner of thanking the person who lent the coin, which can easily be arranged to suit one's fancy. The 6 and 2 have therefore to be transmitted. The performer stands away from the medium or among the audience. The medium being on the stage, securely blindfolded, the performer takes his position, with chalk in right hand, in front of a blackboard, holding coin in his left hand. He does not speak a word, but simply looks at the coin. After a pause the medium calls out: 'The first figure I picture is a one,' or words to that effect. Immediately the lady stops speaking, they both begin to count mentally at the rate agreed upon by practice. In this case the number to be transmitted is 6. As the last word of the sentence is spoken they commence mentally 1-2-3-4-5-6; during this short period the performer glances down at the coin as if to verify what the lady has called out. As soon as they reach the figure 6 the signal 'stop' has to be transmitted. This is done by the performer putting down on the blackboard sharply the figure

called out by the lady, viz.: ' One ' (1).   It will be seen by this method that
the signal is quite easy to transmit, and it is perfectly natural to put down the
figure on the board quickly and sharply.   The third figure of the coin is now
known to the medium.   The last figure, 2, is transmitted in the same manner
as the previous figure.   The lady says, ' The second figure I see is 8.'   As
soon as she ceases speaking, they begin the counting again, 1-2; on the
arrival at the figure 2 the performer puts down the 8, previously called
out, sharply on the board, which is the signal for ' stop.'   The lady now knows
the full date of the coin.   The metal of the coin must be indicated to the
medium previously by the wording of the reply to the owner of the coin after
it has been handed to the performer.   This can easily be arranged.   The value
of the coin or its equivalent number is indicated in the same way as the previous figure; and between the 6 and the 2, that is, after the lady has called
out the 6, they commence to count for the value.   When an 0 occurs in the
date, no pause is made.   The performer puts down the figure on the board
for the ' stop ' signal immediately the lady stops speaking.   This if followed
carefully will be found quite easy and natural in practice. ¨

" Any other system that one may adopt for giving the starting and stopping signals can, of course, be applied, but the method here proposed will be
found to answer the purpose, and cannot be detected."

The bank-note, card, and other tests are arranged on similar lines.

Silent Thought Transference, No. 2.

This clever trick was introduced to the theater-goers of marvel-loving Paris by
Professor Verbeck and Mademoiselle Mathilde.   Guibal and Marie Gréville performed it in England and America, creating a great sensation.   It is based on a
very simple principle.   Abbreviated somewhat from Burlingame's *brochure*, the
effect is as follows: " The pretended mesmerist announces to the spectators the
marvelous intuitive powers of his subject, Miss Venus, remarking: ' Miss Venus
shall be hypnotized by me, and, when launched into the hypnotic sleeep, can and
will perform any rational act that the spectators desire, despite the fact that I
will not speak one word during the séance.   While in the trance state, she will
walk among you and comply with your requests.   This, ladies and gentlemen,
is the *trance-it* of Venus.   When I have her under control and in the hypnotic
trance, I will move about among you, and you can convey to me by whisper
what you would desire the medium to do.'

" Miss Venus is now introduced by the professor.   She bows and seats herself on a chair, facing the spectators.   The professor, by means of any of the
pantomimic gestures, pretends to hypnotize her, after which dramatic scene, he
goes among the audience, asking here and there what the spectators would like
the lady marvel to do.   Having spoken to some twelve or twenty persons, he
solemnly enjoins the strictest silence.   With serious mien he advances toward
the medium, without going on the stage, and motions or waves his right hand
in a downward movement in front of her.   She slowly rises and goes through

each desired performance, finally returning to her chair and allowing herself to be dehypnotized. The professor recapitulates for the benefit of all what each spectator desired, and how Miss Venus was successful in each and every crucial test.

EXPLANATION.

" In this trick a code of signs and things to be done must be learned by the alleged mesmerist. These he forces adroitly into the minds of the people. The following is the forcing code:

" 1. Pull a gentleman's hair.

" 2. Turn up his trousers.

" 3. Tie a number of knots in his handkerchief.

" 4. Take a watch out of a gentleman's pocket and place it in another pocket.

" 5. Open a lady's reticule; take out her purse, or anything she may desire.

" 6. From out of a number of coins placed in a hat, pick out the special one which has been selected.

" 7. Write any number selected on a card.

" 8. Take a gentleman's cane or umbrella and put it in the hands of another gentleman.

" 9. Take glasses off a person and place on own nose.

" 10. Take off lady's or gentleman's gloves.

" 11. Write autograph on programme gentleman holds.

" 13. Take a handkerchief out of some person's pocket and tie it on his neck or arm.

" 14. Tie a knot in a watch chain, and so on.

" This can be varied indefinitely.

" How to force these requests: The professor first pretends to hypnotize the subject; then moving among the audience, he goes to number one, or first person, and asks him what he would like the medium to do. ' Let her tell me what I have in my pocket,' suggests the spectator. ' Oh,' says the professor, ' you forget that she is hypnotized and we cannot have her speak. Get her to do so and so, or this, or that,' and so the professor rapidly shoots out a volley of suggestions from his learned code. As a natural result, the person selects one of these suggestions.

" Going to the next, he forces the questions differently, saying, ' What shall she do for you—turn up your trousers? Pull your hair? Tie a knot in your handkerchief?' etc. In this case a volley of queries is fired before the gentleman has time to make any suggestions not mentioned by the professor. Seeing a lady sitting near with a bag, the ' mesmerist' remarks: ' Madam, have you a purse in it? Yes? Shall the lady remove it, or something from it?' and so on. Again he beholds a gentleman with glasses on, and suggests that the medium remove the spectacles, etc. If, however, the gentleman does not wish this done, the professor suggests some of the other tests. In going through the audience the professor asks each individual his or her request in whispers only, and he generally has each person whom he asks a couple of yards apart.

"Again it is better, when forcing questions, to force only three at a time, and force them in rotation. To do this, suggest three questions, but emphasize or force only one of the three. The professor has to keep his wits about him. Having gone to a sufficient number in the audience, he must keep mental track of the gentleman who selected No. 1 of code, of him who selected No. 2, and so on. When he returns to the stage to wave down Miss Venus, all she has to do is to follow him in front or at his side. The first person he stops at (by signal), she merely does first on code; the second he stops at, she does second on code; and so on right through. The professor must remember where each chooser is seated.

"He directs the medium to the spectator in question by the movements of his hands. He first shows her the rows in which the persons are seated, all the time waving his hands as if making mesmeric passes. As soon as the medium reaches No. 1 the professor drops his left hand at his side, whereupon she stops and pulls the gentleman's hair.

"The professor then directs her to No. 2. She stops and turns up the gentleman's trousers. When she gets to No. 3 the man of mystery tells her how many knots to tie in the handkerchief, by the number of downward waves of left hand, at the same time making passes with the right. To select any special coin out of a hat, or other receptacle, Miss Venus pours the coins from the hat into her right hand, letting them drop one by one into the left hand. When she reaches the proper article, the professor turns to the audience, as if silencing them, and says 'hist!'

"The lady, however, continues pouring the coins into her left hand, and when all are in, picks out the one she knows is correct.

"These methods may be readily varied to suit the taste of the performers.

"The medium's eyes appear to be closed all the time, but in fact are open sufficiently for her to see all the movements of the professor. After becoming expert it will not be necessary to use the forcing code often, because all requests can be whispered to the medium by the so-called mesmerist, without the audience becoming aware of it. He can do this when he escorts her from the stage to the audience, or as he occasionally passes her in the aisles. The waving of his hands and arms in his different 'passes' will partly tell her what she is expected to do.

"This 'hypnotic demonstration' is one of the most puzzling effects in the whole domain of mental magic.

BOOK II.

ANCIENT MAGIC.

CHAPTER I.

TEMPLE TRICKS OF THE GREEKS.

PUPPET SHOWS AMONG THE GREEKS.

The ancients, especially the Greeks, were very fond of theatrical representations; but, as M. Magnin has remarked in his "*Origines du Théâtre Moderne,*" public representations were very expensive, and for that reason very rare. Moreover, those who were not in a condition of freedom were excluded from them; and, finally, all cities could not have a large theater and provide for the expenses that it carried with it. It became necessary, then, for every-day needs, for all conditions and for all places, that there should be comedians of an inferior order, charged with the duty of offering continuously and inexpensively the emotions of the drama to all classes of inhabitants.

Formerly, as to-day, there were seen, wandering from village to village, menageries, puppet shows, fortune tellers, jugglers, and performers of tricks of all kinds. These prestidigitateurs even obtained at times such celebrity that history has preserved their names for us—at least of two of them, Euclides and Theodosius, to whom statues were erected by their contemporaries. One of these was put up at Athens, in the Theater of Bacchus, alongside of that of the great writer of tragedy, Æschylus, and the other at the Theater of the Istiaians, holding in the hand a small ball. The grammarian Athenæus, who reports these facts in his "Banquet of the Sages," profits by the occasion to deplore the taste of the Athenians, who preferred the inventions of mechanics to the culture of mind, and histrions to philosophers. He adds with vexation that Diophites of Locris passed down to posterity simply because he came one day to Thebes, wearing around his body bladders filled with wine and milk, and so arranged that he could spurt at will one of these liquids in apparently drawing it from his mouth. What would Athenæus say if he knew that it was through him alone that the name of this histrion had come down to us?

Philo of Byzantium, and Heron of Alexandria, to whom we always have to have recourse when we desire accurate information as to the mechanic arts of antiquity, both composed treatises on puppet shows. That of Philo is lost, but Heron's treatise has been preserved to us, and has recently been translated in part by M. Victor Prou.

MACHINA SE MOVENTE MOBILE

FIG. 1.—THE SHRINE OF BACCHUS. FROM AN OLD PRINT.

According to the Greek engineer, there were several kinds of puppet shows. The oldest and simplest consisted of a small stationary case, isolated on every side, in which the stage was closed by doors that opened automatically several times to exhibit the different tableaux. The programme of the representation was generally as follows: The first tableau showed a head, painted on the back

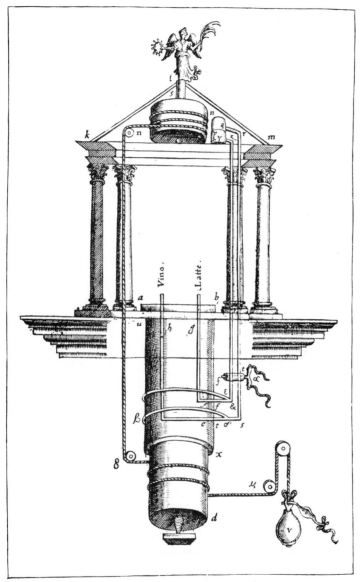

FIG. 2.—THE SHRINE OF BACCHUS. MECHANISM FOR DELIVERING WINE AND MILK. FROM AN OLD PRINT.

of the stage, which moved its eyes, and lowered and raised them alternately. The door having been closed, and then opened again, there was seen, instead of a head, a group of persons.   Finally, the stage opened a third time to show a new group, and this finished the representation.   There were, then, only three movements to be made—that of the doors, that of the eyes, and that of the change of background.

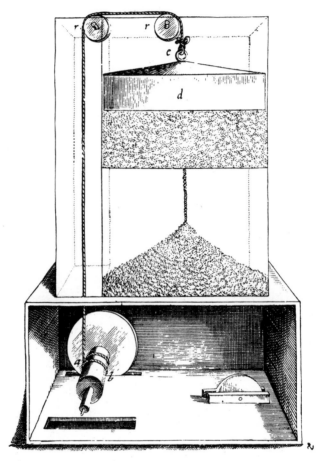

FIG. 3.—THE SHRINE OF BACCHUS.   SECTION SHOWING THE PRO-
PELLING MECHANISM.

    As such representations were often given on the stages of large theaters, a method was devised later on of causing the case to start from the scenes behind which it was hidden from the spectators, and of moving automatically to the front of the stage, where it exhibited in succession the different tableaux, after which it returned automatically behind the scenes.   Here is one of the scenes indicated by Heron, entitled the "Triumph of Bacchus":

    The movable case shows at its upper part a platform from which arises a cylindrical temple, the roof of which, supported by six columns, is conical, and surmounted by a figure of Victory with spread wings and holding a crown in her right hand. In the center of the temple Bacchus is seen standing, holding a thyrsus in his left hand and a cup in his right. At his feet lies a panther. In front of and behind the god, on the platform of the stage, are two altars provided with combustible material. Very near the columns, but external to them, there are Bacchantes placed in any posture that may be desired. All being thus prepared, says Heron, the automatic apparatus is set in motion. The theater then moves of itself to the spot selected, and there stops. Then the altar in front of Jupiter becomes lighted, and, at the same time, milk and water spurt from his thyrsus, while his cup pours wine over the panther. The four faces of the base become encircled with crowns, and, to the noise of drums

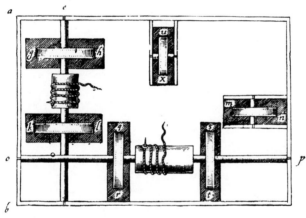

FIG. 4.

and cymbals, the Bacchantes dance round about the temple. Soon, the noise having ceased, Victory on the top of the temple, and Bacchus within it, face about. The altar that was behind the god is now in front of him, and becomes lighted in its turn. Then occurs another outflow from the thyrsus and cup, and another round of the Bacchantes to the sound of drums and cymbals. The dance being finished, the theater returns to its former station. Thus ends the apotheosis.

We shall try to briefly indicate the processes which permitted of these different operations being performed, and which offer a much more general interest than one might at first sight be led to believe; for almost all of them had been employed in former times for producing the illusions to which ancient religions owed their power.

There is a general belief among mechanicians that vehicles containing within themselves the means of their own propulsion are of comparatively recent origin; and the fact of the adhesion of the rims of their wheels to the earth or a supporting rail being sufficient to enable adequate power applied to the wheels to move the vehicle was a discovery of not earlier than the middle of the last century; but in this instance the writers on locomotive machines have not dived deep enough or stayed down long enough among the records of antiquity to discover the bottom facts in the history of such mechanisms.

The first locomotive, or self-moving vehicle, of which we have any account was this invention of Heron of Alexandria. In his work just cited descriptive of automatic or self-moving machines, there is illustrated the mechanism by which the shrine of Bacchus, mounted upon three wheels concealed within its base, is moved. Fig. 3 is a vertical section of that part of the shrine below the canopy, and exhibits the propelling apparatus of this ancient locomotive machine. Within the base are seen two of the supporting wheels; the driving

FIG. 5.

wheel nearest the eye having been removed. On the axle of the driving wheels was the drum, *b,* about which was wound the rope, *a,* which passed upward through the space on one side of the shrine and over the pulleys, *r r,* and was fastened to the ring, *c,* of the ponderous lead weight, *d,* which rested upon a quantity of dry, fine sand. The escape of this sand through a small hole in the middle of the floor of the compartment containing it allowed the lead weight, *d,* to gradually descend, and by pulling upon the cord, *a,* caused the shrine to move slowly forward in a straight line.

Heron describes the method of arranging and proportioning the wheels in case it was desired that the shrine move in a circular path. He also shows how the shrine can be constructed to move in straight lines at right angles to each other.

Fig. 4 shows the arrangement of the wheels for this purpose, and Fig. 5 is a perspective view, showing the screws by which the bearings of either set of wheels could be raised or lowered, so as to cause the shrine to move in the way proposed.

Supposing the motive cords properly wound around vertical bobbins, instead of a horizontal one, and we have the half revolution of Bacchus and Victory, as well as the complete revolution of the Bacchantes. This is clearly shown in the engraving (Fig. 2).

The successive lighting of the two altars, the flow of milk and wine, and the noise of drums and cymbals were likewise obtained by the aid of cords moved by counterpoises, and the lengths of which were graduated in such a way as to open and close orifices at the proper moment, by acting through traction on sliding valves which kept them closed.

Small pieces of combustible material were piled up beforehand on the two altars, the bodies of which were of metal, and in the interior of which were hidden small lamps that were separated from the combustible by a metal plate which was drawn aside at the proper moment by a small chain. The flame, on traversing the orifice, thus communicated with the combustible.

The milk and wine which

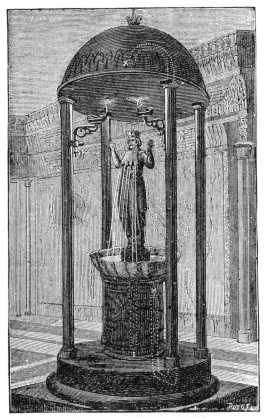

FIG. 6.—THE MARVELOUS STATUE OF CYBELE.

flowed out at two different times through the thyrsus and cup of Bacchus came from a double reservoir hidden under the roof of the temple, over the orifices. The latter communicated, each of them, with one of the halves of the reservoir, through two tubes inserted in the columns of the small edifice. These tubes were prolonged under the floor of the stage, and extended upward to the hands of Bacchus. A key, manœuvred by cords, alternately opened and closed the orifices which gave passage to the two liquids.

As for the noise of the drums and cymbals, that resulted from the falling of granules of lead, contained in an invisible box provided with an automatic sliding valve, upon an inclined tambourine, whence they rebounded against little cymbals in the interior of the base of the car.

Finally, the crowns and garlands that suddenly made their appearance on the four faces of the base of the stage were hidden there in advance between the two walls surrounding the base. The space thus made for the crowns was closed beneath, along each face, by a horizontal trap moving on hinges that connected it with the inner wall of the base, but which was held temporarily stationary by means of a catch. The crowns were attached to the top of their compartment by cords that would have allowed them to fall to the level of the pedestal, had they not been supported by the traps.

At the desired moment the catch, which was controlled by a special cord, ceased to hold the trap, and the latter, falling vertically, gave passage to the festoons and crowns that small leaden weights then drew along with all the quickness necessary.

Two points here are specially worthy of attracting our attention, and these are the flow of wine or milk from the statue of Bacchus, and the spontaneous lighting of the altar. These, in fact, were the two illusions that were most admired in ancient

FIG. 7.—MARVELOUS ALTAR (ACCORDING TO HERON).

times, and there were several processes of performing them. Father Kircher possessed in his museum an apparatus which he describes in "*Œdipus Ægyptiacus*" (t. ii., p. 333), and which probably came from some ancient Egyptian temple as shown in Fig. 6.

It consisted of a hollow hemispherical dome, supported by four columns, and placed over the statue of the goddess of many breasts. To two of these columns were adapted movable brackets, at whose extremities there were fixed lamps. The hemisphere was hermetically closed underneath by a metal plate. The small altar which supported the statue, and which was filled with milk, communicated with the interior of the statue by a tube reaching nearly to the bottom. The altar likewise communicated with the hollow dome by a tube having a double bend. At the moment of the sacrifice the two lamps were lighted and the brackets turned so that the flames should come in contact with and heat the bottom of the dome. The air contained in the latter, being dilated, passed through the tube X M and pressed on the milk contained in the altar, and caused it to rise through the straight tube into the interior of the statue as high as the breasts. A series of small conduits, into which the principal tube divided, carried the liquid to the breasts, whence it spurted out, to the great admiration of the spectators, who cried out at the miracle. The sacrifice being ended, the lamps were put out, and the milk ceased to flow.

Heron of Alexandria describes in his " Pneumatics " several analagous apparatus. Here is one of them. (M. de Rochas translates the Greek text literally.)

" To construct an altar in such a way that, when a fire is lighted thereon, the statues at the side of it shall make libations (Fig. 7).

" Let there be a pedestal, A B Γ Δ, on which are placed statues, and an altar, E Z H, closed on every side. The pedestal should also be hermetically closed, but is connected with the altar through a central tube. It is traversed likewise by the tube, e Λ (in the interior of the statue to the right), not far from the bottom, which terminates in a cup held by the statue, e. Water

FIG. 8.—MARVELOUS ALTAR (ACCORDING TO HERON).

is poured into the pedestal through a hole, M, which is afterward corked up.

" If, then, a fire be lighted on the altar, the internal air will be dilated, and will enter the pedestal and drive out the water contained in it. But the latter, having no other exit than the tube, e Λ, will rise into the cup, and so the statue will make a libation. This will last as long as the fire does. On extinguishing the fire the libation ceases, and occurs anew as often as the fire is relighted.

" It is necessary that the tube through which the heat is to introduce itself shall be wider in the middle; and it is necessary, in fact, that the heat, or rather that the draught that it produces, shall accumulate in an inflation, in order to have more effect."

According to Father Kircher, an author whom he calls Bitho reports that there was at Saïs a temple of Minerva in which there was an altar on which, when a fire was lighted, Dionysius and Artemis (Bacchus and Diana) poured milk and wine, while a dragon hissed.

It is easy to conceive of the modification to be introduced into the apparatus above described by Heron, in order to cause the outflow of milk from one side and of wine from the other.

After having indicated it, Father Kircher adds: "It is thus that Bacchus and Diana appeared to pour, one of them wine, and the other milk, and that the dragon seemed to applaud their action by hisses. As the people who were present at the spectacle did not see what was going on within, it is not astonishing that they believed it due to divine intervention. We know, in fact, that Osiris or Bacchus was considered as the discoverer of the vine and of milk; that Iris was the genius of the waters of the Nile; and that the Serpent, or good genius, was the first cause of all these things. Since, moreover, sacrifices had to be made to the gods in order to obtain benefits, the flow of milk, wine, or water, as well as the hissing of the serpent, when the sacrificial flame was lighted, appeared to demonstrate clearly the existence of the gods."

In another analogous apparatus of Heron's, it is steam that performs the *rôle* that we have just seen played by dilated air. But the ancients do not appear to have perceived the essential difference, as regards motive power, that exists between these two agents; indeed, their preferences were wholly for air, although the effects produced were not very great. We might cite several small machines of this sort, but we shall confine ourselves to one example that has some relation to our subject. This also is borrowed from Heron's "Pneumatics." (Fig. 8.)

"Fire being lighted on an altar, figures will appear to execute a round dance. The altars should be transparent, and of glass or horn. From the fireplace there starts a tube which runs to the base of the altar, where it revolves on a pivot, while its upper part revolves in a tube fixed to the fireplace. To the tube there should be adjusted other tubes (horizontal) in communication with it, which cross each other at right angles, and which are bent in opposite directions at their extremities. There is likewise fixed to it a disk upon which are attached figures which form a round. When the fire of the altar is lighted, the air, becoming heated, will pass into the tube; but being driven from the latter, it will pass through the small bent tubes and . . . cause the tube as well as the figures to revolve."

Father Kircher, who had at his disposal either many documents that we are not acquainted with, or else a very lively imagination, alleges (*Œdip. Æg.*, t. ii., p. 338) that King Menes took much delight in seeing such figures revolve. Nor are the examples of holy fireplaces that kindled spontaneously wanting in antiquity.

Pliny (*Hist. Nat.*, ii.,7) and Horace (*Serm. Sat.*, v.) tell us that this phenomenon occurred in the temple of Gnatia, and Solin (ch. v.) says that it was observed likewise on an altar near Agrigentum. Athenæus (*Deipn.*, i., 15) says that the celebrated prestidigitateur, Cratisthenes of Phlius, pupil of another celebrated prestidigitateur named Xenophon, knew the art of preparing a fire which lighted spontaneously.

Pausanias tells us that in a city of Lydia, whose inhabitants, having fallen under the yoke of the Persians, had embraced the religion of the Magi, " there exists an altar upon which there are ashes which, in color, resemble no other. The priest puts wood on the altar, and invokes I know not what god by harangues taken from a book written in a barbarous tongue unknown to the Greeks, when the wood soon lights of itself without fire, and the flame from it is very clear."

The secret, or rather one of the secrets of the Magi, has been revealed to us by one of the Fathers of the Church (St. Hippolytus, it is thought), who has left, in a work entitled *Philosophumena*, which is designed to refute the doctrines of the pagans, a chapter on the illusions of their priests. According to him, the altars on which this miracle took place contained, instead of ashes, calcined lime and a large quantity of incense reduced to powder; and this would explain the unusual color of the ashes observed by Pausanias. The process, moreover, is excellent; for it is only necessary to throw a little water on the lime, with certain precautions, to develop a heat capable of setting on fire incense or any other material that is more readily combustible, such as sulphur and phosphorus. The same author points out still another means, and this consists in hiding fire-brands in small bells that were afterward covered with shavings, the latter having previously been covered with a composition made of naphtha and bitumen (Greek fire). As may be seen, a very small movement sufficed to bring about combustion.

THE MACHINERY OF THE TEMPLES.

A. Rich, in his " Dictionary of Roman and Grecian Antiquities," relates, under the word *adytum*, that many ancient temples possessed chambers that were known only to the priests, and that served for the production of their mysteries. He was enabled to visit a perfectly preserved one of these at Alba, on Lake Fucino, in the ruins of a temple in which it had been formed under the *apsis*, that is to say, under the large semicircular niche which usually held the image of the god at the extreme end of the edifice. " One part of this chamber," says he, " is sunk beneath the pavement of the principal part of the temple (*cella*), and the other rises above it. The latter, then, must have appeared to the worshippers assembled in the temple merely like a base that occupied the lower portion of the *apsis*, and that was designed to hold in an elevated position the statue of the divinity whose name was borne by the edifice. This sanctuary, moreover, had no door or visible communication that opened into the body of the temple. Entrance therein was effected through a hidden door in an inclosure of walls at the rear end of the building. It was through this that the priests introduced themselves and their machines without being seen or recognized. But there is one remarkable fact, and one which proves without question the purpose of the *adytum,* and that is, that we find therein a number of tubes or hollow conduits which form a communication between this

APPARATUS FOR SOUNDING A TRUMPET WHEN THE DOOR OF A TEMPLE WAS OPENED.

compartment and the interior of the temple, which end at the different parts of the walls·of the *cella,* and which thus allowed a voice to make itself heard at any place in the temple, while the person and the place whence the sound emanated remained hidden.''

Sometimes the *adytum* was simply a chamber situated behind the *apsis,* as in a small edifice which was still in existence at Rome in the sixteenth century, and a description of which has been left to us by Labbacco, an architect of that epoch.

Colonel Fain tells us that he himself has visited an ancient temple in Syria, in the interior of all the walls of which there had been formed narrow passages through which a man could make a tour of the building without being seen.

In the temple of Ceres, at Eleusis, the pavement of the *cella* is rough and much lower than the level of the adjacent portico; and, moreover, the side walls exhibit apertures and vertical and horizontal grooves whose purpose it is difficult to divine, but which served, perhaps, for the establishing of a movable flooring like that spoken of by Philostratus in the '' Life of Apollonius '' (lib. iii., ch. v.). '' The sages of India,'' says he, '' led Apollonius toward the temple of their god, singing hymns on the way, and forming a sacred procession. The earth, which they strike in cadence with their staves, moves like an agitated sea, and raises them to a height of nearly two paces, and then settles again and assumes its former level."

The statues of the gods, when they were of large dimensions, possessed cavities which the priests entered through hidden passages, in order to deliver oracles (Theodoret, *Hist. Eccl.*, vol. xxii.).

We read in Pausanias (*Arcadica*, lib. viii., ch. xvi.) that at Jerusalem the tomb of a woman of the country, named Helen, had a door made of marble like the rest of the monument, and that this door opened of itself on a certain day of the year, and at a certain hour, by means of a machine, and closed again some time afterward. "At any other time," adds he, "had you desired to open it, you had sooner broken it."

According to Pliny (xxxvi. 14), the gates of the labyrinth of Thebes were so constituted that when they were opened they emitted a noise like that of thunder.

Heron, in his "Pneumatics," gives us an explanation of some of these prodigies.

Our first engraving is sufficiently clear to permit of dispensing with a reproduction of the Greek engineer's text in this place. It will be seen that when the door is opened, a system of cords, guide-pulleys, and rods pushes into a vessel of water a hemisphere, to the upper part of which a trumpet is fixed.

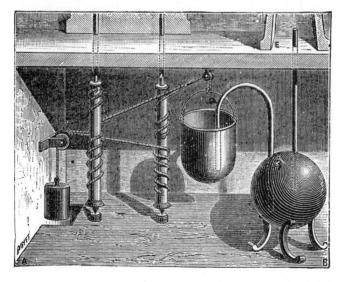

MECHANISM FOR OPENING AND CLOSING THE DOORS WHEN A FIRE
WAS LIGHTED UPON THE ALTAR.

The air compressed by the water escapes through the instrument and causes it to make a sound.

Our second and third engravings are likewise borrowed from Heron.

The altar is hollow, as shown at E, in second engraving. When fire is lighted thereon, the air contained in the interior dilates and presses against the water with which the globe situated beneath is filled.   This water then runs through a bent tube into a sort of pail suspended from a cord that passes

TEMPLE WHOSE DOORS OPENED WHEN A FIRE WAS LIGHTED UPON
THE ALTAR.

over a pulley, and afterward separates into two parts, and winds around two cylinders movable upon pivots, and forming a prolongation of the axes around which the doors revolve.   Around the same cylinders are wound in opposite directions two other cords, which likewise unite into a single one before passing over a pulley, and then hang vertically in order to hold a counterpoise.

It is clear that, when the water from the globe enters the pail, the weight of the latter will be thereby increased, and that it will descend and draw on the cord, which has been wound around the cylinders in such a way as to cause the doors to open when it is drawn in this direction.

The doors are afterward closed again as follows: The bent tube that puts the globe and pail in communication forms a siphon whose longer arm enters the globe. When the fire is extinguished upon the altar, the air contained in the latter and in the globe becomes cooled and diminished in volume. The water in the pail is then drawn into the globe, and the siphon, being thus naturally primed, operates until all the water in the pail has passed over into the globe. In measure as the pail lightens, it rises under the influence of the counterpoise; and the latter, in its descent, closes the doors through the intermedium of the cords wound around the cylinder. Heron says that mercury was sometimes used instead of water on account of its being heavier.

INVENTION IN 1889 A.D. *VS.* INVENTION B.C.

At the railway stations, ferry houses, and even upon the street corners, there may be found in almost every city and village in the United States automatic vending machines, which, for a nickel, or more or less, will deliver the various goods which they are adapted to sell. The purchaser may procure a newspaper and a cigar to smoke, or, if averse to the use of the weed, he may secure a tablet of chewing-gum or a package of sweets. If entertainment is desired, it may be found in the " nickel-in-the-slot " phonograph.

In Europe and America machines of this class are provided for dealing out portable liquors; bouquets are also furnished in a similar way: and if you desire to know how much you have increased in weight since yesterday, all that need be done is to mount the platform of the nickel-in-the-slot scales, and drop in your coin, and the thing is done. One of the latest achievements in this line is the automatic photographic apparatus, which takes your picture for a nickel, while you wait.

The craze has even gone so far as to apply the principle to the distribution of perfumery. In the railway stations and ferry houses may be found machines which, for a penny, will dole out a drop or two of liquid which passes for perfumery, and which, in many cases, serves as a thin mask for bodily uncleanliness.

These various devices, and many others which we might mention, are regarded as very clever inventions, and have certainly proved successful in many cases in a pecuniary sense.

The last automatic vending machine alluded to is shown in our second engraving. The perfume reservoir is located in the upper portion of the vase; the tube communicating with the lower part of the reservoir extends through the side of the vase, and is closed at its upper end by a valve attached to one end of the lever, O. The other end of the lever, O, is connected by a rod with the lever, E, the longer arm of this lever being provided with a pan, R, for receiving coin, while the shorter arm of the lever is furnished with a weight for counterbalancing the pan and closing the valve. A curved piece of metal is arranged concentric with the path of the pan, R, and serves to retain the coin dropped into it through the slot in the top of the vase until the pan, R, is carried down beyond the end of the curved plate, when the

LUSTRAL WATER VESSEL DESCRIBED BY HERON ABOUT 100 B.C.

coin is discharged into the lower part of the vase; the counterweight on the short arm of the lever then returns the lever to the point of starting and closes the valve, thus stopping the flow of the perfume.

NOBLE'S AUTOMATIC PERFUME DISTRIBUTOR. PATENTED IN 1889.

This very clever device was patented by Mr. Lewis C. Noble, of Boston, Mass., on November 19, 1889. Our illustration is prepared directly from the patent drawings. This and other machines for analogous purposes are regarded as the peculiar product of our inventive age, but in turning back the pages of history, we find that in Egypt, something more than two thousand years ago, when a worshiper was about to enter the temple, he sprinkled himself with lustral water, taken from a vase near the entrance. The priests made the distribution of holy water a source of revenue by the employ-ment of the automatic vending machine which is shown in our first engraving. This apparatus would not release a single drop of the purifying liquid until coin to the amount required had been deposited in the vase.

A comparison of the ancient lustral water vase and the modern perfumery vending machine will show that they are substantially alike. The ancient machine has a lever, O, fulcrumed in the standard, N, and connected with the valve in the reservoir, H. The lever is furnished with the pan, R, for receiving the coins dropped through the slot, A, at the top of the vase. An enlarged view of the valve belonging to the vase is shown at the left of the engraving.

The mechanism is almost identical with that shown in the modern device; in fact, this ancient vase, described by Heron more than two thousand years ago, is the prototype of all modern automatic vending machines, and simply serves as another proof of the truth of the saying, "There is nothing new under the sun."

It is a curious fact that this ancient invention escaped the notice of the Patent Office until long after patents were granted for the earlier automatic vending machines. It was only a comparatively short time ago that the Patent Office began to cite the vase of Heron as a reference. It was discovered in an ancient work on natural philosophy, and it is a matter of considerable interest to us now to know that this device was well known to the Patent Office during the middle of this century. The vase of Heron is illustrated and described in a work on hydraulics and mechanics published in 1850 by Thomas Ewbank, who was at that time Commissioner of Patents.

AN EGYPTIAN LUSTRAL WATER VESSEL.

Two thousand years ago the Egyptian priests sold holy water to the faith-ful by a similar process to that which we have just described, although the apparatus did not partake of the nickel-in-the-slot character. Heron says of them, that there are placed in Egyptian sanctuaries, near the portico, movable bronze wheels which those who are entering cause to revolve "because brass passes for a purifier." He says that it is expedient to arrange them in such a way that the rotation of the wheel will cause the flow of the lustral water. He describes the apparatus as follows:

"Let A B Γ Δ be a water vessel hidden behind the posts of the entrance doors. This vessel is pierced at the bottom with a hole, E, and under it there is fixed a tube, Z H Θ K, having an aperture opposite the one in the bottom of the vessel. In this tube there is placed another one, Λ M, which is fixed to the former at Λ. This tube, Λ M, likewise contains an aperture, Π, in a line with the two preceding. Between these two tubes there is adapted a third, N Ξ O P, movable by friction on each of them, and having an aperture, Σ, opposite E.

"If these three holes be in a straight line, the water, when poured into the vessel, A B $l'\varDelta$, will flow out through the tube, $\varLambda$ M; but if the tube, N $\varXi$ O R, be turned in such a way as to displace the aperture, $\varSigma$, the flow will cease. It is only necessary, then, to so fix the wheel, N $\varXi$ O P, that, when made to revolve, the water shall flow."

This ingenious system of cocks having several ways was reproduced in the sixteenth century by Jacques Besson, in his "*Theatrum Instrumentorum et Machinarum.*" Besson applied it to a cask provided with compartments, which gave at will different liquors through the same orifice. Some years later, Denis Papin proposed it for high-pressure steam engines. Further improved, it has become the modern long D valve.

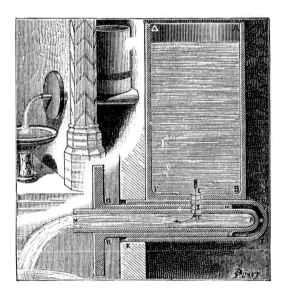

EGYPTIAN LUSTRAL WATER VESSEL.

CHAPTER II.

MIRACULOUS VESSELS OF THE GREEKS.

THE DICAIOMETER.

Heron, in his " Pneumatics," describes a large number of wonderful vessels that were used by the ancients, and, among them, one called the " dicaiometer " (a correct measure), which allowed of the escape of but a definite quantity of the liquid that it contained.

This was constructed as follows: Let us suppose a vessel (see the illustration) whose neck is closed by a diaphragm. Near the bottom there is placed a small sphere, T, of a capacity equal to the quantity that it is desired to pour out. Through the diaphragm there passes a small tube, $\varDelta$ E, which communicates with the small sphere. This tube contains a very small aperture, $\varDelta$, near and beneath the diaphragm. The sphere contains at its lower part a small aperture, Z, whence starts a tube, Z H, that communicates with the hollow handle of the ewer. Alongside of this aperture the globe contains another one, $\varLambda$, through which it communicates with the interior of the ewer. The handle is provided with a vent, $\varTheta$. After closing the latter, the ewer is filled with liquid through an aperture that is afterwards stopped up. The tube, $\varDelta$ E, may likewise be made use of, but in this case it is necessary to form a small aperture in the body of the ewer in order to allow the air to make its exit. The globe, T, fills at the same time that the ewer does. Now, if we turn the ewer over, leaving the vent $\varTheta$ open, the liquid in the globe, T, and in the small tube, $\varDelta$ E, will flow out. If we close the vent and bring the ewer to its former position, the globe and the tube will fill up anew, since the air that they contain will be expelled

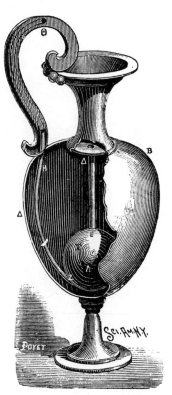

THE DICAIOMETER.

by the liquid that enters thereinto. The ewer being again turned over, an equal quantity of liquid will flow anew, save a difference due to the small tube, $\varDelta E$, since this latter will not always be full, and will empty in measure as the ewer does; but such difference is very insignificant.

MIRACULOUS VESSELS.

Ctesias, the Greek, who was physician to the Court of Persia at the beginning of the fourth century of our era, and who has written a history of that country, narrates the following fact: Xerxes, having caused the tomb of Belus to be opened, found the body of the Assyrian monarch in a glass coffin which was nearly full of oil. "Woe to him," said an inscription at the side, "who, having violated this tomb, does not at once finish the filling of the coffin."

Xerxes, therefore, at once gave orders to have oil poured into it; but whatever the quantity was that was put in, the coffin could not be filled. This miracle must have been effected by means of a siphon, analogous to the one found in the Tantalus cup, and which becomes primed as soon as the level rises in the vessel above the horizontal; that is, on a line with the upper part of the tube's curve. In fact, proof has been found of the use of the siphon among the Egyptians as far back as the eighteenth dynasty, and Heron, in his "Pneumatics" (book xii., chap. iii.), describes a very large number of vessels that are founded upon its use.

The ancients, likewise, solved a problem contrary to that of the tomb of Belus, and that was one connected with the construction of a vessel that should always remain full, whatever was the quantity of water that was removed from it, or, at least, which should remain full even when a large quantity of water was taken from it.

The annexed engraving (Fig. 1) shows one of the arrangements employed.

"Let A B be a vessel containing a quantity of

FIG. 1.—A MIRACULOUS VESSEL OF HERON.

water equal to that which may be demanded, and $\Gamma\varDelta$ a tube that puts it in communication with a reservoir, H Θ, lower down. Near this tube there is fixed a lever, E Z, from whose extremity, E, is suspended a cork float, K, and to whose other extremity, Z, there is hooked a chain that carries a leaden weight, Ξ.

"The whole should be so arranged that the cork, K, which floats on the water, shall close the tube's orifice; that when the water flows out, the cork, in falling, shall leave such aperture free; and, finally, that when a new supply of water enters, the cork shall rise with it and close the orifice anew. To effect this the cork must be heavier than the leaden weight suspended at Ξ. Now, let $\varLambda$ M be a vessel whose edges should be at the same height as the level of the water in the reservoir when there is no flow through the tube because of the cork float. Again, let Θ N be a tube that connects the reservoir with the base of the vessel, $\varLambda$ M.

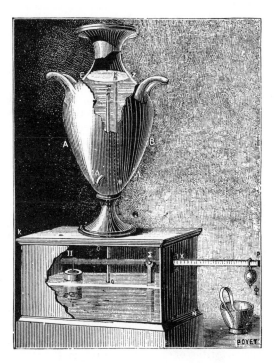

FIG. 2.—MIRACULOUS VESSEL OF HERON.

"So, then, when we remove water from the vessel, $\varLambda$ M, after it has once been filled, we shall at the same time lower the level of the water in the reservoir, and the cork, in falling, will open the tube. The water thereupon running into the lower reservoir, and from thence into the external vessel, will cause the cork to rise and the flow to cease, and this will occur every time that we remove water from the tazza."

There were, also, vessels which discharged but a certain definite quantity of the liquid that they contained. We have already described one of these, but here is another that is more complicated, wherein the quantity of liquid that it measures out may be caused to vary in the same vessel.

A vessel containing wine, and provided with a spout, being placed upon a pedestal, to cause the spout, by the simple moving of a weight, to allow a given quantity of wine to flow ; now, for example, half a cotyle (0.13 liter), and now a whole cotyle ; or, briefly, any quantity that may be desired.

"Let A B be the vessel into which the wine is to be put (Fig. 2). Near its bottom there is a spout, $\varDelta$. Its neck is closed by a partition, E Z, through which passes a tube that runs to the bottom, but leaving, however, sufficient space for the passage of the water. Let K $\varLambda$ M N be the pedestal upon which the vessel stands, and $\varXi$ O another tube that reaches as far as the partition and enters the pedestal. In the latter there is sufficient water to stop up the orifice of the tube, $\varXi$ O. Finally, let $\varPi$ P be a lever, half of which is in the interior of the pedestal and the other half external to it, and which pivots on the point $\varSigma$, and carries suspended from its extremity, $\varPi$, a clepsydra having an aperture, T, in the bottom.

"The spout being closed, the vessel is filled through the tube, H $\varTheta$, before putting water into the pedestal, so that the air may escape through the tube, $\varXi$ O. Then, through any aperture whatever, water is poured into the pedestal in such a way as to close the orifice, O; and, after this, the spout, $\varDelta$, is opened. It is clear that the wine will not flow, since the air cannot enter anywhere. But, if we depress the extremity, P, of the lever, a part of the clepsydra will rise from the water, and the orifice, O, being freed, the spout will flow until the water lifted up in the clepsydra has, on running out, closed this same orifice again. If, when the clepsydra has become full again, we still further depress the extremity, P, the liquid in the clepsydra will take longer to flow out, and more wine will consequently be discharged from the spout. If the clepsydra rises entirely from out the water, the flow will last still longer yet. Instead of depressing the extremity, P, by hand, we may use a weight, $\varPhi$, which is movable on the external part of the lever and capable of lifting the whole of the clepsydra out of the water when it is placed near P. This weight, then, will lift a portion only when it is farther away from such point. We must proceed, therefore, with a certain number of experiments upon the flow through the spout, and make notches on the lever arm, P X, and register the quantities of wine that correspond thereto, so that, when we desire to cause a definite quantity to flow, we shall only have to put the weight on the corresponding notch, and leave it."

The miracle of changing water into wine is one of those upon which the ancients exercised their imaginations most. Heron and Philo describe fifteen apparatus designed for effecting this, and more generally for causing different liquors to flow at will from the same vessel.

Here is one of the simplest of them (Fig. 3): "There are," says Heron, "certain drinking-horns which, after wine has been put into them, allow of the flow, when water is introduced into them, now of pure wine, and now of pure water.

"They are constructed as follows: Let A B $\varGamma\varDelta$ be a drinking-horn provided with two diaphragms, $\varDelta$ E and Z H, through which passes a tube, $\varTheta$ K, this being soldered to them and containing an aperture, $\varLambda$, slightly above the diaphragm, Z H. Beneath the diaphragm, $\varDelta$ E, there is a vent, M, in the side of the vessel.

"Such arrangements having been made, if any one, on stopping the orifice, $\varGamma$, pours wine into the horn, the liquor will flow through the aperture, $\varDelta$, into the compartment, $\varDelta$ E Z H, since the air contained therein can escape through the vent, M. If, now, we close the vent, the wine in the compartment, Δ E Z H, will be held there. Consequently, if, on closing the vent, M, we pour water into the part, A B Δ E, of the vessel, pure water will flow out through the orifice, Γ; and if, afterward, we open the vent, M, while there is yet water above the upper diaphragm, a mixture of wine and water will flow out. Then, when all the water has been discharged, pure wine will flow.

"On opening and closing the vent, M, oftener, the nature of the flow may be made to vary; or, what is better still, we may begin by filling the compartment, Δ E Z H, with water, and then, closing M, pour out the wine from above. Then we shall see a successive flow of pure wine and of wine and water mixed, when we open the vent, M, and then, again, of pure wine when the vent is closed anew; and this will occur as many times as we desire it."

The apparatus represented in Fig. 4 is very curious, and might be put to some useful application, without mentioning that which wine merchants might make of it by changing the order of the liquids and leaving in view only the vessel, A B, and the cock.

FIG. 3.—HERON'S DRINKING-HORN.

"Being given," says Heron again, "two vessels, one of them containing wine, it is required that whatever be the quantity of water poured into the empty one, the same quantity of a mixture of wine and water, in any proportion whatever (two parts of water to one of wine, for example), shall flow out through a pipe.

"Let A B be a vessel in the form of a cylinder, or of a rectangular parallelopipedon. At the side of it, and upon the same base, we place another vessel, $\Gamma \Delta$, which is hermetically closed, and of cylindrical or parallelopipedal form, like A B. But the base of A B must be double that of $\Gamma \Delta$ if we desire that the quantity of water shall be double that of the wine in the mixture. Near $\Gamma \Delta$ we place another vessel, E Z, which is likewise closed, and into which we have poured wine. The vessels, $\Gamma \Delta$ and E Z, are connected by a tube, H Θ K, which traverses the diaphragms that close them at their upper part, and which is soldered to these. In the vessel, E Z, we place a bent siphon, Λ M N, whose inner leg should come so near to the bottom of the vessel as to leave just enough space for the liquid to pass, while the other leg runs into a neighboring vessel, Ξ O. From this latter there starts a tube, Π P, which passes through all the vessels, or the pedestal that supports them, in such a way that it can be easily carried under and very near the bottom of the vessel, A B. Another tube, Σ T, traverses the partitions in the vessels, A B and $\Gamma\varDelta$. Finally, near the bottom of A B we adjust a small tube, Υ, which we inclose, with the tube H L, in a pipe, Φ X, that is provided with a key for opening or closing it at will. Into the vessel, E Z, we pour wine through an aperture, Ω, which we close after the liquor has been introduced.

FIG. 4.—AN APPARATUS OF HERON PERMITTING OF MIXING WINE AND
WATER IN DEFINITE PROPORTIONS.

" These arrangements having been made, we close the pipe, X Φ, and pour water into the vessel, A B. A portion, that is to say, one-half, will pass into the vessel, $\Gamma\varDelta$, through the tube, Σ T, and the water that enters $\Gamma\varDelta$ will drive therefrom a quantity of air equal to itself into E Z, through the tube, H Θ K. In the same way this air will drive an equal quantity of wine into the vessel, O Ξ, through the siphon, $\varLambda$ M N. Now, upon opening the pipe, Φ X, the water poured into the vessel, A B, and the wine issuing from the vessel, O Ξ, through the tube, Π P, will flow together, and this is just what it was proposed to effect."

The accompanying figures, borrowed from a work on "Scientific Recreations," by the late editor of *La Nature*, M. Gaston Tissandier, represents a magic vase and pitcher such as the ancients were accustomed to employ for the purpose of practicing a harmless and amusing deception on those who were not acquainted with the structure of the apparatus. For instance, if any one should attempt to pour wine or water from the pitcher shown in the

cut, the liquid would run out through the apertures in the sides.   But the
person who knew how to use the vessel would simply place his finger over the
aperture in the hollow handle (Fig. 6) and then suck through the spout, A,
when the liquid would flow up through the handle and through a channel running around the rim of the vessel and so reach the spout.   These magic vases,
cups, pitchers, etc., were not only in use among the ancients, but were quite

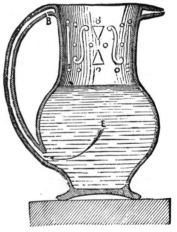

FIG. 5.—MAGICAL VESSELS OF THE EIGHTEENTH
CENTURY.

FIG. 6.—SECTION OF A MAG-
ICAL PITCHER.

common in the eighteenth century, and numerous specimens are to be seen in
European collections.   The ones shown in the accompanying cuts are preserved in the Museum at Sèvres.   These apparatus are all based on the use of
concealed siphons, or, rather, their construction is based on the principle
of that instrument.   Devices of this kind admit of very numerous modifications.   Thus tankards have been so contrived that the act of applying
them to the lips charged the siphon, and the liquid, instead of entering the
mouth, then passed through a false passage into a cavity formed for its recep-

tion below. By making the cavity of the siphon sufficiently large, a person ignorant of the device would find it a difficult matter even to *taste* the contents, however thirsty he might be. Dishonest publicans, whose signboards announced "entertainment for man and beast," are said to have thus despoiled travelers in old times of a portion of their ale or mead, as well as their horses of feed. Oats were put into a perforated manger, and a large part forced through the openings into a receptacle below by the movements of the hungry animal's mouth. Heron, in the eighth problem of his "*Spiritalia*," figures and describes a magical pitcher in which a horizontal, minutely perforated partition divides the vessel into two parts. The handle is hollow and air-tight, and at its upper part a small hole is drilled where the thumb or finger can readily cover it. If the lower part of the pitcher be filled with water and the upper with wine, the liquids will not mix as long as the small hole in the handle is closed; the wine can then be either drunk or poured out. If the hole be left open for some time, a mixture of both liquids will be discharged. "With a vessel of this kind," says an old writer, "you may welcome unbidden guests. Having the lower part already filled with water, call to your servant to fill your pot with wine; then you may drink unto your guest, drinking up all the wine; when he takes the pitcher, thinking to pledge you in the same, and finding the contrary, will happily stay away until he be invited, fearing that his next presumption might more sharply be rewarded." Another old way of getting rid of an unwelcome visitor was by offering him wine in a cup having double sides and an air-tight cavity formed between them. When the vessel was filled, some of the liquid entered the cavity and compressed the air within, so that when the cup was inclined to the lips and partly emptied, the pressure being diminished, the air expanded and drove part of the contents in the face of the drinker. Another goblet was so contrived that no one could drink out of it unless he understood the art. The liquid was suspended in cavities, and discharged by admitting or excluding air through several secret openings.

The apparatus represented in the illustration (Fig. 7) represents an arrangement similar to that of the inexhaustible bottle of Robert-Houdin, but it is more ingenious. The problem proposed, as enunciated by Heron, the Greek engineer, who describes the apparatus, is as follows: "Being given a vessel, to pour into it, through the orifice, wines of several kinds, and to cause any kind that may be designated to flow out through the same orifice, so that, if different persons have poured in different wines, each person may take out in his turn all the wine that belongs to him.

"Let A B be a hermetically closed vessel whose neck is provided with a diaphragm, E Z, and which is divided into as many compartments as the kinds of wine that it is proposed to pour into it. Let us suppose, for example, Π Θ and K Λ are diaphragms forming the three compartments, M, N, and Ξ, into which wine is to be poured. In the diaphragm, E Z, there are formed small apertures that correspond respectively to each of the compartments. Let O, Π, and P be such apertures, into which are soldered small tubes, Π Σ, O T, and P Υ, which project into the neck of the vessel. Around each of these tubes there are formed in the diaphragm small apertures like those of a sieve, through which the liquids may flow into the different compartments. When, therefore, it is desired to introduce one of the wines into the vessel, the vents, Σ, T, and Γ are stopped with the fingers, and the wine is poured into the neck, Φ, where it will remain without flowing into any of the compartments, because the air contained in the latter has no means of egress. But, if one of the said vents be opened, the air in the compartment corresponding thereto will flow out, and the wine will flow into such compartment through the apertures of the sieve. Then, closing this vent in order to open another, another

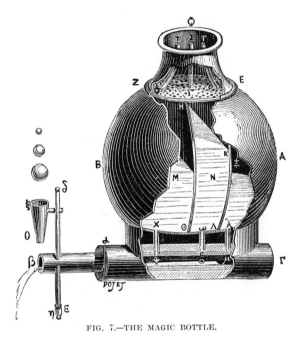

FIG. 7.—THE MAGIC BOTTLE.

quantity of wine will be introduced, and so on, whatever be the number of wines and that of the corresponding compartments of the vessel, A B.

" Let us now see how each person in turn can draw his own wine out through the same neck. At the bottom of the vessel, A B, there are arranged tubes which start from each of the compartments, to wit: The tube, $\chi\psi$, from the compartment, M; the tube $\omega\sigma$, from N, and the tube $\lambda\mu$, from Ξ. The extremities, ψ, σ, and μ, of these tubes should communicate with another tube, α, in which is accurately adjusted another, $\beta\Gamma$, closed at Γ at its lower extremity and having apertures to the right of the orifices, ψ, σ, and μ, so that such apertures may, in measure, as the tube revolves, receive respectively the wine contained in each of the compartments and allow it to flow to the exterior through the orifice, β, of the said tube, $\beta\Gamma$. To this tube is fixed an iron rod, $\delta\varepsilon$, whose extremity, ε, carries a lead weight, η. To the extremity, δ, is fixed an iron pin supporting a small conical cup whose concavity points upward. Let us therefore suppose this truncated cone established, its wide base at ε, and its narrow one (through which the pin passes) at θ.* Again, one must have small leaden balls of different weights, and in number equal to that of the compartments, M, N, and Ξ. If the smallest be placed in the cup, $\varepsilon\theta$, it will descend on account of its weight until it applies itself against the internal surface of the cup, and it will be necessary to so arrange things that it may thus cause the tube, $\beta\Gamma$, to turn so as to bring beneath ψ that one of the apertures that corresponds to it, and that will thus receive the wine of the compartment, M. This wine will then flow as long as the ball remains in the cup. If, now, the ball be removed, the weight, η, in returning to its first position, will close the orifice, ψ, and stop the flow. If another ball be placed in the cup, a further inclination of the rod, $\varepsilon\delta$, will be produced, and the tube, $\beta\Gamma$, will revolve further, so as to bring its corresponding aperture beneath σ. Then the wine contained in the compartment, N, will flow. If the ball be removed, the weight, η, will redescend to its primitive place, the aperture, σ, will be closed, and the wine will cease to flow. Finally, upon placing the last ball (which is the heaviest), the tube, $\beta\Gamma$, will turn still more, so as to cause the flow of the wine contained in the compartment, Ξ.

"It must be remarked that the smallest of the balls should be so heavy that when placed in the cup it shall outweigh the weight, η, and consequently bring about the revolution of the tube, $\beta\Gamma$. The other balls will then be sufficient to cause the revolution of the said tube."

ANCIENT ORGANS.

The hydraulic organ filled with its powerful voice the vast arenas in which the gladiators fought, and Petronius relates that Nero one day made a vow to play one of them himself in public if he escaped a danger that threatened him. The invention of them is attributed to Ctesibius.

Fig. 1 gives a reproduction of one of these instruments as described by Heron in his "Pneumatics."

Let B$\varDelta$ be an altar† of bronze containing water. Let there be in the latter an inverted hollow hemisphere, E Z H (called a damper), that allows the water to pass all around its bottom, and from the top of which rise two tubes that communicate with the interior. One of these tubes, H K, is bent in the interior and communicates with a small inverted box,‡ N $\varPi$, the aperture of which is at the bottom, and the interior of which is bored out so that it may receive a piston, P I, which should fit very accurately so as to allow no air to

---

* The text does not agree with the figure given by the MSS. Moreover, there is an arrangement here that it is difficult to understand from Heron's description.

† Altars were cylindrical or square pedestals, characterized by a cavity in the upper platform, in which a fire was lighted.

‡ This box performs here the office of a pump chamber.

pass. To this piston is fixed a very strong rod, $T\gamma$, with which is connected another rod, $\gamma\Phi$, movable around a pin at γ.* This lever moves upon a fixed vertical rod, ΨX. Upon the bottom of the box, $N\Pi$, is placed another box, Ω, which communicates with the first, and which is closed at the upper part by a cover that contains an aperture to allow of the passage of the air into the box, $N\Pi$. Under the aperture of this cover, and in order to close it, there is arranged a thin disk, held by means of four pins which pass through aper-

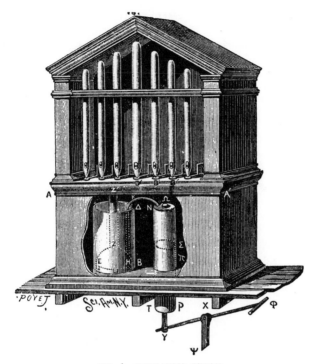

FIG. 1.—HYDRAULIC ORGAN.

tures in the disk, and are provided with heads in order to hold it in place. This disk is called a platysmatim (Fig. 2). The other tube, ZZ', is carried by the hemisphere, EZH, and ends in a transverse tube, $A\Lambda'$,† upon which rest pipes communicating with it and having at their extremities glossocomiums‡ that communicate with these pipes, and the orifices, B', of which are open. Across these orifices, covers provided with holes § slide in such a way that when they are pushed toward the interior of the organ their holes correspond to the orifices of the pipes (and to those of the tube AA'), and that when they are pulled back, the pipes are closed, since there is no longer any correspondence.

---

* The figure shows another arrangement.
† Called a wind-chest in modern organs.   ‡ Flute mouths.   § Registers.

If, now, the transverse rod, $\gamma \Phi$, be lowered at Φ, the piston, P Σ, will rise and compress the air in the box, N Σ O Π, and such air will close the aperture of the small box through the intermedium of the platysmatim described above. It will then pass into E Z H by means of the tube, K H, then into the transverse tube A A', though the tube Z Z', and finally from the transverse tube into the pipes, if the orifices correspond to those of the covers, and this will occur when all the covers (or only a few of them) have been pushed toward the interior.

In order that their orifices may be open when it is desired to make certain pipes resound, and that they may be closed when it is desired to cause the sound to cease, the following arrangement is employed: Let us consider isolately one of the mouths placed at the extremity (Fig. 3). Let $\gamma \delta$ be this mouth, δ its orifice, A A' the transverse tube, and σ the cover that is adapted and the aperture of which does not coincide with the apertures of the pipes at this moment. Let us now suppose a jointed arrangement composed of three rods, δ, μ, and ν, the rod, $\varepsilon \delta$, being attached to the cover, σ, and the system as a whole moving around a pin, μ. It will be seen that if we lower with the hand the extremity, ν, of the system toward the orifice of the glossocomiums, we shall cause the cover to

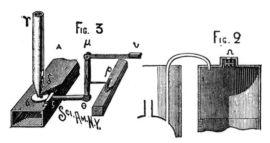

FIGS. 2 AND 3.—DETAILS OF THE HYDRAULIC ORGAN SHOWN IN FIG. 1.

move toward the interior, and that, when it arrives there, its orifice will coincide with the orifices of the pipes. In order that, upon removing the hand, the cover may be carried back toward the exterior and close all communication, an arrangement such as the following may be employed. Beneath a number of glossocomiums, there is established a bar equal in length to and parallel with the tube, A A', and to which are fixed strong curved plates of horn, such as γ, placed opposite $\gamma \delta$. A cord is fixed to the end of this plate and winds around the extremity, δ, in such a way that when the cover is moved toward the exterior the cord shall be taut. If the extremity, ν, then be lowered, and the register be thus pushed into the interior, the cord will draw upon the horn plate, and by its force, right it. But as soon as the pressure ceases, the plate will resume its former position and draw the cover back in such a way as to prevent its orifice from establishing a communication. This arrangement being adopted for all the glossocomiums, it will be seen that in order to cause any one of the pipes to resound, it will suffice to depress the corresponding key with the finger. When, on the contrary, it is desired to cause the sound to cease, we shall merely have to lift the finger, and the effect will be produced by the motion of the cover.

Water is poured into the small altar in order that the compressed air that is driven from the box, N *II*, may, owing to the pressure of the liquid, be retained in the damper, E Z H, and thus supply the pipes. When the piston, P Σ, is raised, it therefore expels the air from the box into the damper, as has been explained. Then, when it is lowered, it opens the platysmatim of the small box. By this means, the box, N *II*, becomes filled with air from the exterior, which the piston, raised anew, drives again into the damper.

It would be better to render the rod, T γ, immovable at T, around a pin, and fix at the bottom, P, of the piston a ring through which this pin would pass, so that the piston would have no lateral motion, but would rise and descend with exact perpendicularity.

Porta, at the beginning of the seventeenth century, constructed at Naples a hydraulic organ according to the arrangement just described. A few years afterward, in 1645, Father Kircher constructed another at Rome for Pope Innocent X. These organs had the defect of not preserving the note, but of giving a series of harmonies. On the other hand, they produced an exceedingly agreeable tremolo. It was probably these unusual variations in sound that charmed the ears of the Greeks and Romans.

Heron afterwards describes a bellows organ, motion to which is communicated not by manual power, but by a windmill. Fig. 4 shows the arrangement with sufficient clearness to permit us to dispense with a description. It is interesting to reproduce, in that it carries the origin of windmills (which it is claimed were unknown to antiquity, because Vitruvius and Varro do not speak of them) back at least to the second century before our era.

FIG. 4.—WINDMILL ACTUATING THE BELLOWS OF AN ORGAN.

CHAPTER III.

THE ORIGIN OF THE STEAM ENGINE.

All works that treat of the history of the steam engine speak of the eoli-pile of Heron as the most ancient manifestation known of that power which to-day fills the world. But very few persons know that we also find in the "Pneumatics" of the Greek engineer the germs of the tubular boiler and of the Papin cock which has been replaced in modern engines by the long D-valve. Here, in the first place, is a literal translation of the two passages that have reference to the apparatus, so often cited, of Heron:

"*Balls may be held in the air by the following method:*

"Fire is lighted under a boiler that contains water and is closed at its upper part. From the cover starts a tube which rises vertically, and at the extremity of which a hollow hemisphere is in communication with it. On placing a light ball in this hemisphere it will happen that the steam, on rising through the tube, will raise the ball in such a way that it will remain suspended.*

"*To cause the revolution of a sphere on a pivot by means of a boiler placed over a fire.*

"Let A B (Fig. 2 †) be a boiler containing water and placed over a fire. It is closed by means of a cover, $\Gamma' \Lambda$, which is traversed by a bent tube, E Z H, whose extremity, H, enters the hollow sphere, Θ K, in the direction of the latter's diameter. At the other extremity is placed the pivot, A M N, which is fixed upon the cover, $\Gamma \Lambda$. There are added to the sphere, at the two extremities of one of its diameters, two tubes bent at right angles and perpendicular to the line, H N. When the boiler is heated, the steam will pass through the tube, E Z H, into the small sphere, and, issuing through the bent tubes into the atmosphere, will cause it to revolve *in situ*."

The following apparatus, likewise described by Heron, but not so well known as those that preceded, shows that the ancients employed steam (mixed with hot air, it is true) for causing liquids to rise. According to Father Kircher, who reports it on the faith of an author named Bitho, there was at Sais, Egypt, a temple dedicated to Minerva in which there was an altar upon

---

* Fig. 1 is borrowed from a MS. of the "Pneumatics" dating back to the Renaissance. The boiler should have been represented over a fireplace.

† This figure, likewise borrowed from a MS. of the Renaissance, is sufficiently clear to allow letters to be dispensed with.

which, when a fire was lighted, Dionysius and Artemis (Bacchus and Diana) poured, one of them wine, and the other milk.

The miracle was performed as follows:

" *On lighting a fire upon an altar, figures make libations and serpents hiss* (Fig. 3).*

" Let A B be a hollow pedestal upon which there is an altar, *Γ*, in whose interior there is a large tube, *Δ* E, that descends from the fireplace into the pedestal and divides into three small tubes. One of the latter, E Z, runs to the serpent's mouth; another, E H *Θ*, to a vessel, K *Δ*, suitable for containing

FIG. 1.—HERON'S EOLIPILE.   FIG. 2.—HERON'S WHIRLING EOLOPILE.

wine, and the bottom of which should be above the figure, M, as this tube has to be connected with the cover of the vessel, K *Δ*, by a grating; and the third tube, E N *Ξ*, rises likewise to a vessel, O, suitable for receiving wine, and is connected in the same way with its cover. The two latter tubes are soldered to the bottoms of the vessels, and in each of these vessels there is a siphon, P *Σ* and T *Υ*. One extremity of each of these tubes dips into the wine, while the other, which ends in the hand of the figure that is to make the libation, traverses the side of the wine vessel. When you wish to light the fire, you will first put a little water into the tubes so that they shall not be burst by the dryness of the fire, and you will stop up all the apertures so that the air shall not escape. Then the blast from the fire, mixed with the water, will rise through the tubes up to the gratings, and, passing through these, will press

---

* The letters on the engraving are again dispensed with.

upon the wine and cause it to flow through the siphons, $P \Sigma$ and $T \Upsilon$. The wine issuing thus from the hands of the figures, the latter will appear to make libations as long as the altar is burning. As for the other tube, which leads the blast to the serpent's mouth, it causes the latter to hiss."

FIG. 3.—HERON'S MARVELOUS ALTAR.

As regards the cock and the tubular boiler, we find these in a hot-water stove which Heron calls by the Græco-Latin name *miliarion*, because of its resemblance to a milestone.

Fig. 4 shows us, in the center, the fireplace in the shape of a vertical cylinder, which should have beneath it an air vent that is not shown in the cut. All around this there is a boiler, likewise cylindrical, filled with water. A certain number of tubes, such as O K and M N, put its different parts in communication by passing through the fireplace, and thus increase the heating surface.

The cock, T, serves to let off hot water, and the funnel, Σ, to introduce cold water into the boiler through a tube which runs to the bottom of the latter. The object of the bent tube is to allow of the escape of air when

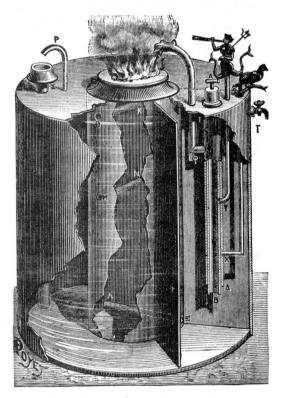

FIG. 4.—HERON'S TUBULAR BOILER.

water is poured in, and to give exit to the steam that may be formed, and thus avoid the ejection of water through the funnel, Σ. Heron, in his text, says that this tube debouches in the interior of the funnel so that it shall not be perceived, and not as we have shown it for the sake of greater clearness. In the figure there may be seen a compartment formed by two vertical plates that make an angle into which water cannot enter. This is designed for actuating different figures through the play of the steam and of the several way cocks that I have mentioned. This latter consists of two concentric tubes capable of revolving with slight friction one within the other. The external tube, $\Gamma\varDelta$, is fixed to the upper side of the stove, and traverses it. It contains three apertures, φ, ψ, and χ, placed at different levels, and communicating, through small tubes, with the figures that are to be presently mentioned. The internal tube, A B, is open at its lower part, and thus communicates with the interior of the compartment, but is closed at its upper part, which latter debouches above the stove and may be manœuvered by the handle, A. It contains three apertures at the same levels as apertures φ, ψ, and χ, but differently placed, so that when, through a rotary motion of the tube, A B, one of them is brought opposite an aperture of the same level in the tube, $\varGamma\varDelta$, the two others do not correspond. The positions that it is necessary to give them in order that such correspondences shall occur are denoted by marks engraved on the visible portions of the tubes. The tube, φ, terminates in a serpent's head which bends toward the fireplace, and tube, ψ, terminates in a triton who holds a trumpet to his mouth. Finally the tube, χ, carries at its extremity a whistle that debouches in the body of a bird filled with water.

It will now be seen what will occur. The tube, A B, is removed and a little water is put into the compartment. This water flows into the tube, $\varLambda\varXi$ (which passes under the fireplace and is closed at the side opposite its aperture, $\varXi$), and is converted into steam. When the tube, A B, has been replaced, the steam may at will be passed into the body of the bird, which will warble, or into that of the triton, who will blow his trumpet, or, finally, into that of the serpent, which will blow into the fire and quicken the flames.

CHAPTER IV.

GREEK LAMPS, TOYS, ETC.

PERPETUAL LAMPS.

The ancients utilized, in their prestiges, combustible gases, which, in many places, were disengaged naturally from the earth.

The Arab Schiangia, in a passage quoted by Father Kircher, expresses himself in this wise:

"In Egypt there was a field whose ditches were full of pitch and liquid bitumen. Philosophers, who understood the forces of nature, constructed canals which connected places like these with lamps hidden at the bottom of subterranean crypts. These lamps had wicks made of threads that could not burn. By this means the lamp, once lighted, burned eternally, because of the continuous influx of bitumen and the incombustibility of the wick."

It is possible that it was to an artifice of this same nature that were due some of the numerous perpetual lamps that history has preserved a reminiscence of, such as that which Plutarch saw in the temple of Jupiter Ammon, in Egypt, and that in the temple of Venus, which Saint Augustine could only explain as due to the intervention of demons. But the majority of them owed their peculiarity only to the precautions taken by the priests to feed them without being seen. It was only necessary, in fact, that the wick, which was made of asbestos threads or gold wire, should be kept intact, and that the body of the lamp should communicate with a reservoir placed in a neighboring apartment in such a way that the level of the oil should remain constant. Heron and Philo have left us descriptions of a certain number of arrangements that permittted of accomplishing such an object.

The same authors likewise point out different processes for manufacturing portable lamps in which the oil rises automatically. The most ingenious one is that which is at the present day known under the name of "Heron's Fountain." *

The following is the Alexandrine engineer's text:

"Construction of a candelabrum such that upon placing a lamp thereon, there comes up through the handle, when the oil is consumed, any quantity

---

* In 1801, Carcel and Carreau applied Heron's system to lamps without, perhaps, knowing that they were thus returning to the primitive apparatus.

that may be wished, and that, too, without there being any need of placing above it any vessel serving as a reservoir for the oil.

"A hollow candelabra must be made, with a base in the shape of a pyramid. Let A B $\Gamma \Delta$ be such pyramidal base, and in this let there be a partition, E Z. Again, let H Θ be the stem of the candelabrum, which should also be hollow. Above, let there be placed a vessel, K Λ, capable of containing a large quantity of oil. From the partition, E Z, there starts a tube, M N, which traverses it and reaches almost to the cover of the vessel, K Λ, upon which latter is placed the lamp in such a way as to allow only a passage for the air. Another tube, Ξ O, passes through the cover and runs down, on the one hand, to the bottom of the vessel, K Λ, in such a way that the liquid may be capable of flowing, and on the other, forms a slight projection on the cover. To this projection there is carefully adjusted another tube, Π, which is provided with a stopper at its upper part, and, traversing the bottom of the lamp and united with it, is wholly inclosed within the interior of the lamp. To the tube, Π, there is soldered another and very fine one which communicates with it and reaches the extremity of the lamp handle. This tube debouches in the latter in such a way that its contents may empty into the lamp, the orifice of which is of the usual size. Under the partition, E Z, there is soldered a cock that enters the compartment, $\Gamma \Delta$ E Z, in such a way that when it is open the water from the chamber, A B E Z, may pass into the compartment, $\Gamma \Delta$ E Z. Through the upper plate, A B, there is pierced a small hole, through which the compartment, A B E Z, may be filled with water, the air within escaping through the same aperture.

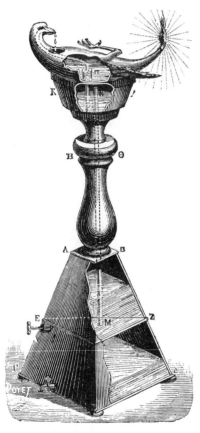

PLATO'S LAMP.

"Let us now remove the lamp and fill the vessel with oil by the aid of the tube, Ξ O. The air will escape through the tube, M N, and afterward through a cock which is open near the bottom, $\Gamma \Delta$, when the water has flowed out from the compartment, $\Gamma \Delta$ E Z. Let us place the lamp upon its base, connecting it at the same time with the tube, Π. When it becomes necessary to pour oil into it, we will open the cock near the partition, E Z. The water that is in the compartment, $\Gamma \Delta$ E Z, as well as the air therein, being forced through the tube, M N, into the vessel, will cause the oil to rise and pass into the lamp through the tube, Ξ O, and the one that forms a continuation of it. When it is desired to cause the oil to stop coming over, the cock is closed, when the flow will cease. This may be repeated as often as may be necessary."

Such was, perhaps, Plato's lamp, of which Athenæus speaks in the "Banquet of the Sophists," and by means of which the illustrious philosopher was enabled to have a light for himself during the longest nights in the year.

AN ANCIENT AUTOMATON.

In his "*Spiritalia*" (written about 150 B.C.) Heron describes several automata of which figures of birds form a part; but perhaps the most remarkable for its ingenious simplicity is No. 44, the illustration of which we reproduce.

The description of this, as given by Heron, is somewhat meager and unsatisfactory, but the drawing is so very plain that, taken in connection with other mechanism in his work, operated in a similar way, it is easy to understand how the desired result was accomplished.

An air-tight box of metal was provided, which was divided into four compartments, 1, 2, 3, 4, by horizontal diaphragm plates. On the top of this box was a basin, O, for receiving the water of a fountain. Around this basin were four birds, A, B, C, D, perched upon branches or shrubs, which apparently grew out of the top of the box. Each of these branches was hollow, and communicated with one of the compartments already named, by one of the pipes, 9, 10, 12, and 13, which passed but a very short distance through the tops of the several compartments. The bodies of the birds were also hollow, and were connected with the hollow branches by tubes in their legs. In the hollow body of each bird were two musical reeds or whistles of different note. One of these would sound when air was forced outward through the beak of the bird, and the other would only respond to air drawn inward. This alternate action of the air, and consequent variation of note, was produced by the peculiar way in which the water supplied by the fountain was made to pass through the several compartments.

The water from the basin, O, entered compartment 1 near its bottom by the pipe 11, and as it rose in the compartment, it compressed the air above it, which escaped through the beak of the bird, A, and caused its first note to sound; but when the water reached the top of the bend of the siphon 5, it at once began to discharge by that siphon into compartment 2; but as the siphon 5 was so proportioned that it discharged the water much faster than it was supplied by pipe 11, the level of the water in compartment 1 gradually fell, and the air in passing into this compartment through the beak of the bird, A, caused its second note to sound. As the water rose in compartment 2, it compressed the air above it, which passed by the pipe 10, to the bird, B, which then sounded its first note, while the bird, A, was sounding its second, and this state of affairs continued until all of the water was discharged from the compartment 1, and compartment 2 was filled to the top of the bend of siphon 6, which then began to discharge into compartment 3; and as siphon 5 had ceased to operate, the water gradually fell in compartment 2, and the air entering by the beak of the bird, B, sounded its second note. While this was taking place, compartment 1 was again filling, and the first note of bird, A, sounding; and compartment 3 was also filling, and the air above the water therein was being forced by the pipe 12 into the bird, C, and causing its first note to sound.

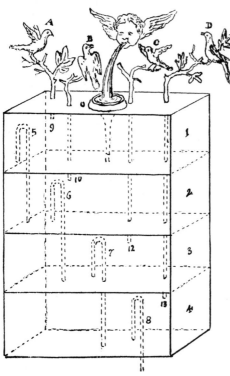

AN ANCIENT AUTOMATON.

By following out the operations described, and tracing the action of the flux and reflux of the water in the compartments 3 and 4, it will readily be seen that the bird, C, will sound its second note when the compartment 3 is being discharged by siphon 7 into compartment 4, and at the same time the bird, D, will sound its first note, and that eventually the water will escape from the automaton by the siphon 8, causing the second note of the bird, D, to be heard.

It is evident that by simple and well-known means any or all of the bird notes can be made to trill, and that it is only necessary to properly proportion the discharging capacity of the siphons to insure the repetition and admixture of the notes in a bird-like manner; and it is further evident that the employment of the ideas involved is not of necessity confined to but four birds, as several birds, each having different notes, might be operated from the same compartment, and of course as many compartments as may be wished can be used. Furthermore, the wings of the birds could be made to move, and their beaks to open and shut, by the movement of the same air which acted upon the musical reeds or whistles.

Each of the siphons in the automaton was intermittent in its action, ceasing to flow when its compartment was emptied, and beginning again spontaneously when the water reached the level of the top of its bend. The antiquity of intermittent siphons is of special interest from the fact of their comparatively recent application in sanitary plumbing.

Chaucer was not much in error as regards his own time (1328–1400), and his words are only somewhat less true to-day:

> " For out of the old fieldes, as men saithe,
>   Cometh al this new corne fro yere to yere;
>   And out of old bookes, in good faithe,
>   Cometh all this new science that men lere."

A GREEK TOY.

Upon a pedestal there is fixed a small tree around which is coiled a dragon. A figure of Hercules stands near by, shooting with a bow, and there is an apple lying upon the pedestal. If this apple be lifted from the latter, Hercules will shoot his arrow at the dragon, and the latter will hiss.

Mechanism of the Toy.—Let A B be the water-tight pedestal under consideration, provided with a diaphragm, $\Gamma \varDelta$. To this latter there is fixed a small, hollow, truncated cone whose apex points toward the bottom of the vessel, and from which it is just sufficiently distant to permit the water to pass. To this cone there is adjusted with care another one, Θ, which is fixed to a chain that, passing through an aperture, connects it with the apple. Hercules holds a small horn bow, whose string is stretched and laced at a proper distance from the right hand. The left hand is provided with a detent. To the ex-

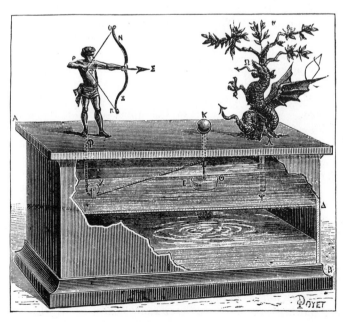

A GREEK TOY.

tremity of this latter there is fixed a small chain or a cord that traverses the top of the pedestal, passes over a pulley fixed to the diaphragm, and connects with the small chain that joins the cone with the apple. This cord passes through the hand and body into the interior of Hercules. A small tube, one of those used for whistling with, starts from the diaphragm, rises through the top of the pedestal, and passes into the interior of the tree or around it.

Now, if the apple, K, be raised, the cone, Θ, will be raised at the same time, the cord, $X\Phi$, will be tightened, the catch will be freed, and this will cause the arrow to shoot. The water in the compartment $A\Gamma$, running into the compartment $B\Gamma$, will drive out the air contained in the latter, through the tube, and produce a hissing. The apple being replaced, the cone, Θ, will adjust itself against the other, stop the flow, and thus cause the hissing to cease. The arrow and its accessories will then be adjusted anew.

When the compartment $B\Gamma$ is full, it is emptied by means of a spout provided with a key, and $A\Delta$ is again filled as we have indicated.

THE DECAPITATED DRINKING HORSE.

The optical delusion known as the talking decapitated person has already been described in Book I., Chapter I., of the present work. The ancients invented an analogous trick, but one that was founded upon a very ingenious mechanical combination. This is found described at the end of Heron's "Pneumatics," under the title, "To cut an animal in two and make him drink." It is as follows:

"Let us suppose a hollow pedestal, A B C D, divided in its center by a diaphragm, E F. Above the pedestal there is fixed a statuette representing a horse and traversed by a tube, M N, which terminates on the one hand in the horse's mouth, and in the other in the upper part of the compartment, A B E F, after following one of the legs. It will be conceived, in the first place, that if the said compartment be filled with water through an aperture, T, which is afterwards stopped up, and that then a cock be opened, so as to form a communication between the upper compartment and the lower (which latter is itself provided with an open air-hole), the water will flow, and, in doing so, tend to cause a vacuum in the tube, M N, so that when a vessel of water is brought near the animal's mouth the water will be sucked up.

"If the cock be so arranged as to present its key upon the top of the pedestal, and if to the key there be adapted a statuette representing a man armed with a club, things may be so arranged that the animal shall drink when the man has his back turned, for example, and that he shall stop drinking when the man threatens him with the club.

"The following is the way in which a knife may be passed through the animal's neck without causing the head to fall or interrupting communication

between the mouth and pedestal. The head and body form two distinct
pieces, which are adjusted according to the plane, O P (Figs. 1, 2, and 3).
The tube, M N, is interrupted to the right of this slit, and the two parts of it
are connected by a smaller tube, $\alpha\beta$, which enters by slight friction into the
interior of each of them; and to this small tube, $\alpha\beta$, there are fixed two
racks, δ and ε. Above δ and under ε are placed two segments of toothed
wheels, π and ρ, which are movable around axles fixed in the body of the animal. Over the whole there is a third wheel, which is likewise movable around

HERON'S DECAPITATED DRINKING HORSE.

an axle fixed in the animal's body, and the thickness of which keeps increasing
from the centre to the circumference. This wheel is cut out into three parts
of circles, μ, ν, and ξ, which have for diameters three of the sides of the
inscribed hexagon. It is inclosed in the neck in such a way that the circular
cavity containing it embraces just four of the sides of the inscribed hexagon,
the two other sides projecting outside of the plane, O P. In the piece that
forms the head a circular cavity is formed capable of containing this projecting
portion of the wheel, and a wedge-shaped profile is given it, so that when one
tooth of the wheel, σ, is engaged therein by the edge, it can also only leave it
by the edge. Let us now suppose the wheel, σ, free; let us engage one of its
teeth in the cavity, $\chi\psi$; let us cause the head and body to approach; let us
fix the wheel, σ, in the body by means of the movable axle traversing it; and
let us introduce a knife into the slit, O P, and see what will happen.

"The blade, on entering the space, ξ, will press against one of the teeth,
and cause it to descend until it, as well as the knife, is disengaged. The tooth
above the space, ξ, will then be disengaged in its turn and connect the head

with the body again.   The knife-blade, which is now under the wheel, σ, rests on the inclined plane that the figure shows in the segment, π, and, on pressing thereupon, causes the wheel to turn, and with it the rack, δ, and the tube, $\alpha\beta$, which latter leaves the tube, M, and gives passage to the blade between it and the extremity, α.   Then the blade comes in contact with the lower projection of the sector, ρ, which has been carried upward by the motion of the rack, ε, that is connected with the rack, δ.   On pressing against such projection the blade causes the segment, ρ, to revolve in a contrary direction, brings ε toward the left, and causes the small tube, $\alpha\beta$, to enter anew the tube, M.   Communication between M and N is thus reëstablished.''

M. de Rochas has never found elsewhere than in the '' Pneumatics '' a description of this system of toothed wheels, although he has read the majority of books treating of this class of ideas.   The description given by Heron is itself so confused and so mutilated, and the figure that accompanies it is so incomplete, that in all the Latin editions it is suppressed as incomprehensible.

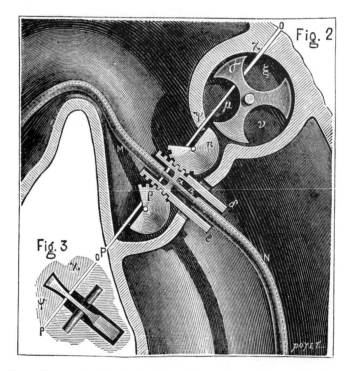

THE DECAPITATED HORSE.   DETAILS OF THE MECHANISM IN THE NECK.

ODOMETERS.

In the inventory of the objects sold after the death of the Emperor Commodus, drawn up by Julius Capitolinus in the life of Pertinax, we find mentioned, among other valuable things, "vehicles that mark distances and hours."

Vitruvius (X, 14) describes the mechanism of these vehicles, but the figures that must have served to throw light upon the text have been lost, so that his description is somewhat obscure. Fortunately, as a sequel to a manuscript of the Dioptra of Heron, there have been found two Greek fragments upon this same subject, dating back probably to the Alexandrine epoch and accompanied with figures. The following is a translation, says M. de Rochas:

To Measure Distances upon the Surface of the Earth by Means of an Apparatus called an Odometer.

Provided with this instrument, instead of being obliged to measure land slowly and laboriously with the chain or cord, it is possible in traveling in a vehicle to know the distances made, according to the number of revolutions of the wheels. Others, it is true, have, previous to us, made known certain methods of accomplishing the same object; but every one will be able to decide between the instrument described here by us and those of our predecessors.

Let us imagine an apparatus in the form of a box (Fig. 1) in which is contained the entire machine that we are to describe. Upon the bottom of the box rests a copper face wheel, AB, having, say, eight teeth. In the bottom there is an opening in which a rod, fixed to the hub of one of the wheels of

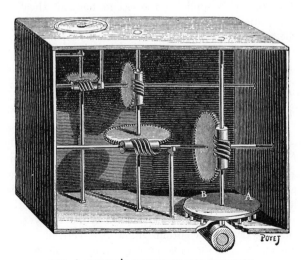

FIG. 1.—HERON'S ODOMETER FOR VEHICLES.

the vehicle and engaging at every revolution, pushes forward one of the teeth, which is replaced by the following one, and so on indefinitely.   Whence it results that when the wheel of the vehicle has made eight revolutions, the face wheel will have made one.   Now, to the center of the latter there is fixed perpendicularly, by one of its extremities, a screw which, by its other extremity, engages with a crosspiece fixed to the sides of the box.   This screw gears with the teeth of a wheel whose plane is perpendicular to the bottom of the box. This wheel is provided with an axle whose extremities pivot against the sides of the box.   A portion of this axle is provided with spirals formed in its surface, so that it becomes a screw.   With this screw there gears a toothed wheel parallel with the bottom of the box.   To this wheel is fixed an axle, one of the extremities of which pivots upon the bottom, while the other enters the crosspiece fixed to the sides; and this axle likewise carries a screw that gears with the teeth of another wheel placed perpendicular to the bottom. This arrangement may be continued as long as may be desired, or as long as there is space in the box; for the more numerous are the wheels and screws, the longer will be the route that one will be able to measure.

In fact, every screw, in making one revolution, causes the motion of one tooth of the wheel with which it gears; so that the screw carried by the face wheel, in revolving once, indicates eight revolutions of the wheel of the vehicle, while it moves only one tooth of the wheel upon which it acts.   So, too, the said toothed wheel, in making one revolution, will cause the screw fixed to its plane to make one revolution, and a single one of the teeth of the succeeding wheel will be thrust forward.   Consequently, if this new wheel has again thirty teeth (and this is a reasonable number), it will, in making one revolution, indicate 7,200 revolutions of the wheel of the vehicle.   Let us suppose that the latter is ten cubits in circumference, and this would be 72,000 cubits, that is to say, 180 furlongs.   This applies to the second toothed wheel.   If there are others, and if the number of teeth likewise increases, the length of the journey that it will be possible to measure will increase proportionally.   But it is well to make use of an apparatus so constructed that the distance which it will be able to indicate does not much exceed that which it is possible to make in one day with the vehicle, since one can, after measuring the day's route, begin anew for the following route.

This is not all.   As one revolution of each screw does not correspond with mathematical accuracy and precision to the escapement of one tooth, we shall in an express experiment cause the first screw to revolve until the wheel that gears with it has made one revolution, and shall count the number of times that the wheel will have revolved.   Let us suppose, for example, that it has revolved twenty times while the adjacent wheel has made a single revolution. This wheel has thirty teeth; therefore, twenty revolutions of the face wheel correspond to thirty teeth of the toothed wheel moved by the screw.   On the other hand, the twenty revolutions allow 160 teeth of the face wheel to escape, and this makes a like number of revolutions of the wheel of the vehicle, that is to say, 1,600 cubits; consequently, a single tooth of the preceding wheel indicates $53\frac{1}{3}$ cubits. Thus, for example, when, in starting from the origin of the motion, the toothed wheel will have revolved by fifteen teeth, this will indicate 800 cubits, say two furlongs; upon this same wheel we shall therefore write $53\frac{1}{3}$ cubits. Making a similar calculation for the other toothed wheels, we shall write upon each one of them the number that corresponds to it. In this way, after we ascertain how many teeth each has moved forward, we shall know by the same the distance that we have traveled.

Now, in order to be able to determine the distance traveled without having to open the box in order to see the teeth of each wheel, we are going to show how it is possible to estimate the length of the route by means of an index placed upon the external faces. Let us admit that the toothed wheels of which we have spoken are so arranged as not to touch the sides of the box, but that their axles project externally and are squared so as to receive indexes. In this way the wheel, in revolving, will cause its axle with its index to turn, and the latter will describe upon the exterior a circle that we shall divide into a number of parts equal to that of the teeth of the interior wheel. The index should have a length sufficient to describe a circumference greater than that of the wheel, so that such circumference may be divided into parts wider than the interval that separates the teeth. This circle should carry the number already marked upon the interval wheel. By this means we shall see upon the external surface of the box the length of the trip made. Were it impossible to prevent the friction of the wheels against the sides of the box, for one reason or another, it would then be necessary to file them off sufficiently to prevent the apparatus from being impeded in its operation in any way.

Moreover, as some of the toothed wheels are perpendicular to and others parallel with the bottom of the box, so, too, the circles described by the indexes will be some of them upon the sides of the box and others upon the top. Consequently, it will be necessary to so manage that the side that carries no circle shall serve as a cover; or, in other words, that the box shall be closed laterally.

Another engineer, probably Græco-Latin, since he expresses distances sometimes in miles and sometimes in stadia, has pointed out an arrangement of a different system for measuring the progress of a ship.

We shall describe this apparatus, which we illustrate in Fig. 2.

Let A B be a screw revolving in its supports. Let us suppose that its thread moves a wheel, $\varDelta$, of 81 teeth, to which is fixed another and parallel wheel, E (a pinion), of nine teeth. Let us suppose that this pinion gears with another wheel, Z, of 100 teeth, and that to the latter is fixed a pinion, H, of 18 teeth. Then let us suppose that this pinion gears with a third wheel, $\varTheta$, of 72 teeth, which likewise is provided with a pinion, K, of 18 teeth, and again that this pinion engages with a wheel, $\varLambda$, of 100 teeth, and so on; so that finally the last wheel carries an index so arranged as to indicate the number of stadia traveled.

On the other hand, let us construct a star wheel, M, whose perimeter is five paces. Let us suppose it perfectly circular and affixed to the side of a vessel in such a way as to have, upon the surface of the water, a velocity equal to that of the vessel.   Let us suppose, besides, that, at every revolution of the wheel, M, there advances, if possible, one tooth of $\varDelta$.   It is clear, then, that at every distance of 100 miles made by the vessel the wheel, $\varDelta$, will make one revolution; so that, if a circle concentric with the wheel, A, is divided into 100 parts, the index fixed to A will, in revolving upon this circle, mark the number of miles made by the number of the degrees.

Odometers, like so many other things, have been reinvented several times, notably in 1662 by a member of the Royal Society of London, and in 1724 by Abbot Meynier.

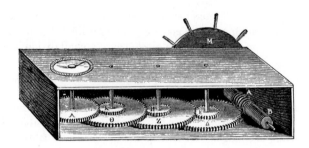

FIG. 2.—ODOMETER FOR VESSELS.

BOOK III.

SCIENCE IN THE THEATER.

CHAPTER I.

BEHIND THE SCENES OF AN OPERA HOUSE.

It would be difficult to find anyone who would not like to go behind the curtain of a great opera house to see how realism is given to the performance, and, incidentally, to gain an insight into that mysterious world upon the stage which always has such an attraction to opera-goers. Before describing in detail the commodious stage of the Metropolitan Opera House, New York City,* we will consider for a moment a typical English stage which is the predecessor of most stages in America. America is unfortunate in having so few really great opera houses, so that the description of the English stage will answer for most of the theaters and opera houses, with the exception of the Metropolitan Opera House and the Auditorium in Chicago, both of which have features of interest. For our description of the English form of theater stage we are largely indebted to a series of papers by Mr. Edwin O. Sachs, architect, in the London "Engineering," beginning January 17, 1896, and appearing at irregular intervals for a year and a half. This valuable series is most profusely illustrated, and forms a treatise of great value. Mr. Sachs has written other works on opera houses. In this connection may be mentioned the French work "*Trucs et Décors*," by M. Georges Moynet, architect. This book is of rather more popular interest than the series of Mr. Sachs. It describes the ordinary equipment of the stage, but includes the obtaining of special effects on a large scale. The modern adjuncts of the theater stage, such as hydraulic platforms and bridges, are not neglected. Many of the illusions which are illustrated in the present work are described in it, and at least one of them appeared first, we believe, in the "Scientific American."

Before describing the ordinary English stage and that of the Metropolitan Opera House, a few generalities are in order. The audience really sees a very small proportion of the stage, for behind the curtain is an enormous rectangu-

---

* The editor is indebted for courtesies to Mr. William Parry, stage manager of the Metropolitan Opera House ; to Mr. C. D. McGiehan, the stage machinist ; to Mr. Edward Siedle, the property master ; and to Mr. Stewart, the electrician.

lar structure which is usually much higher than the roof of the auditorium. This great height is rendered necessary in order to raise the hanging scenes up bodily without resorting to the necessity of rolling them up.   Great space is also needed for the ropes, pulleys, and other mechanism used for working the curtains, drop scenes, and borders.   Everything above the arch of the proscenium is termed the "flies."   The stage proper is the rectangular platform upon which the drama is given.   Its width is usually regulated by the width of the space devoted to the orchestra.   There is considerable space at each side of the stage for working space.   It is here that the "wing" or "side" scenes are stored for the various scenes of the opera, and it is here that the singers and the ballet wait before going before the curtain, through the so-called "entrances" into which the depth of the stage is divided, the number of entrances depending upon the number of wings.

The floor of the stage runs from the footlights to the rear wall of the building, but usually the last few feet of the stage are not utilized by the performers, as the scenery is usually painted there in what is called the "paint room." It is here that a platform, called the "paint bridge," was formerly raised or lowered, giving access to all parts of the canvas which was being painted. But now the paint frames are usually run up and down, while the bridge remains stationary.   The stage is divided widthwise into sections, and these sections of the stage floor can be raised or lowered as desired, and it is also arranged so that scenes, or portions of scenes, may be dropped down through the floor.   As the scenes raised upwards have to be taken out of sight, the scenes which are lowered below the stage floor have likewise to disappear from the view of the audience.   This results in deep cellars under the stage.   The cellar should, of course, be as high as the proscenium aperture through which the audience views the scene; but this is often impossible, and various means are employed to give a great depth to the cellar.   This is sometimes managed by raising the orchestra, or pit, above the ground, but this is apt to make the theater unpopular with those who patronize the galleries, as it necessitates a greater climb; and if the orchestra is depressed below the street level, it requires that the cellar shall be sunk in so much further.   This increases the difficulty of drainage, and the presence of water may be a constant source of annoyance.

We will now describe a typical wooden stage of the English type.   England is the home of excellent stage management, and an English property master is known all over the world by the excellence of his work.   In England large sums are spent on costly productions, and the arrangements which are provided when the stage is built permit of lightning changes, which are so popular there.   In this country the question of expense prevents such elaborate fittings as those in England.   There are, of course, important exceptions to this rule. In the commoner English and American stages there has been so little progress that Mr. Sachs notes the fact that there is little difference between "the ordinary London stage of 1895 and the stages of 1750."   One reason that the theaters on the continent of Europe have such excellent stages—stages in which the ability of the architect and engineer are taxed to the utmost—is that they are very largely assisted by subventions from either the government or the municipalities; so it is little wonder, then, that we have so many splendid examples of the most modern stages in Europe. In the present chapter the word "theater" may be considered to mean either a theater for the spoken drama or an opera house.

The top of the stage is known as the "rigging-loft," or "gridiron," and consists of a wooden or iron stage composed of an open floor laid upon the tie-beams of the principal roof trusses. A considerable weight has to be supported

TOP OF THE GRIDIRON.

upon this gridiron, for from it depend all the "cloths" (drops), "borders," and "gas battens." The strength of the roof is, therefore, calculated so as to sustain this great weight. In some continental theaters there are two gridirons. The gridiron is also called the rigging-loft on account of the fact that the scenes are "rigged up" by ropes from this floor. The scenes are raised and lowered from this level by means of ropes passing through the spaces in the floor, over blocks with wheels in them, on to the drum, and thence down to the "fly floors" below.

Our engravings show the upper and the under side of the gridiron of the Castle Square Theater, in Boston, Mass. This gridiron has some interesting features not possessed by the stage of the Metropolitan Opera House, which will be described a little further on, as at the Metropolitan Opera House there are no windlasses on the gridiron. The windlasses are used to raise heavy weights suspended from the gridiron, and are of the greatest possible use in aërial ballets and other theatrical performances. It will be seen that the gridiron is in reality nothing but a slatted floor supported by iron girders. The ropes will be seen passing over the pulleys to where they descend, at regular intervals, to raise the drops. Our second engraving shows the under side of the gridiron, and the drops and borders which are suspended from

THE GRIDIRON FROM UNDERNEATH, SHOWING DROP AND BORDERS.

it. It gives an excellent idea of the maze of ropes which hang from the gridiron.

The flies consist of galleries, on both sides of the stage, running from the proscenium wall to the back wall. The "fly rail" consists of a girder made especially strong, to take the weight and pull of the ropes and scenes which are brought down from the gridiron. Each cloth or gas batten hung from the gridiron has four or five ropes by which it hangs, and these are all brought over the pulleys in the gridiron floor down to the flies, where they are made fast on belaying-pins or cleats fixed to the fly rail. The "fly floor" is supported by joists running from the fly-rail girder into the wall of the stage.

On the fly floor are often placed windlasses used to raise the heavy weights which are suspended from the gridiron. The load is usually relieved by counterweights which are placed against the wall. The counterweights are usually encased, to minimize the danger of accident in case the rope breaks. The "fly galleries" are usually two tiers in number, but in very large theaters there are often three tiers of fly galleries, one above the other. Nearly all the working of the flies is done from one side of the stage. The flies are often connected by a bridge against the back wall of the stage, and sometimes there are intermediate narrow bridges among the scenery. These enable the "fly men" to cross the stage quickly without necessitating their coming down to the level of the stage. In modern stages of the better class, iron and steel construction is very largely used for the gridiron, flies, etc., and, of course, tends to decrease the danger from fire.

Nearly all of the older stage floors fall three-eighths to one-half inch in a foot, from the back to the front, in order to enable the audience to see the actor or singer as he retires "up" the stage; but in modern stages the floors are usually level, as then the scenery can be set plumb. The divisions of the stage are numerous, and include the imaginary divisions called for by the stage directions, and the actual divisions of the stage into "traps," "sliders," and "bridges." The imaginary divisions need not concern us here.

In the front and center of the stage is a trap called the "grave trap," on account of its use in the grave scene of "Hamlet." It is a small wooden platform made to rise up and down in grooves between four uprights. The stage may have other traps. The trap as an aid in stage illusions is referred to in Chapter IV. of Book III. of the present work.

In ordinary stages the traps are floored over, and before they can be used a portion of the floor of the stage has to be removed. This is done by releasing a lever and letting the section of the floor drop into a groove and slide under the immovable parts at the side of the stage. The opening left in the stage is filled by the floor of the ascending trap. Back of the grave trap there are three narrow strips of openings which are technically called "sliders," then a wider opening which is known as the "bridge." The rest of the stage is taken up by alternate bridges and sliders. The sliders consist of narrow strips of wood which are made to slide horizontally, right and left, under the stage. They slide in grooves cut in the joists, and are moved backwards and forwards by means of ropes which wind around windlasses which are operated from the mezzanine floor underneath the stage. When both sliders are slid away right and left, the open space in the floor and the space underneath is known as the "cut," and it is in the "cut" that the scenery is placed which is to be raised up from below. Scenes are raised up the "slider cuts" by means of lengths of wood sliding up and down in grooves forming very wide and narrow elevators. The scene is attached to the lower bar. The floor of the bridge is like the slider floor in construction; the only difference is in the width of the opening left in the stage when the section of the floor has been removed. To fill this space a platform of the same dimensions as the opening which is left in the stage where the bridge is removed is used. The bridge is used to raise bodily any heavy scene, furniture, or a group of figures, but it only raises its load level with the stage, while some of the new hydraulic bridges, or the counterbalanced rising bridge, which we will shortly describe, permit of lifting the part of the scene to any height. There have recently been many reforms in this part of stage management. The level underneath the stage floor is known as the mezzanine floor. This is the working level for all the traps, sliders, and bridges, and it is on this level that all the windlasses are placed which work the ropes to remove the sliders, bridges, etc. The mezzanine takes the same position regarding the manipulation of the stage machinery below as does the fly gallery above. In some cases the mezzanine floors are multiplied so that there are three or four. The lowest level of the stage is known as the "cellar," or "well." From the cellar spring the uprights which support the joists of the stage floor. At the bottom of the cellar are placed the drums and shafts used for lifting the bridges. In many theaters there is what is known as the "back stage." It has no movable portion, no gridiron, flies, or cellar. This space is most useful for distant scenes. In the finest stages, as that of the Vienna Court Theater, the entire cellar is constructed of iron and steel, and everything is worked by hydraulic power. Scenes are not only raised up from the cellar and let down from the gridiron, but are also "built up" on the stage. Such scenes may be only small "profile strips," or they may be large constructions like a throne, in which the heavy foundations called "rostrums" run in on wheels. Where the run of the opera is to be long, sometimes they are built at great expense and are very ingenious; but they always take up considerable room, and require time to adjust.

In continental theaters what is called the "chariot and pole" is largely used. Narrow slits in the stage permit of an upright pole passing through it, the scene being fastened to it. The truck, or "chariot," which supports the pole runs on the floor of the mezzanine on rails. This manner of shifting the scenes is sometimes very useful. The chariots can be worked singly or in gangs, and they can be worked simultaneously with the borders and the drops, as the ropes which manipulate them can all be brought under the control of one drum or windlass.

Having now described a stage of the ordinary variety, we will take up a large stage built on conservative lines. The stage of the Metropolitan Opera House is one hundred and one feet wide, and the depth is eighty-four feet. The height from the stage to the gridiron is ninety feet, to the first fly gallery thirty-six feet, and the depth of the cellar is twenty-eight feet. The stage is divided widthwise into four bridges which run entirely across the stage. Each bridge is divided into four parts, so there are really sixteen working bridges. The wings, or side scenes, are held in place by means of sliding scene posts. The general method of securing the side scenes by scene frames and extension braces will be understood by reference to the engravings in the chapter entitled "Fireworks with Dramatic Accessories,"

in the present work. When not in use, the wings for the opera are temporarily piled against the side of the house. At each side of the stage are huge
scene-rooms. The stage proper is supported upon an iron framework, and
there are three mezzanine floors, though one only is used. When it is desired
to raise any part of the stage above the level in order to represent broken
ground, or for what is called a "runway," or for any other purpose, a narrow
trap door is lifted and a man at each end of the bridge raises it up to the
desired height. The bridges can be raised to a height of twenty-three feet.
They are counterweighted, so that it requires very little effort to raise them.

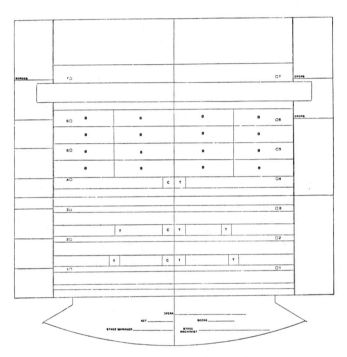

PLAN OF STAGE OF METROPOLITAN OPERA HOUSE.

It is considered that with this system the stage can be worked about as well
and quickly as in the far more elaborate hydraulic stages, as those of Buda-
Pesth and Chicago; certainly the simplicity of arrangement is a point in its
favor, and, being purely mechanical, it is not liable to break down at a critical
moment. The simple bridges are not favored by all stage machinists, however.
The wing posts slide up and down through the floor and drop down flush into
it. They are at the ends of the bridges.

In the Metropolitan Opera House no use is made of the cellar for raising
up the scenes, as they find it more satisfactory to operate the scenes from
overhead, and nothing of the London pantomime order is done. The cellar is

STAGE SHOWING BRIDGES.

valuable, however, for storage purposes. Going up several flights of stone stairs, the visitor arrives at the first fly gallery. Here, as in the other parts of the house, every precaution is taken to guard against fire. The floor is of cement resting upon iron girders, and the visitor is at once struck with the solidity of everything. On each side of the fly gallery is a large iron pipe through which passes at frequent intervals a series of belaying-pins to which are secured the ropes. All of the drops and borders, as well as the curtain,

STORING SCENES IN THE CELLAR.

are worked from the left fly gallery. In theatrical parlance, a scene which is lowered to the stage is called a "drop," while the scenes which represent the sky are called "borders." The drops at the Metropolitan measure forty-five by seventy feet. The painted canvases, whether drops or borders, are secured at the top. The canvas is hemmed so as to permit of a wooden pole, or batten, being thrust through it. This bar is secured by means of clamps to the ropes which are to raise the scenes or drops. At the very top of the building, underneath the roof, is what is called the gridiron. It is an iron framework which supports the pulleys over which the ropes run to raise the drops, borders, and the border lights. Each scene-drop is supported by five ropes, and most of the borders are also supported by five ropes, though three are sometimes used. These ropes are attached at equal intervals along the length of the scene or border.

Each of the five ropes passes over a pulley on the gridiron, or rigging-loft. The ropes are then assembled and pass down on the left of the stage to

WORKING FLY GALLERY.

the first fly gallery, where the fly men are located. In raising or lowering a scene, the five ropes are pulled at the same time, and are secured to the fly rail by means of the belaying-pins. In all theaters the arrangement is not the same as in the Metropolitan ; in some cases there are two or three fly rails, each provided with belaying-pins. Usually one rail will be in front, as shown in our engraving, and the others back and at a slightly higher level. The ropes for the drops, etc., which are not in immediate use, are fastened to the be-laying-pins on this rail. The fly men climb up to the second and third fly galleries when heavy scenes are to be raised, and, catching hold of the ropes, descend to the first fly gallery on the ropes.

There were one hundred and eighty coils of rope used in the stage machinery of the Metropolitan Opera House, each containing one thousand one hundred feet, and one thousand feet of wire rope was required to hang each border light, they being, of course, very heavy. Twelve thousand feet of wire rope was needed for the curtains and border lights.

The curtain is raised by hand, by means of a winch using wire ropes. An asbestos curtain is also provided, and may be dropped instantly from the level of the stage in case of fire, so that the conflagration can be confined to the "back of the house."

We present an engraving of a corner of the stage, showing the great switchboard and the prompter's desk, though, of course, in Grand Opera the prompter takes up his position under a hood directly in front of the conduc-

ELECTRIC SWITCHBOARD.

tor, just beyond the footlights. This hood can be dropped down under the stage when not in use.

Just before the conclusion of the act the conductor of the orchestra rings an electric bell in the working fly gallery. This is a signal to the fly man to get ready to lower the curtain, for the conductor knows the exact bar in the music at which the curtain should descend. At the proper moment the conductor rings again, and the curtain descends. When the men in the fly gallery receive the first signal—that is, the signal to get ready—they turn a switch which lights a colored electric lamp directly over the small prompt desk shown in our engraving, where the stage manager or his assistant takes up his position. When the conductor rings the curtain down, another colored electric lamp is lighted on turning on a switch by the men in the fly gallery. Of course, audible signals would not answer. The stage manager or his assistant stands in front of the little desk and orders the curtain up and down, depending upon the applause of the audience, which governs the appearance of the artists.   This little corner very much resembles the interior of the conning tower of a ship.   Here are speaking tubes and electric bells which connect with all parts of the house, from the box office to the cellar.

The inscriptions under the bells are as follows: " Prompter," " Stage," " Office,"   " Carpenter,"   " Music-Room,"   " Wardrobe,"   " Engineer," " Orchestra,"   " Gas Table,"   " Thunder,"   " Trap,"   " Fly,"   " Property Artist,"   " Box Office."   This means of communication for giving orders and " cues " is very useful; for instance, when the proper moment for thunder has arrived, the stage manager pushes the button and it thunders.   Here is also a book upon which is inscribed the exact time of beginning and finishing the various acts.   A door at the right of the desk gives access to the stage in front of the curtain; there is a corresponding door on the other side of the house. These doors are very useful, as they enable the artists to appear in response to *encores*, without raising the curtain, which means loss of time which is much needed in changing the scene.   It is a wonderful sight to look through the little peep-hole in the door at the audience.   Tier upon tier of splendidly clothed humanity rises up to the family circle at a dizzy height above.   The whole is bright and gay, and is very different from the practical world behind the stage, where stand the stalwart stage hands ready for their duties; but, after all, the world behind the stage has a charm which even the casual visitor willingly admits.

The electric lighting of the Opera House is very interesting, the switchboard especially.   It is believed to be the finest theater switchboard in the world, and cost a good-sized fortune.   It is known as the Kelly-Cushing switchboard. From the switchboard every light in the house is controlled both in front of and behind the curtain.   Of course, the necessity of arranging all the lights used upon the stage so that the colors may be changed, greatly complicates the switch-board.   It is arranged so that the operator can move all the rheostats at once, if desired, thus producing a gradual brightening or dimming of the lights. This is done by the large lever at the right of the switchboard.   Underneath will be seen the fuses.   At the right will be noticed a number of small switches. These control the pilot lights which are fastened at the top of the switchboard. These pilot lights show the exact condition of every light both in the house and on the stage; and the electrician, who has absolute control over all the lights from the great switchboard, can see at a glance what lights he has on, whether red, blue, yellow, or white, and their brightness.   The footlights, which are between the conductor and the curtain, are provided with fifty candle-power lamps.   The drop scenes, and especially the borders, are lighted by means of what are called border lights.   The border lights consist of a batten which runs clear across the stage and which is suspended from the grid-iron by means of wire ropes.   The batten is backed with a tin reflector. There are two hundred and thirty-four lamps in each of the border lights, which are eight in number.   The electric lamps are of thirty-two candle-power, and are arranged alternately in colors of red, white, blue, and yellow. It is, of course, possible for two of the colors to be turned on at once if desired.

Any degree of brightness may be obtained by manipulating the rheostats on the switchboard.

The cables for furnishing the electricity for the border lights are attached at the level of the first fly gallery on the right side, or the side opposite to the working fly gallery. The border lights are usually maintained at a height just above the first fly gallery. In case of any breakdown in the electrical system, gas is provided for the borders and the footlights, the burners being secured to the battens of the border lights the same as the electric lights. Rubber tubes which furnish the supply of gas are attached on the same side as the electric cable. At the sides of the proscenium opening are what are called "side lights." They are one hundred in number, and are of sixteen candle-power. They are provided in the four colors already mentioned. Up in the first fly gallery, at the side of the border lights, are eighteen arc-light projectors, nine to the side, seven of which are what are called "open boxes," that is, they have a ground-glass front, and two of them are provided with lenses and are called "lens boxes." These arc lights take the place of the old calcium lights, and are better and more economical. The wings are lighted by what are called "bunch lights," several incandescent lights being placed in front of a reflector. They are supported by a standard. The electric light can be obtained at nearly all parts of the stage from boxes which are provided with an iron cover. Gas may also be had for use in various effects. In some operas, as many as a thousand incandescent lights may be going on the stage at one time, in addition to the arc-light projectors already referred to. There is little wonder that under this intense light the ordinary complexion is paled, and artifice is required to come to the aid of nature. There are about nine thousand incandescent lights in the entire house, although they are not all used at one time. Every part of the house is beautifully lighted, even to the cellars.

When the Opera House is used for balls, splendid chandeliers are used, which are stored in the cellar when not in use. The whole stage and orchestra are boarded over, making a superb ballroom. The Opera House does not have its own plant for generating electricity. It is all obtained from the street circuit. It is believed that there is less risk of a breakdown or from fire than if an isolated plant was provided. Electricity is used in many of the effects and for running the ventilating fans and the elevators.

When the house was rebuilt after the fire, the gas table made way for the switchboard. The complicated gas plot is not used at the present time at the Opera House, the electrician carrying the lighting in his mind, the effects being determined upon at the rehearsal. Much of the lighting depends on "cues;" thus, in the first act of "Siegfried," when Wotan appears in the mouth of the cave, this is the signal for light being turned on him with a projector; and further on, when he strikes the stage with his spear, white light is thrown on him.

The electrical organ at the Metropolitan Opera House is interesting. The organ itself is fixed in the first fly gallery on the right, but it may be played from any part of the stage.   At the extreme right of the stage is the organ trap.   When it is wished to use the organ either for rehearsal or for a performance, the keyboard is raised by the trap and carried to any part of the stage, a large cable carrying the wire which runs up to the organ.   This arrangement gives great satisfaction.

Every precaution is taken to guard against fire, which once played such havoc with the Opera House.   Lines of hose are on every floor, and automatic

PAINTING SCENERY FROM THE PAINT BRIDGE.

sprinklers are in all of the rooms.   Axes and fire-hooks are disposed at frequent intervals.   A fireman is on the stage at all the performances, and the men are carefully trained in a fire drill.   The asbestos curtain affords absolute protection to the audience, as even a fire of the most serious character in the "back of the house" would give the most ample time for all of the audience to get out comfortably.   It may be dropped either from the flies or the stage.   It is lowered at night as a precaution.

The paint bridge is a wide platform at the level of the first fly gallery, and furnishes a means of communication between the two fly galleries.   The canvas which is to be painted is run up the side of the paint bridge. The scenic artist thus has access to all parts of the canvas. On the paint bridge are long tables covered with large earthenware dishes in which the paint is kept. The visitor will probably be surprised to see the enormous quantity of color which is used in painting scenery; the color is mixed with a size. At the Metropolitan the scenery is painted by daylight, but it can also be lighted artificially by incandescent lights. The production of a new opera necessitates the making of large quantities of scenery.

The property-rooms are most interesting. Here you may see Siegfried's anvil, his forge, Wotan's spear, the Lohengrin swan, or the "Rheingold;" while under the second fly gallery will be seen the parts of "Fafner," the dragon in "Siegfried," which will be described in another chapter. The armory is a room containing a vast collection of helmets, casques, breastplates, swords, spears, lanterns, daggers, etc.; while in a case lighted by electricity are the splendid jewels, crowns, etc., which make such an effective appearance when seen on the stage. Here will also be found a model of the old dragon which was burned up in the fire. Hung up on one side of the wall is an elephant's head with a trunk which is freely flexible, and in the next room will be found the head of a camel which winks his eyes. In here are also stored the shields and weapons which the great artists use when they impersonate Northern gods and warriors. Under the property master's charge are modeling-rooms and carpenter shops.

The day on which the opera is to be performed the property master gets out all of the things which will be needed in the production. They are carefully stowed away convenient to the stage, or upon it, so that they may be brought to their proper place without a moment's delay. When it is considered that the size of the objects varies from the dragon to a pack of cards, it will be seen that there is a great chance of forgetting something; but should this occur, everything is arranged so that the error can be remedied with the smallest loss of time. With properties, as with stage carpentry, everything depends upon invention, and for every new opera the property master is obliged to devise new properties and new effects for which he has often no precedent.

When the curtain falls for good after the *encores*, the stage machinist blows a sharp blast on his whistle, and as if by magic all the singers and the chorus who have not gone already, leave the stage, and their places are taken by a swarm of stage hands. The fly men raise the drops and the borders out of the way, while the men on the stage take away the movables and the set scenes. The wing scenes are unfastened and are placed at the sides of the stage temporarily, while the new set scenes are brought out and take their place. If rising ground is to be made, the men raise the trap doors and, reaching underneath the bridges, haul them up to the proper height and secure them with pins. Then canvas to represent the ground is placed over the front of the stage and up over the broken ground. Rocks and trees of *papier maché* and canvas are brought in and placed in position. If any things like chandeliers are used, ropes are dropped from the gridiron to secure them at the proper height. The stage machinist stands in the middle of the stage and gives an order now and then to some of the men, the scenes and the drops and borders are raised or lowered, or the set scenes straightened until all are in order and able to pass the critical eyes of the machinist and the stage manager. All of this is done without confusion, so carefully is every man trained in his duties. Then calls are sent to the various dressing-rooms, and the chorus or " supers " are brought out and placed in position. When everything is in readiness, and the proper time has arrived, according to the music, the prompter, from his little box under the stage, gives a signal which is transmitted to the fly men, who wind away on the windlasses and raise the curtain. It might naturally be supposed that all is now quiet at the back and sides of the stage, but this is not always the case; the wings and the stage back of the last drop are filled with those who are to go on next, and one may encounter Sicilian bandits, peasants, Northern gods, or the *première danseuse* nervously practicing her steps with the master of the ballet. The favored visitor is allowed to walk around in this new world without being molested, and the opera as seen from the floor of the stage or from the " flies " is a sight never to be forgotten.

After any one has viewed the production of an elaborate opera from behind the scenes he will never again be in the slightest degree annoyed by the length of the *entr'acte*. The only wonder is that the elaborate scenes can be gotten ready in the fifteen or twenty minutes which elapse between the falling of the curtain at the close of one act and the raising of the curtain at the beginning of the next act; and it must be remembered that the artists are frequently the cause of the delay.

The dressing-rooms at the Metropolitan are not luxurious, but often the artists fix them up attractively. The dressing-rooms for the supers, chorus, and ballet are, of course, large.

Few of those who hear the first production of a new opera realize that the successful performance is the result not only of the singing of celebrities and perfect orchestration, but also of the patient care which has been bestowed upon the opera for months by the stage manager and those who have helped him.

When the director of the opera company decides to produce a new opera the libretto is given to those who are charged with the construction of scenery, costumes, and properties. The first thing to be avoided is the gross anachronisms which are so often seen upon even the stages of first-class theaters. The examples of chronological errors which might be cited are almost endless, and for interesting examples the reader is referred to " Pictorial Art on the Stage," by E. W. and E. H. Blashfield, in the " Century," vol. xxxv. At the present time celebrated artists are often engaged to make drawings of the scenes and costumes. The results obtained for spoken dramas by Mr. Frank Millet and Mr. Hamilton Bell are noteworthy. If artists are not engaged to do the work it is entrusted to carefully trained specialists. They first consult books of costume and works bearing upon the period which is to be illustrated. These matters are discussed by the director, and the designs are modified if necessary. The scenic artist is then called in to sketch and model the scenery. He has a miniature stage on the scale of half an inch to a foot. Little scenes are made for it of pasteboard, and carefully painted. They are placed in position, and are modified from time to time, as required. It is really wonderful to the layman to see how many things have to be taken into consideration in modeling a scene. The number of persons upon the stage, the properties, the music, and the difficulties of setting the scenes, all have to be most carefully considered, as well as arrangements for traveling on the road. Finally the miniature stage with all its properties is fully equipped, then the whole force at the disposal of the stage manager is set to work to prepare costumes, properties, and scenery. All possible care must be taken to insure the proper effects of color when the costumes and scenery are brought into juxtaposition. Frequently over two hundred and fifty costumes must be made for a single opera, so that the costume-rooms of an opera house resemble a mammoth dressmaking and tailoring establishment. It is no small task to preserve the thousands of costumes from dust and moths. Before each performance all the costumes required must be gotten out, brushed, and placed in the proper dressing-rooms. All repairs are made to the garments before putting them away again. The number of properties which are required for an opera is frequently several hundred, and they are of all sizes, from finger rings to immense constructions which require the united efforts of a dozen men to move them. It is naturally to be supposed that *papier maché* and plaster of paris are two of the most valuable adjuncts of the property master's art. Probably nothing in the way of an opera requires such Yankee ingenuity as does the office of property master. We have not space to go into the subject of rehearsals and how the final production of the opera is accomplished, but we shall endeavor to give a few examples in the next chapter of how some of the effects are produced.

Before taking up the minor stage effects, as well as those which might be called "theater secrets," we will first describe some interesting old stages, then stage effects in which the entire stage is required for the production of a certain effect. In leaving the subject of opera it is only fair to say that the enormous expense attending the maintenance of the opera house itself, the cost of properties, lighting, etc., to say nothing of the remarkable salaries of the singers, really warrants the exaction of what are seemingly high prices. Opera is such an education to music lovers that it is unfortunate that it cannot receive such financial aid from the state that its success under good management will be assured. On the Continent every care is taken to foster the opera. In Paris, we believe, the government allots an annual subvention of 800,000 francs.

CHAPTER II.

SOME REMARKABLE STAGES, ANCIENT AND MODERN.

AN ELECTRIC CURTAIN.

We present an engraving of the electric drop scene of the Comédie Française, at Paris. The curtain is held by five ropes, *a*, which pass over pulleys, *o*, at the upper part, and wind round a wooden drum, B, to which motion is given in one direction or the other in order to cause the curtain to rise or descend. Such motion is obtained by the aid of a belt connected with an electrical shunt motor, F; a counterpoise, D, held by a rope which passes around a drum, assures an equilibrium at every point. It is an easy matter to maneuver the curtain by means of the motor, the curtain being raised as required. Three different velocities in descent and two in ascent are obtained. The maximum velocity of descent is five feet per second, the medium is three feet six inches, and minimum is three feet five inches. The velocities of ascent are respectively two and one-half and three and one-half feet per second. This was, we believe, the pioneer of all theater curtains which were worked by electricity. There have been many since.

THE FAN–DROP CURTAIN.

In Japanese ballets a large fan is sometimes used in place of a drop curtain, and in some of the Paris *cafés* a fan is also used, as this enables them to make evasion of the law relating to theatrical performances. We present an engraving showing the fan at the Paris Opera House, in a ballet called "*Le Rêve*" (The Dream).

It scarcely differs in principle from an ordinary fan, but the sticks are twenty-three feet in length; that is to say, two stories high. There are in all ten sticks that revolve around the same axis (letter K in our second engraving). They are connected by strips of canvas of the same width. The two extreme sticks, A and B, and the two center ones, C and D, are prolonged beneath the axis of rotation. It is these four sticks only that are acted upon in order to open and close the fan. Others participate in their motion through arcs of iron which connect one with the other. The maneuvering apparatus is readily

ELECTRIC DROP SCENE OF THE COMÉDIE FRANÇAISE.

understood by reference to our engraving, the ropes from the four working sticks of the fan running over windlasses.   The fan is arranged in advance

FIG. 1.—VIEW OF THE FAN AT THE PARIS OPERA HOUSE.

under the stage.   In the middle of the first act it is mounted vertically, all closed, upon the stage, behind the streamer which completely hides the maneu-

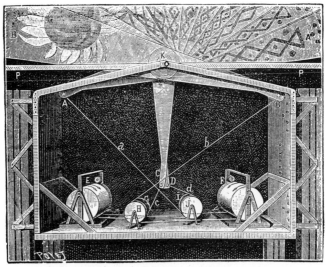

FIG. 2.—APPARATUS FOR MANEUVERING THE FAN.

ver.   The fan is manipulated by two men, one at each windlass; moreover, the work is facilitated by the use of cables, provided with counterpoises, which are hooked above to the four principal sticks and pass over guide pulleys placed in a semicircle. The cables are concealed behind a decoration representing foliage which hides the edges of the fan.

AN ELEVATOR THEATER STAGE.

We present an engraving of the theater stage of the Madison Square Theater, New York City, which shows a remarkable advance in stage management. The first movable stage is probably that which the late Steele Mackaye patented in 1869. The details of Mackaye's patent were not completely worked out, but this was done by Mr. Nelson Waldron, the stage machinist, who elaborated the system and obtained a patent on it. The stage in the theater we refer to is moved up and down in the same manner as an elevator car, and is operated so that either of its divisions can be easily and quickly brought to the proper level in front of the auditorium. This enables the stage hands to get one scene ready while the other one is in view of the audience. The shaft through which the huge elevator moves up and down measures one hundred and fourteen feet from the roof to the bottom. The stages are moved up and down in a compact, two-floored structure of timber strapped with iron, and knitted together with truss-beams above and below, and substantially bound by tie and tension rods. The whole construction is fifty-five feet high and twenty-two feet wide and thirty-one feet deep, and weighs about forty-eight tons. A vertical movement of the structure or car is twenty-five feet two inches at each change. The car is suspended at each corner by two steel cables, each of which would be capable of supporting the entire structure. These cables pass upward over sheaves or pulleys set at different angles, and thence downward to a saddle to which they are all connected. Secured to this saddle is a hoisting cable attached to a hoisting drum, by the rotation of which the stage is raised or lowered. Only about forty seconds are required to raise or lower the stage in position, and the entire structure is moved by four men at the winch. The movement is effected without sound, jar, or vibration, owing to the balancing of the stage and its weight with counterweights, which are suspended from the saddle to which the cables supporting the stage are attached.

The borders and border lights are supplied to each of the movable stages, and each stage has its own trap floor, with traps and guides and windlasses for raising the traps. The space for operating the windlass under the top stage is about six feet. Our illustration shows that while the play is proceeding before the audience, the stage hands are setting the scene on the stage above.

STAGE OF THE MADISON SQUARE THEATER, NEW YORK CITY.

SOME REMARKABLE AMERICAN STAGE INVENTIONS.

The fact that there have been many important and brilliant inventions relating to stages made by Americans has been overlooked, and nearly all of the literature of the subject does not consider them at all. This is probably owing to the fact that in many cases the inventions have been planned out on so large a scale they can hardly be used, and, unfortunately, they usually exist only on paper. Still, we cannot help but admire the genius of such men as Steele Mackaye, whose inventions in this line were most remarkable, and to whom we have already referred in reference to the elevator stage. We now purpose to describe one of the most gigantic affairs that was ever devised for obtaining scenic effects. It was intended for the "Spectatorium" at the World's Fair at Chicago, in 1893. It will be remembered that the unfinished building was just outside the lower end of the Fair grounds. Unfortunately the scheme was not carried out.

In brief, Mr. Mackaye's idea was to increase realism in the performances, and, at the same time, lessen the time of the waits between the scenes. To this end he devised means for producing various scenic effects in imitation of natural or other scenery, with special reference to the proper presentation of important historical or other events, as, for instance, the discovery of America by Columbus or the burning of Rome by Nero. His arrangements permitted of the exhibition of various occurrences, either on land or water, in such a manner as to give the effect of the actual occurrence. Thus, near and distant moving objects were to be moved at different rates of speed for the production of perspective moving scenic effects. His invention consisted primarily of the combination of movable stages adapted to support and carry the scenic arrangements and properties or persons. The building might, of course, be of any desired form; a proscenium wall or arch was to be provided, and Mr. Mackaye devised an adjustable proscenium opening to meet the various requirements of the drama. Back of the proscenium arch was a series of stages which could be made in any desired shape and fitted to support and carry scenes, properties, or persons. They were provided with rollers or wheels and ran on tracks or floated on tanks. These stages, or cars, as they might be termed, were to be moved over a track which was really a segment of a circle. In order to save space the cars were so arranged that they would telescope. As already mentioned, the cars could be driven at any rate of speed; thus, where there were four concentric stages, the one the furthest away from the audience could be moved much slower than the one nearest the spectators. Electric motors and cables were to haul the moving stages over the curved tracks, or guideways. Ample facilities were to be provided for the use of vessels; the various tracks on which ran the scenic car being arranged so that they could be flooded without interfering with the moving of the scenes.

Waves were to be produced by what was known as a "wave maker," consisting of a plate pivoted to a reciprocating frame which works in guideways fitted within channel bars, which are secured to plates forming a canal connected with the curved water ways or channels. The wave plates were to be connected by a pitman rod to the crank wheel or shaft of an electric motor. When it was desired to give the effect of waves upon the surface of the water contained in the reservoir of the foundation floor of the scenic department which overspreads this department to sufficiently conceal the tracks in the water channel, the wave maker could be set in motion by the operator or prompter turning on the current to the motor. Channels, conduits, sluices, and gates were to be provided to cause the water to flow from one channel into another. The current was to be made by spiral blades or archimedean screws journaled in proper supports and geared to electric or other suitable motors. The rotary motion was to be imparted to the blades to force the water through the channel and thereby produce a current.

Powerful electric fans were to be provided for the purpose of forming currents of air for producing the effect of a gale of wind blowing in either direction, and a motor in the dome over the scene would permit of the currents of air descending, ascending, or moving in a rotary course, so that the effect of a stiff gale, a hurricane, or a cyclone could be produced. The air could also be sent through flexible tubes, so that it could be guided in any desired direction.

Mr. Mackaye had several other devices, also, for producing atmospheric effects upon the stage. What he termed "cloud creators," or "nebulators," consisted essentially of a cloud cloth having the cloud forms of shadows placed thereon and adapted to move in front of an illuminating lamp so as to cast the cloud shadows over the landscape or scenic arrangement, or produce the effect of moving clouds upon a sky foundation or other surface. The cloud cloth may consist of any suitable material, on which may be placed various cloud effects or forms, the cloth being secured to a sliding frame or fitted over rollers, so as to move in proximity to an illuminating coloring device, from which light may pass through the transparent or semi-transparent material on which the cloud effects or shadows are placed so as to cast the shadows upon the scenic arrangements or sky foundations, thereby imitating clouds moving through the sky, or cloud shadows moving over land and water. Rain was provided for by a series of perforated pipes connected with a water supply, so that a gentle rain or a hard shower could be produced. These pipes were to cross the stage, being secured to the fly galleries. The fog producer consisted of a trough containing lime. This trough, which was suspended from the fly galleries and the roof, was to be lowered into another tank, slacking the lime, and thus forming a fog, the wind-making permitting of the lifting or the dissipating of the fog. A whole series of the "nebulators," "umbrators," and fog and rain producers was arranged for, the patent drawings showing six. The audience could see nothing of the mechanism, as each was masked by borders. The scenes, with Mr. Mackaye's system of lighting, could be painted in their natural color, the high lights not needing to be emphasized as in ordinary scene painting.

Another curious invention is what Mr. Mackaye was pleased to term a "lux-auleator." It was a stage appliance which was intended to prevent the audience from witnessing the operations or movements of the actors behind the proscenium opening between the acts or when it was desired to shift or rearrange stage scenery. The invention consisted of a series of lights, set in backings or reflectors, placed in the form of a border or other suitable arrangement around the proscenium opening so as to throw the space in the rear of the opening into complete shade while flooding the other space, as the auditorium, in front of the opening, with rays of light, and so crossing each other and blending in such a manner as to intercept all sight of anything that may be placed or moved in the shaded portion of the stage. By this means the ordinary drop curtain may be dispensed with, and, at the same time, it renders it unnecessary to extinguish the light in the auditorium when removing or shifting stage scenery. This was tried in a model and was found to be satisfactory. In view of Mr. Mackaye's remarkable invention, it can never be said that America is behind England and the Continent in the matter of stage business, and the inventions of Mackaye are representative ones of a whole class of American inventors, although their work was perhaps not so brilliant as his.

Another interesting theatrical construction is that of Mr. Claude L. Hagen, the master machinist of the Fifth Avenue Theater, New York City. In brief, the invention provides for a building preferably of circular form, in the center of which is a circular pit or cistern provided with an entrance which may be used by carriages and persons on foot. This entrance is provided with a lock gate which can be closed, so that the cistern or pit can be filled with water for aquatic purposes. The pit can also be used for a circus ring, horse show, etc., or can be filled with chairs, or used for a standing audience or promenade; the center may be occupied by an electric fountain.

From the edge of the pit rise the tiers of seats and boxes in a similar form to that of the Coliseum at Rome. The stage is designed to permit of a series of tableaux or pictures being built permanently, so that it will not be necessary to resort to the scene painter's art to give light and shadow. There are no borders or overhead scenery, but the light is arranged to move in the same manner as the sun, surrounded with large cylinders of glass so covered as to cause the lights on the scenes to be the same as in nature.

The proscenium opening is at one end of the circular building, and the circular stage surrounds the entire auditorium, revolving into the empty space underneath the tiers of seats and boxes. The space underneath the tracks in which the stage runs being used as an arcade, connection with the lower portion of the tiers is by means of stairways at the foot of each aisle, there being similar exits midway of the aisle, connected with drawbridges to the stairways on the exterior of the building. The top of the tiers of seats opens on to a wide promenade which connects with a roof garden or *café* on the portion of the building over the stage, behind the proscenium aisle. Entrance to this promenade is made by means of endless traveling stairways which form parts of a broad stairway. The moving stairway in case of accident is automatically locked with and into the solid portion of the stairway, thereby forming an ample means of egress. The arrangement for the stage is of great interest, as the scenes can be built in the most elaborate manner, and the effect is, of course, far more realistic where real earth, trees, fences, etc., can be used. Where a piece is to have a long run, as a spectacular performance, this added realism will prove of great value, and the labor and time which is expended in preparing the stage for each performance will be saved; for at the termination of the scene the electric motors or other sources of power are put into motion, the entire stage is rotated, and the next scene is moved in front of the proscenium aisle.

A portion of the revolving stage consists of a tank filled with water, so that marine scenes with ships and boats can be produced. For example: in case a drama of "Columbus" was to be produced, Columbus is discovered bidding his friends farewell on the shores of Spain; he then gets into his boat, and the stage is caused to slowly revolve, bringing into view his ship. The land then disappears from view, and this is succeeded by scenes of the voyage, storms, etc. Then the floating branch of the tree is discovered; then the coast of America appears; then the disembarkment takes place; and this is followed by the journey into the interior. Of course, the movement of the stage can be reversed, and the return journey made.

The circular stage platform can at any time be cleared of all its appurtenances, and the stage can be used as a race track, being caused to move in a direction opposite to that in which the horses run, and at such a speed as to keep the horses in view through the proscenium opening. Thus, the whole course of a steeple chase, a hurdle or other race, or even a fox hunt, can be shown to an audience, with the fences, walls, waterways, and other scenery moving in the most natural manner. The whole plan seems to have great flexibility, and it is to be hoped that at some time one of these interesting buildings will be built.

A REVOLVING STAGE.

For some years past the public has been demanding more and more realistic representations of plays. Managers have found great difficulty in satisfying this demand, owing to the time required to set elaborate scenery. The public will not stand long waits, which are often sufficient to cause the failure of a play or opera. These delays are bad enough between the acts, but in plays or operas which necessitate changes of scene during the acts, the waits become well nigh unbearable ; and many of the works of Schiller, Goethe, and Shakespeare become well nigh monstrosities, as many of them are divided into interminable acts and scenes. This difficulty has been sometimes avoided by the use of an elevating stage such as we have just described, or by the so-called "Shakespeare stage," in which the front part of the stage remains unchanged, while on the raised rear stage different scenes succeed one another.

Kgl. RESIDENZ u. HOFTHEATER. MUENCHEN.

DON GIOVANNI - TANZSAAL I ACT. BILD IV.

DON GIOVANNI GARTEN I ACT. BILD III.

CHANGE FROM THE THIRD TO THE FOURTH SCENE OF THE FIRST ACT OF "DON JUAN."

This is regarded as eminently unsatisfactory. Baron von Perfall, manager of the Munich Theater, published a book setting forth his ideas in regard to the thorough transformation of the stage as it then existed. The manager of the royal stage in Munich made a practical and successful test of the invention of Herr Lautenschlager, the mechanical director of the Royal Theater of Bavaria. The revolving stage was used in a representation of Mozart's "Don Juan." When the nature of the invention first became known, many people associated it with a device used on Japanese stages, which consists of a revolving platform in the center of the stage, a similar device being employed in America and England for displaying "living pictures;" but this arrangement has only a superficial resemblance to the revolving stage we are considering. The arrangement used at the Court Theater at Munich is essentially as follows:

On the ordinary stage floor is placed a revolving disk, or platform, which raises the floor slightly. This circular platform is fifty-two feet five inches in diameter, and presents not quite a quarter of a circle to the proscenium opening, which is thirty-two feet nine inches wide. It turns on rollers that run on a circular track; the revolving mechanism is driven by electricity. If a scene is set on the quarter circle presented to the audience—perhaps a closed room of considerable depth—something similar can be arranged on the opposite side of the platform which opens to the rear of the stage, as well as on the other quarters, so that four different scenes are set on the stage at the same time. For a play of four acts, requiring a different setting for each act, all four scenes can be prepared beforehand, and at the end of the first act the stage is turned a quarter of a circle (which requires about ten or eleven seconds), and the scene desired for the next act is presented to the audience; and so on at the end of each act. In case three changes were required in one act, after the portion of the stage occupied by the first scene had been turned away from the audience, it would be cleared and set for the first scene of the next act. The scenes need not be limited to representations of closed rooms; any desired scene can be set on the turning stage, and, if necessary, the whole stage can be used the same as any ordinary stage. Difficulties will occur only when two scenes requiring great depth—for instance, two landscapes with distant views—follow one another. But Herr Lautenschlager has shown that even these difficulties can be overcome by setting the scene along the radius of the circular stage so that the portion used decreases considerably toward the rear, and in this way he gains the entire depth of the stage for another scene. Much more of the artistic element enters into the setting of a stage of this kind than of a stage that is set on straight lines.

The reader will understand the above after an examination of the accompanying plans, which show the stage set for the third and fourth scenes of the first act of "Don Juan." The third scene shows Don Juan's garden, in which the peasants invited to the *fête* gather and the maskers meet. This is changed to the hall in which the first act closes. As shown by the plan, considerable depth was required for this scene. Our large illustration shows how this change is accomplished, or how it would appear if darkness did not

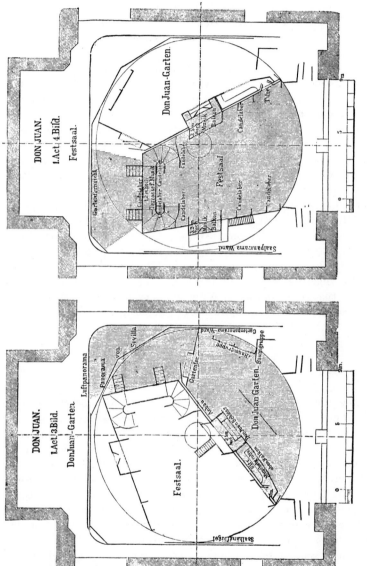

PLAN SHOWING THIRD AND FOURTH SCENES OF FIRST ACT.

prevail when the stage was being turned.   Before the garden had completely disappeared, a portion of the hall would be visible, with all the life and motion, the dancers, and the gaily dressed crowd of guests.

The " under machinery "—the traps, chariots, bridges, etc.—are worked in various ways, and they are as accessible and as easily managed as in the ordinary stage.   The overhead work is about the same as in any other modern iron theater.

A stage of this kind, constructed of iron, and equipped with electrical driving devices, would meet the most exacting requirements of the present age. The success of Herr Lautenschlager's plan in the Munich Theater gives ground for the hope that it will soon be adopted in other theaters.

The inventor of this stage, Karl Lautenschlager, was thoroughly educated as an engineer, and has had so much experience in the management of the mechanical devices of different theatres that he is admirably fitted to plan a thoroughly practical stage which meets the entire approval of those interested in " stage reform."

A revolving stage was patented by an American, Mr. Charles A. Needham, in 1883.   It certainly seems to contain the germ of Herr Lautenschlager's invention.   A Mexican, J. Herrera y Gutierrez, of the City of Mexico, invented in 1892 a theatrical arrangement in which the conditions of the revolving stage are reversed.   In the center of a circular building were five auditoriums forming a circle which was capable of turning.   The stages were rectangular and surrounded the auditoriums.   A different scene was set upon each, and the auditoriums were turned, facing each scene in turn.

THE " ASPHALEIA " STAGE.

In some theaters there is a whole series of traps worked by hydraulic power.   These traps are capable of raising a whole section of the stage if desired.   In the so-called " Asphaleia " stage—in which each trap goes right across the stage and is divided into three parts, each of which rests on the plunger of a hydraulic press, so that it can be raised and lowered either independently or simultaneously with the rest of the traps in that division—the whole of the floor can be raised or lowered as desired.   It will be readily seen that by this means a stage manager has at his disposal a very effective aid in setting a large scene.   Each section of the floor of the stage can be fixed in an oblique position, and the traps can be arranged one after the other so as to form a succession of steps, bridges, balconies, or even a ship, in a moment, with perfect safety, and without previous preparation.   The old clumsy timberwork set pieces and the building up of scenes is avoided, and the method of working is in many ways an ideal one, but, after all, does not seem to possess the flexibility of a series of divided bridges such as are used at the Metropolitan Opera House, New York.   The hydraulic traps permit of the easy representation

THE "ASPHALEIA" STAGE, SHOWING HYDRAULIC TRAPS AND HORIZON.

of uneven ground, which strengthens the possibility of illusion and gives a chance for a far more picturesque arrangement than is permitted on the plain ordinary stage. The trap arrangement of the "Asphaleia" stage should be regarded as something more than a mere arrangement of traps. In this theater it is arranged so that entire scenes can be raised and lowered through the slides simultaneously. It is possible to raise up from below the stage, in view of the audience, a complete scene representing a room. With these facilities the waits are very much shorter. The hydraulic stage of the Chicago Auditorium is a fine example of good hydraulic work. In the "Asphaleia" stage even the drop scenes are manipulated by hydraulic power from a central point. The fire curtain is also actuated by a hydraulic cylinder fixed to the middle of the fire curtain. Valves are provided in various parts of the stage, which permit of dropping the curtain. For detailed information concerning the splendid stages at Halle, Buda-Pesth, and Chicago, the reader is referred to Mr. E. O. Sachs's series of articles on "Modern Theater Stages," in "Engineering" for October 23d and November 13, 1896, and to his monumental books upon the same subject.

In our engraving it will be noticed that the horizon is represented by a canvas background like a panorama. In the "Asphaleia" theater the back of the stage is much wider, as compared with the opening of the proscenium, than it is in ordinary theaters. Its whole area is surrounded by a continuous cloth scene, on which there is painted a sky called the horizon, which runs from the back of the stage and up each side for quite a distance. In order to produce the effect of an unbroken surface the corners are rounded off very carefully so that the eye of the spectator is not brought up by the wings. With this system it is no longer necessary to use so much rock and tree work, and it is quite possible to represent boundless plains or the illimitable expanse of the sea. This continuous horizon not only helps in the illusion, but it reaches so high up that borders are no longer needed. The horizon, like the canvas in a cyclorama, represents a uniformly illuminated surface, which gives the same impression as the sky. The horizon is carried by the rollers, and it may be painted so that at a moment's notice the different aspects of the sky can be represented, from the deep blue of Italy to the mists and fogs of the North, and from the fleeciest clouds to a sky heavy with thunder. It is even possible to change the nature of the sky during the action of the play or opera.

Another very important feature of the "Asphaleia" stage is the system of lighting; gas battens and footlights are dispensed with. In the "Asphaleia" theater there is a special arrangement of the proscenium; all the lighting is done from the side. There are many other interesting features of the "Asphaleia" stage, which is almost entirely fireproof, and tends not only to minimize the danger of fire, but also to insure the safety of the workmen and artists. This form of theater stage is, of course, expensive in its initial outlay, but it is much cheaper in its actual working. Opinions seem to be very much divided as to its merits; at any rate, it is a most interesting example of the most modern form of engineering talent being devoted to the building of a thoroughly scientific stage. M. Georges Moynet says in " *Trucs et Décors,*" from which we take our engraving, that the manipulation of the scenery at Buda-Pesth is very slow and that the cellar is very damp.

We have just described the "direct ram" system of operating traps and bridges, but it will be readily seen that the space required for the rams is practically lost, so another system is sometimes used. This is called the "crane" system. In this the bridges and traps are maneuvered by wire ropes which are worked by hydraulic rams placed against the walls of the stage building. Some of these systems are very complicated, but the results are very satisfactory, and are said to be economical, doing away with much handwork, especially so in the day-time.

The Court Theater at Weisbaden possesses a very novel feature. The entire space occupied by the musicians is really a gigantic trap, the whole floor being raised or lowered by hydraulic power, noiselessly and in a moment. This device was installed by Herr Fritz Brandt, of the Berlin Court Theater. The idea of having an orchestra movable was to permit of the musicians playing at the bottom of the pit when the production of a Wagnerian opera was given, as Wagner believed that the musicians should be out of sight. He made arrangements at the theater at Bayreuth by which the orchestra is entirely concealed from view, the sound coming from the bottom of the deep orchestra well. At Wiesbaden, if a small operetta is to be given, the platform for the musicians is raised to the normal height. This arrangement is valuable in other ways, for in the case of a ball the platform may be run to any height. The hydraulic rams are powerful enough to raise the entire load of sixty-five musicians, so that if desired the orchestra can be see-sawed up and down according to the requirements of the score. The Lyceum Theater, New York City, is similarly equipped.

A THEATER WITH TWO AUDITORIUMS.

The people of New York City have the reputation of being the most tireless theater-goers in all America; a statement which is verified by the ever-increasing number of large and well-filled places of amusement. Of late years the growth of the popularity of the style of entertainments which are classed under the name of "vaudeville" has called into existence a special type of theater, which, in addition to the regulation stage and auditorium, includes special halls of entertainment, with lounging-rooms, *cafés*, etc., and, for use in the hot summer months, the inevitable roof garden. To judge from the nightly programme of a first-class house of this type, the excellence of the performance is measured, after its quality, by its length and variety. The more rapidly the various artists can make "their exits and their entrances," the more concentrated amusement can be packed into any given hour of a "continuous performance."

It was with a view to enlarging the stage capacity that the proprietor of Proctor's Pleasure Palace, in New York City, resorted to the bold expedient

A THEATER IN NEW YORK CITY WITH TWO AUDITORIUMS.

which is shown in the illustration on page 284, from which it will be seen that a single stage is made to do duty for two separate auditoriums. The way in which this was accomplished will be seen by reference to the sectional diagram, which is taken longitudinally through the auditorium proper, the stage, and the new auditorium, which is known as the Palm Garden, being so named after the palms and tropical plants and vines with which it is decorated. The part of the diagram which includes the auditorium and the stage shows the construction of a typical summer theater of to-day—the *café* in the basement and the roof garden being special features in a house of this kind—which introduces no new structural features of much consequence beyond a strengthening of the roof supports. Stripped of its galleries and scenery, a theater consists of two four-walled structures, the auditorium being about square in plan, and the stage floor about the same width as the auditorium, and half the depth. The walls of the stage are carried considerably higher than the roof of the auditorium, in order to accommodate the drop curtains, which are hung by ropes that pass over pulleys attached to what is known as the gridiron, a stout framework located near the roof of the scene loft. When the drop curtains are not in use they are raised clear of the proscenium, as the opening from the stage to the audience is called, and hang in parallel rows as shown in the diagram. Below the stage floor are shown the traps. Here, in the older theaters, were frequently located the dressing-rooms of the performers, though the more modern arrangement is to build them at the sides or the rear of the stage.

In carrying out the idea of a double stage a hall was built immediately behind the theater proper, and a proscenium arch was cut through the rear wall of the stage, the floor of which was carried out into the hall and provided with the regulation footlights. The new proscenium was provided with its own curtain, and all that was then necessary was to paint the backs of the existing wings and drop curtains with scenery, and the doubling of the stage was complete.

The original intention was to have three or four performances of such a character that they would not interfere with each other going on upon the stage at the same time, and during the summer months this was frequently done. Ordinarily, however, the curtain opening to the palm garden is kept lowered, and it is raised only during the intermissions, or when special acrobatic, gymnastic, or animal acts are in progress. A passageway leads from the auditorium to the palm garden, which are both accessible to the audience at all times.

This is the first time that such an experiment as this has been tried, and its results will be watched with considerable interest. The effect as one looks through the stage may be judged from the larger engraving.

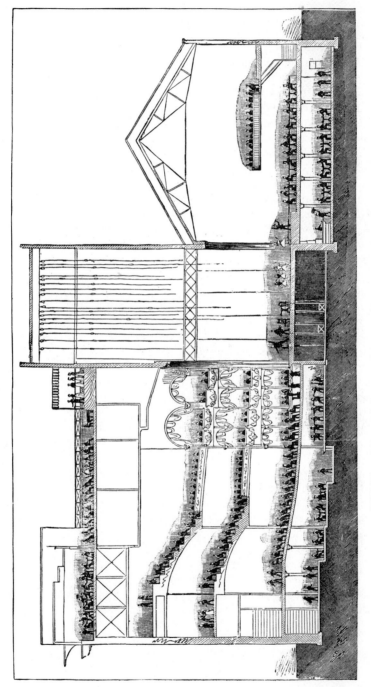

SECTIONAL VIEW SHOWING THE STAGE AND THE TWO AUDITORIUMS.

CURIO'S PIVOTED THEATER.

One of the most ingenious of the ancient theaters of which we have any record is that devised by Curio, which is described by Pliny. In the half century before Christ, a wealthy Roman citizen constructed a theater capable of holding eighty thousand persons. The stage of this theater was ornamented with three hundred and sixty columns, and between these columns there were in all three thousand statues. Curio not being able to do anything more magnificent, was, according to Pliny, obliged to substitute ingenuity for extravagance; he therefore constructed two large wooden theaters near each other, and they were so arranged that each could be revolved upon a pivot. In the morning plays were put upon the stages of each of the theaters, the latter being back to back. In the afternoon the theaters were all at once revolved so as to make them face each other, the people being carried with them. It was only necessary to connect the corners of the two theaters in order to have an amphitheater in which gladiatorial combats might be exhibited.

It is rather extraordinary that the Romans should have allowed themselves

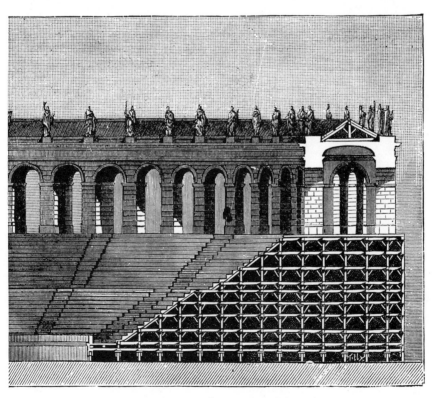

SECTION OF CURIO'S PIVOTED THEATER.

to be carried around in this unstable machine. The theater, of course, was only for temporary use, but during the last day of the celebration, Curio was obliged to change the order of his magnificent entertainments, since the pivots became strained and out of true. The amphitheater form was therefore preserved. The mode in which these theaters were constructed has occupied the attention of several learned persons. The architects in the first century before Christ were accustomed to build wooden theaters; the first stone one was built in Rome by Pompey. It will be seen that the transformation due to Curio's imagination might have been effected, as Pliny indicates, by a rotation around the pivots, P and Q, of the two great theaters, whose framework rested upon a series of small wheels movable on circular tracks. The stages, C and D, of the theaters were constructed of light framework, and were so arranged that they could be taken down and pushed back at C' and D', and thus allow the two theaters to revolve on their own axes so as to come face to face, while leaving between them only the space necessary for rotary motion. This space was then filled with light and movable pieces of framework, A and B, which formed on the ground floor vast doors for the entrance of the gladiators, and, in the story above, boxes for the magistrates.

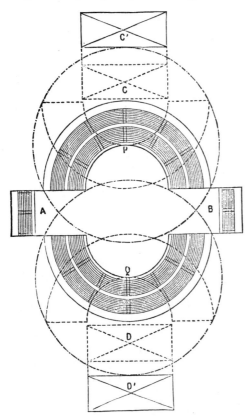

PLAN OF CURIO'S PIVOTED THEATER.

THE OLYMPIAN THEATER OF PALLADIO AT VICENZA.*

The oldest permanent theater in Europe, at least of those built since the time of the Romans, is the Olympian Theater at Vicenza, Italy, and it is the last of its race.   Before considering this curious theater it would, perhaps, be well to glance for a moment at the history of the theater in ancient and modern times.   In the old Greek Theatre the spectators were seated in a semicircle in front of a raised platform on which a fixed architectural screen was provided.   The action took place upon this stage.   The dramas of the Greeks and Romans were of the simplest kind, the dialogue being simple, rhythmical, and often intoned.   The amphitheater, in which the seats rose in tiers, could accommodate a large number of spectators.   A theater with a radius of three hundred feet could seat twenty thousand spectators.   The best counterparts of the Greek theater are some of the concert halls which were built specially for oratorios and concerts.   The Greeks fully understood that the facial expression of the actors was lost, the spectators being so far away from the scene of the action of the drama.   They attempted to overcome these difficulties by requiring the actors to wear masks with strongly marked features, and to increase their height they were provided with high-heeled shoes.   The opera glass in the modern theater has, of course, done away with all objections of this kind.

The modern theater is the result of the blending of the old circular theater of the Greeks with the rectangular theater (so-called) of the Middle Ages. The earliest mediæval theaters in Italy and Spain consisted of courtyards with balconies which were impressed into the service, and plays were often performed in churches ; but in France the climate was so bad that the tennis courts were used.   The trouble with the tennis court was that, owing to the difficulty of roofing a large open space, the room could be only forty or fifty feet wide, and only six hundred to one thousand persons could see and hear to advantage.   The accommodations had to be increased by tiers of boxes.   The conch-like arrangement of classical times was soon found to be unfit for a spoken dialogue, which cannot be well heard more than seventy-five or eighty feet away, or the expression of the actors' faces appreciated at a greater distance, so that the next improvement was the rounding off of the corners of the room and the multiplication of boxes, which were placed tier upon tier in the same manner as high office buildings are erected, to give increased accommodation, owing to the smallness and great value of some of our city blocks. In 1675 Fontana invented the horseshoe form of theater, which has not been departed from.   In opera houses and lyric theaters the curve is elongated into an ellipse with the major axis towards the stage.   In theaters for the spoken drama, where people must see and hear, the contrary process was necessary and the front boxes were brought near the stage.   The introduction of

---

* By Albert A. Hopkins.

painted movable scenery seems to have been due to Baldassare Peruzzi, who used it in 1508 in the production of "*La Calandra*," which was played before Leo X. Further improvements led to the necessity of a recessed stage with a framing like that of a picture. Such is in brief the development of the modern theater.

Palladio (1518–1580) was a native of Vicenza, a town in northern Italy, forty-two miles west of Venice. He was an architect of the first order, and it is difficult to mention any architect who exercised a greater influence on the men of his time as well as on those who succeeded him. He was an enthusiastic student of antiquity, and, fascinated by the stateliness and charm of the buildings of ancient Rome, he did not reflect that reproductions of these, even when they possessed great archæological accuracy, were often lifeless and unsuited to the uses of the sixteenth century. His writings and architectural work rendered it easy for those who came after him to reproduce buildings which were faultless in their details, but which were cramped, formal, and cold. The Certosa of Pavia would have been impossible in London, yet under the inspiration of Palladio, Sir Christopher Wren was enabled to construct in London the Cathedral of St. Paul, which would have done honor to the great Italian master himself.

Palladio died before the theater at Vicenza was completed, and it was finished, though not altogether after the original design, by his pupil and fellow-citizen, Scamozzi. It was an attempt to reproduce the classic theaters of Greece and Rome, and his friends assisted him by sending designs of antique buildings to help him. It consists of an auditorium under an awning in the form of a semi-ellipse, it not being possible, from the narrowness of the situation, to use a semicircle. Its greater diameter is ninety-seven and one-half feet, and its lesser as far as the stage is fifty-seven and one-half feet. Fourteen ranges of seats for the spectators follow the curve of the ellipse. At the summit of these receding steps, or seats, is a corridor of the Corinthian order, which, from the narrowness of the ground, could not be detached from the outer wall at all places. Palladio therefore filled up the nine center and the three external columnations, where the statues touch the external wall, with pieces of statuary. The orchestra is five feet below the seats. The scene, which is sixty feet broad, is an architectural composition of two orders of the Corinthian style superimposed, which are surmounted in turn with a light and well-proportioned attic. On the stylobate of the second story are placed statues, and the inter-columnations are enriched with niches and statues. The panels of the attic are ornamented with reliefs of the "Labors of Hercules," and the center panel over the largest of the three openings in the proscenium, which is arched, with a representation of an ancient hippodrome. Over the arch is the following inscription: "Virtvti ac Genio Olympicorvn Academia Theatrvm hoc a Fvndamentis Erexit Anno MDLXXXIIII. Palladio Archit."

In the lower order the middle interval has a high open arch, and the two others, on the side, have square openings through which are seen streets and

SCENE AT THE OLYMPIAN THEATER AT VICENZA.

squares of stately architecture, each ending in a triumphal arch.   The position
of the diverging avenues will be understood by reference to the plan.   The
magnificent palaces and private dwellings which are here portrayed furnish a
very effective setting for the plays which were performed in the theater.
Though the distance to the back of the theater is only forty feet, yet by skillful
and ingenious perspective and foreshortening it appears to be four hundred feet
distant.   For this skillful and ingenious conceit, which is unclassical in spirit,
we are indebted to Scamozzi.   The exterior of the theater is by no means com-
parable to its internal beauty.   It was built not at the expense of the government, but by some private Vicentine gentleman of the Olympic Academy.
The theater was completed in 1586, and was inaugurated by the performance
of the "*Œdipus Tyrannus*" of Sophocles.

The general lines of the interior of the theater are noble and calm.   The
theater looks as well on paper as in reality, for, like so many of Palladio's
buildings built of brick and stucco, which are now in a dilapidated condition,
it has an enduring shabbiness.   It must be said that in this remarkable building
Palladio conciliated the precepts of Vitruvius and the needs of a contempora-
neous society.   M. Eugène Müntz has expressed the conception of the theater
when he said that it was a "mirage of a Paolo Veronese in architecture," and
indeed, with its profusion of statues and niches and columns, it does resemble
the works of the great painter of Verona, who, in his great light-filled fres-
coes and canvases, crowds the space with monumental architecture, and fills the
buildings with the well-dressed courtiers of Venice, until the whole becomes a
gorgeous pageant.

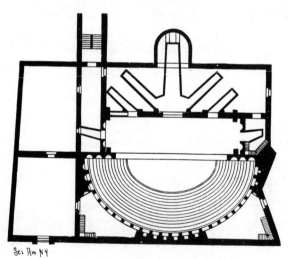

PLAN OF PALLADIO'S OLYMPIAN THEATER.

CHAPTER III.

STAGE EFFECTS.

The present chapter deals with the various effects which are liable to be called for in almost any opera or other dramatic production. It should be remembered that the effects of sunrise, moonlight, thunder, lightning, wind, rainbows, fires, etc., may be obtained in a great variety of ways, so that only an outline of some of the methods of producing the illusion can be given. Stage management is a constant study. Stage managers and stage machinists and property masters vie with one another in producing more and more realistic illusions. It is a curious fact that this business is largely a matter of invention, and it is little wonder that it is in the hands of exceptionally clever men.

SCENE PAINTING.

Scene painting is an art by itself. There is no other branch of painting like it, either in the variety of subjects embraced or in the methods employed. The scenic artist must be at home in landscape, marine, or architectural painting. He must be able to produce at any time the mountainous passes of Switzerland, the flat meadows of Holland, the palace of Versailles, or the Windsor Hotel. The method by which he works and many of the materials he employs are altogether different from those used by the ordinary oil or water-color painter. The scene painter works upon canvas. He first makes a pasteboard model of his scene and gives it to the stage carpenter or stage machinist, who builds the framework and secures the canvas to it. It is then ready for the "paint frame." This is a huge wooden affair hung up with ropes with counterweights attached. It is usually placed against the wall at the back or side of the stage, and has a windlass attached by which it may be raised or lowered. The artist works upon a bridge built in front of this frame, the paint bridge usually giving a passage between the two fly galleries. A paint bridge is illustrated in Chapter I. of the present division of this work. By hoisting or lowering the paint frame the artist is enabled to reach any part of the scene. He is provided with plenty of brushes, ranging from a heavy two-pound brush, such as is used by house painters, to a small sharp one used for drawing fine lines. In addition to these he has several whitewash brushes for laying in flat washes and skies. The colors are kept in buckets, tin cans, and earthenware vessels. His other requisites are a palette knife, plenty of twine, and sticks of charcoal. He is then ready to go to work. His first duty is to "prime" the scenes. This is done with a plain coat of white. Distemper color is used in scene painting. The colors are mixed with sizing, which is simply a weak solution of glue. The priming coat is laid on with a heavy whitewash brush. After the canvas is primed and dry, the artist is ready to draw. After the rough charcoal sketch is made, it is carefully gone over with an ink specially prepared for the purpose. The architectural work must be done with precision; regularity of outline and accuracy are absolutely essential. The perspective requires to be laid off with the greatest possible care, as the effect of many scenes depends almost entirely upon it. The next step is the laying in of the groundwork. The sky is, of course, the first point. This is done with whitewash brushes. The principal point is to get it on thickly, and here the great advantage of painting in distemper is made plain. The color dries very quickly, thus affording the artist a high rate of speed in working; and, secondly, the color dries precisely the same shade it had before being mixed. Scene painters of different nationalities have various methods of working, some using a great deal of color, others very little. Some idea of the rapidity of working can be obtained when it is stated that a scene painter of the English school has been known to paint a scene of twenty by thirty feet in less than four hours. Some of the colors used cost as much as $2.75 per pound. Indigo is used in very large quantities by scenic artists. Ten pounds of indigo are sometimes used in a single scene. A scenic painter, however, is not confined to colors in producing effects. A number of other materials are of great importance in this kind of painting. Gold and silver leaf are freely used for certain kinds of scenes, as well as foil papers and bronze powders. Jewels in the wall of the Eastern palace cannot be imitated with a sufficient degree of realism to stand the glare of the light, so jewels are made of zinc and set in the canvas; they are made of all colors; they are often covered with colored lacquers, or the painted surface is lacquered. In ice scenes mica powders are used in large quantities to produce the glitter and sparkle. Nearly every scene painter has a large collection of stencils which are very useful for producing architectural decorations. The last thing the scene painter does before the introduction of a new play is to have his scenes set upon the stage at night in order that the lighting of them can be arranged. The artist sits in the center of the auditorium and minutely observes every nook and corner of the scene under the glare of the gas or electric light. Here a light is turned up and there one is lowered until the proper effect is obtained. The gas man or electrician takes careful note of his directions, and the stage manager oversees everything.

SUNRISE EFFECT.

The sunrise effect is obtained in several ways. A semicircular screen is placed across the stage and forms the background, as for mountains. Upon a platform immediately behind the center of the stage is placed an arc projector that is maneuvered by hand, and throws a luminous disk upon the canvas of the screen. Upon the stage are suspended colored incandescent border lights. In other suitable places there are arranged groups of lamps provided with reflectors of special form. These lamps may be introduced successively into the circuit. Colored gelatine plates may be slid over the reflectors so as to give the light the color desired. Our engravings show the various systems of lighting employed, showing the cords, pulleys, and other devices for turning the gelatine shades around or raising them so as to give the desired effect. The electrician first puts into the circuit the group of lamps that produce the blue light, and at the same time turns the blue shades over the lamps. At a given signal the operator pulls the rope so as to bring the red colored shades in front of the lamps. When the signal is given to him, the operator in charge of the arc lamp places a red glass in front of the lenses of the projector and switches the current on to the lamp. The resistances in the circuit of the various incandescent lamps are successively withdrawn so as to heighten the red light of the rising sun. In some theaters colored incandescent lamps are used, as at the Metropolitan Opera House, New York City, as described in Chapter I. of the present division of this work. This system is, of course, preferable in many ways.

To return to the sun-rising effect: after the sun has risen above the mountains the red light is diminished, the red glass placed before the aperture of the projector is gradually removed, and the color screens are removed from in front of the lamps. Motion is given to the sun by means of an inclined plane up which the arc lamp is carried by means of a winch which is slowly manipulated by the assistant.

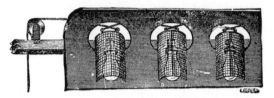

COLOR SCREEN CHANGING.

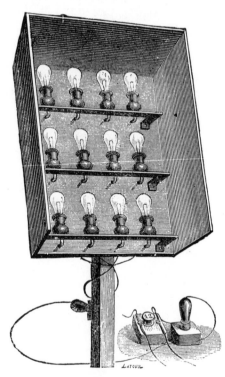

COLOR SCREEN CHANGING.   BUNCH OR SIDE LIGHTS.

SUNRISE EFFECT.

SUN EFFECT.

The stage effect which we are about to describe is produced by the mechanism which was formerly in use in the Metropolitan Opera House, New York City. The electrical sun was a big glass disk with an arc lamp of two thousand candle-power behind it. It showed through a hole cut in a drop curtain, and was set firmly in a frame covered with colored gauze to represent the various hues which the sun imparts to the atmosphere, and the colors it projects upon the clouds, during ascension and declination. It is very effective in many operas, as in "The Prophet" and "Tannhauser."

CHANGE FROM DAY TO NIGHT.

One of the most beautiful effects produced upon the stage is the change from day to night or from night to day, especially the former. This is accomplished in various ways, as the following: To produce the proper effect the back drop is made nearly double the height of the usual scene; the upper half is painted to represent a sunset sky, and the lower half to represent moonlight. It is hung so that the upper half alone is visible. The scenery of the distance is then painted upon a separate piece, which is profiled—that is, cut irregularly —to represent trees, mountains, or houses. This piece is placed immediately in front of the sky drop. A few feet further in front is held what is known as a cut gauze drop. This has sides and a top of canvas painted as the case requires, while the center is filled with fine gauze which lends an aërial effect to the distance. Red lights are employed to give a soft sunset glow to the scene. At the proper moment the back drop is slowly and steadily raised. While the red lights are slowly dimmed, the green lights are slowly turned on. The moon effect is obtained in different ways, as we will shortly describe. The moon is sometimes made in the night-half of the sky drop and rises with it. When it rises above the distant horizon, the green lights are turned on to their full power.

STARS.

The star which we illustrate consists of a single sixteen candle-power incandescent lamp fixed to a metal frame set in a drop curtain; only the star itself, with a covering of red gelatine tinctured with blue, showing through.

STAR.

MOON EFFECTS.

There is hardly any illusion on the stage which is seen as often as the moonlight effect, and there is nothing which can be as well counterfeited on the stage as moonlight scenery. The artist usually begins his task by painting a moonlight scene; by daylight such a scene is ghastly, being painted in cold grays and greens, in which Prussian blue and burnt umber play an important part, and the lights are put in with white, slightly tinged with emerald green. The strong moonlight of the foreground is produced by a calcium light thrown through a green glass. A fainter light upon the scenery at the back of the stage is obtained from what are called " green mediums "—lamps with green shades. They are placed upon the stage just in front of the main scene, and are " masked in " by scenery. A row of them is often suspended from the flies in order to light the top of the scenes. In this case they are hidden from view by what are called the sky borders; thus a soft green light is given to the entire stage without the source of it being visible. The position of the moon being determined upon, immediately under it a number of small irregular holes are cut in the drop, beginning at the horizon. These are covered on the back with muslin, and are painted over on the front to match the rest of the scene. Behind these holes is placed an endless towel about eight feet in height, running around rollers at the top and bottom; the lower roller has a crank by which the towel is turned. In the towel are cut a number of holes similar to those cut in the drop. A strong gas burner is placed between the two sides of the towel. When the crank is turned, the flashing of the light through the passing holes in the towel and the stationary ones in the drop scene produces a fine effect. Instead of a towel a large tin cylinder may be used. Other interesting moon effects are described in the chapter entitled " A Trip to the Moon," in the present work.

We now come to the moon proper, which is produced in a number of ways. The form which we illustrate is one in use in the Metropolitan Opera House, New York City. It is about eighteen inches in diameter, and is made of porcelain or milk glass and is oval in form. Within are six incandescent lamps of sixteen candle-power, connected with a rheostat.

It is very effective in many operas, as in "Tannhauser." The moon is moved by means of a batten, a thin piece of wood let down from above, the course being marked for the operator

ELECTRIC
MOON.

by the apparent, though exaggerated, movements of the moon as we see them in an orrery. The mimic sun moves behind the drop, but the moon moves before it, and therefore to keep up the illusion the wires it draws after it must be colored the same as the drop.

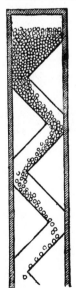

RAIN MACHINE.

RAIN EFFECT.

The rain machine is usually placed high up in the flies. A hollow wooden cylinder five feet in circumference and four feet in length is provided. Upon the inside are placed rows of small wooden teeth. A quantity of dried peas are placed in the cylinder, and a belt is run around one end of it and down to the prompter's desk. By turning these cylinders the peas run down between the teeth, and the noise produced by them makes a good imitation of rain falling upon a roof. Traveling companies often have to go to small theaters where such luxuries as "rain machines" are unknown. A sufficiently good substitute is, however, easily obtained. A sheet of heavy brown paper is pasted over a child's hoop and a handful of bird shot is placed upon the paper. The hoop is tipped from side to side, and the shot rolls around the paper, producing a fairly good rain effect. Our engraving shows a French form of rain machine. It consists of a wooden box seven or eight feet long, divided into compartments, as shown in our engraving, by oblique pieces of tin which transform the interior into a tortuous passage for the dried peas.   The quantity of peas is regulated at the top, and the violence of the drops of rain depends upon the quantity of peas and the inclination of the box.

RAINBOW EFFECT.

In the last scene of "Rheingold" the gods enter Walhalla over the rainbow bridge.   The rainbow is a magnificent stage illusion, and is produced as follows: The prisms are fastened one above the other in front of an electri-

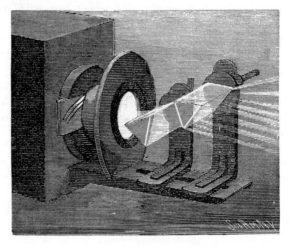

RAINBOW EFFECT.

cal projector.   The light from it passing through the prisms produces the various colors of the prismatic spectacle due to the influence of the raindrops. As in nature, there appear to be two arches, the primary and the secondary.

WIND EFFECT.

Wind is very useful in heightening the effect of stage storms, especially in melodramas.   Where the effect is well done the pitiless blast is very realistic. The wind machine is portable, and may be placed anywhere the property master wishes.   The wind machine is made in various ways, of which the following is one: A heavy frame is made in which to set a cylinder provided with paddles, and resembling very much the stern-wheels seen on Ohio River towboats.

Across the top of the cylinder is stretched as tight as possible a piece of heavy gros-grain silk, but canvas is often substituted instead. The rapid passage of the paddles over the surface of the silk or canvas produces the noise of the

wind. Often traveling companies are in theaters where there is no wind machine. In this case one of the stage hands selects a heavy piece of flexible hose and whirls it around his head. The extraction of wind from the hose is not entirely satisfactory, however.

Our engraving shows a French form of machine for imitating the noise of the wind. It consists of a cylinder mounted on an axle. The staves are triangular in shape, and end in a sharp point. Instead of running these staves over silk or canvas, cords are substituted. The cords are secured below, so that they can be tightened so as to cut into the staves.

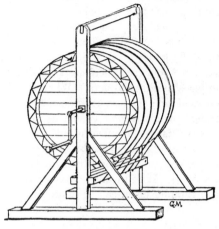

WIND-PRODUCING MACHINE.

The cylinder is turned by a crank, and by turning it rapidly the friction of the cord produces a good representation of wind.

THUNDER EFFECT.

The thunder and lightning effect is somewhat complicated, especially the thunder, which may be regarded as the result of the combination of a number of effects. First a large piece of sheet iron is shaken, which produces an imitation of sharp, rattling thunder. This fails to give the dull roar, a reverbera-

RUMBLE CART.

tion which is usually heard in storms. To produce this effect a heavy box frame is made, and over it is tightly drawn a calf skin. Upon this the stage hand operates with a stick, one end of which is padded and covered with chamois skin. This is called the thunder drum, and when accompanied with a flash of lightning produced with the aid of a magnesium flash torch renders the illusion very realistic. Often two thunder drums are used at the same time. Then the "rumble cart" is also used. The rumble cart is a box filled with some heavy material, and mounted upon irregularly shaped wheels.

Our engraving shows a rumble cart as used in the Paris Opera House. With this a little wind is added from the wind machine, and the rain effect is sometimes worked simultaneously. The result of this complicated effect is very good, and, of course, the effect may be varied as the stage manager may think proper for the opera.

In large opera houses a more complicated system is employed than those which we have just described. It is usually placed against the wall of the third fly gallery. It consists of a kind of cabinet with five or six slanting shelves. On each shelf are kept a half dozen cannon balls which are retained in place by hinged doors. When the signal is given, the stage hands open the doors of one or more compartments, and the balls drop down into a zinc-lined trough, which is some twenty feet long. The trough being built with inequalities of surface, the effect is enhanced. At the end of the trough the balls drop through the flooring to the gallery below by means of special slants. Arrangements are provided by which the balls can be stopped before they pass through the floor. It will readily be seen that by regulating the number of balls almost any thunder effect can be produced.

LIGHTNING.

Lightning is produced in a number of ways, of which the following is an example. A metal box having a large opening in the top is provided. At the bottom is placed an alcohol lamp having a wide-spreading flame. Immediately above the flame is a shelf or partition punched with fine holes. This is, of

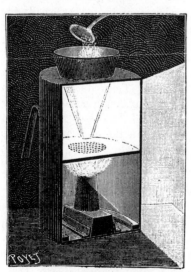

course, heated very hot by the flame. The mixture which is used to give the effect of lightning consists of three parts of magnesium powder and one part of potassium chlorate. This is poured upon the heated grill, through the top of the metal box. The sudden combustion of the composition produces very vivid flashes of lightning. A similar device has long been used by photographers for taking instantaneous photographs in dark places or at night.

Another method of producing lightning flashes is to secure two large files to an electric circuit. The files, when they are rubbed over each other, produce a series of brilliant flashes.

The magnesium flash pistol, which we show in our engraving, is very useful for

APPARATUS FOR PRODUCING LIGHTNING.   producing lightning flashes. It consists of a barrel which is slotted. The barrel is filled with asbestos which is soaked in alcohol. When the lightning effect is to be used the alcohol is lighted and magnesium powder is projected into it by means of the blower on the top of

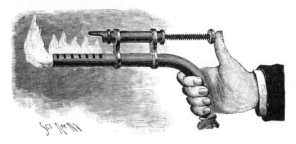

THE MAGNESIUM FLASH PISTOL.

the pistol. It is worked with the thumb. When a thunderbolt is to strike an object, a wire is run from the flies to the object which is to be struck. A rider runs on the wire. The rider consists of a section of iron pipe. Around it is secured asbestos by means of wire. The asbestos is soaked with alcohol, and is lighted just at the instant when it is to be projected upon the object.

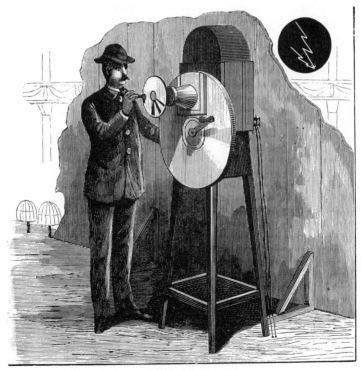

LIGHTNING PROJECTOR.

It is usually held by a string, which is cut.   It rushes flaming through the air, and produces the effect of a ball of fire striking the object.

Our engraving illustrates still another method of producing lightning.   It consists of an electric projecting lantern with attachments for giving the effect. The lightning and the clouds are scratched and painted on small pieces of glass. Devices are provided for rotating them so that they produce the effect of clouds rolling across an apparently immense expanse of sky, as the operator revolves the disks one over the other, and the forked lightning seems to shoot across the heavens.

SNOW EFFECT.

The effect of snow is obtained in a number of ways.   Sometimes pieces of paper, linen, or white kid are thrown from one of the intermediate bridges, if the theater is provided with them.   If well done the effect is very pleasing.   The flakes of snow are usually illuminated by the electric light.   It is often necessary to have the actors appear with traces of snow upon them. One way of doing this is to sprinkle them with soapsuds by means of a birch broom before they appear upon the scene.   Of course, the soapsuds disappear in a few moments, corresponding to the melting of the snow.   In the case of rich costumes it is impossible to use soapsuds, so that bone shavings or ground corn are used instead.   This forms a light coating which resembles snow.   It adheres to the hair, the shoulders, and the creases in the clothing, and produces no ill effects upon the costume.

WAVE EFFECT.

An ocean of heaving waters is usually made as follows: Each wave is cut out separately.   The first row is set up at a distance of three or four feet between each billow, and the second row is set so as to show in the openings left by the first; small boys are usually employed to furnish the motive power.   The waves are rocked back and forth, not from side to side, and the effect is very good.   The noise of the surf upon the beach is obtained by allowing two or three ounces of bird shot to roll around in a box of light wood lined with tin. This is a variation of the rain machine we have already referred to.

CRASH EFFECT.

The noise on the stage is produced by what is called the crash machine, which is one of the oldest implements of imitation on the stage.   It is similar to the wind machine in construction.   It consists of a wheel with paddles set at an angle of about forty-five degrees. Upon the top of the wheel one end of a stout piece of wood is placed down by fastening the other end to a portion of the framework. When the wheel is turned, the slats passing under the stationary piece produce a rattling crash. The principle of the machine is illustrated by a boy running along a picket fence with a stick, allowing it to slip from picket to picket. In many theaters a gigantic rattle is used in place of a machine of this kind; it is more portable.

FIRE AND SMOKE EFFECTS.

Conflagrations are produced in a number of ways, and if proper precautions are taken, they are perfectly safe. Usually the buildings which are to be destroyed by fire are constructed of separate pieces of stage carpentry, through which the painted canvas is attached. They are raised and lowered by means of hinges, slides, cords, and pulleys, so as to give the effect of tumbling down. The fire proper consists of chemical red fire and powdered lycopodium used separately, the former to give a red glow and the latter to represent flames. Variously colored electric lights and small pieces of fireworks simulate the leaping of the sparks. In some cases the shutters on the houses appear to burn off and fall down upon the stage; this is accomplished as follows: They are secured to the scene with a preparation called "quick match." This is made of powder, alcohol, and a lamp wick. The window frames and sashes are made of sheet iron. They are covered with oakum soaked in alcohol or naphtha. These sashes and frames are not fastened to the canvas scene at all, but are placed a short distance behind it upon platforms. The quickest possible touch of flame ignites the oakum, and in a moment the fire runs around the sash, and nothing is apparently left but the blackened and charred wood. Steam is used to represent the smoke, and one method of using it is described below. An occasional crash, followed by the ignition of a little powder, produces a sudden puff of smoke which gives the spectator the idea of a fall of a rafter.

Apparatus for producing the smoke of a conflagration is more complicated than that for producing lightning. Steam is largely used for producing smoke, and is conducted to a place where the smoke is to appear, by means of rubber hose; but this is apt to cause considerable noise when it escapes into the air. This difficulty has been surmounted in at least one stag eillusion which we illustrate, this being the "Magian," the opera of Massenet. It was particularly necessary in the case to have the smoke produced as noiselessly as possible, because the orchestral music at the moment of the fire is relatively soft and low. The difficulty was surmounted as follows: The steam, generated by a boiler in the Paris Opera House, was led to special devices shown in our engraving, the steam being admitted to triangular boxes at the apex opposite the base of the triangle. The boxes at the point of attachment with the steam pipe have a considerable thickness, which gradually diminishes as the base of the triangle is approached, so that the steam, which is distributed throughout the whole extent of the box, escapes without any noise through a narrow

APPARATUS FOR IMITATING THE SMOKE OF A CONFLAGRATION ON THE STAGE OF A THEATER.

orifice between the two faces of the apparatus.   In the interior of the boxes there are pieces of felt, the principal object of which is to absorb the drops

of water which are carried along mechanically or which may condense.   The advantage of this arrangement is that it permits of the disengagement of the steam everywhere where it is necessary.   The boxes are easily manipulated, and hooks fastened to them permit of their being attached to the scenery with ease.   After a simple coupling pipe has been connected with a steam pipe, the apparatus is ready to operate.   In the opera we have referred to, twenty-nine double boxes are employed; seventeen are distributed over the stage at different points, and nearly up to the pipe of the soffit curtains.   The twelve others are beneath the stage, and the orifices through which the steam escapes are flush with the floor.

The realistic fire clouds and flame in the last act of " The

Prophet," when the Prophet, learning that he is betrayed, orders the fire of the palace of Münster, are done by concentrating the arc light upon colored gelatine; usually, first yellow for the fumes, then yellow and white, then yellow and red, red and white, and red and black. The sandstorm in the last act of the "Queen of Sheba" is done in yellow and black and pink gelatine before the light, and the rain by parallel scratches on a black surface, the arc light being dimmed and brightened alternately, and the glass turned this way and that, so that the parallelism of the drops shall follow a supposed changing of the direction of the wind.

GRADUAL TRANSFORMATIONS.

One of the greatest triumphs of Wagner's scenic art is his method of scene shifting, which is carried almost to perfection. He was very much opposed to sudden changes of scenes, which are so frequent in Shakespearian plays, as he was desirous of avoiding everything which broke the continuity of the dramatic action. In the greater part of his operas he lets a single scene suffice for the entire act. Once in a great while he was obliged to provide for a shifting of a scene during an act, but in "Rheingold" the curtain remains, or should remain, raised during the whole of the performance. These changes are usually accomplished in plain sight of the audience, or else the setting of the new scene is hidden behind clouds. These effects are accomplished by means of successive gauze curtains which are raised and lowered, and by the clever use of light which is gradually diminished until almost total darkness reigns. The effect is largely enhanced by the orchestra, which symbolizes the changes which are taking place. The two best examples of this perfection of scene shifting are probably those in "Parsifal," when the magic garden changes to the sanctuary of the Holy Grail; and the other effect is in the third act of "Götterdämmerung," when the warriors place the dead Siegfried upon the bier and carry the body up the rocky path, while the orchestra is playing the funeral march of unearthly beauty. As the procession gradually disappears, mists rise from the Rhine. The mist gradually thickens into fog, then clouds rise upward, hiding the whole scene from view. Then the clouds rise and dissipate into mists which finally disclose the moonlit hall of the Gibichungen. The effects are produced by steam and a series of gauze curtains. The clouds really serve as a screen to prevent the scene shifters being viewed by the audience. A satisfactory effect can only be obtained when every detail is carried out with the greatest care. The superiority of this method over the conventional curtain is apparent.

Sometimes the gauze curtains are not dropped from the flies, but are run across from the side. They are "profiled," or, in other words, they are irregular in shape, so that they help to produce the effect without any noticeable line of demarcation between the two halves of the curtain. The steam curtain is often very effective, especially in Wagnerian operas. The steam is admitted through a perforated steam pipe in a sink cut, the floor being perforated.   As the steam curtain is in a straight line, the effect is apt to be a little formal.

BATTLE SCENES.

Battle scenes are particularly effective upon the stage when they are well produced, and in the midst of a desperate battle a shell is seen to fall and burst, carrying death and destruction in its wake.   Our engraving shows the method of obtaining this result. A *papier maché* shell is formed of separate pieces glued together.   This contains the quantity of powder sufficient to separate the pieces and produce the bursting.   In the powder there is an electric

BOMB EXPLOSION EFFECT.

primer which is ignited by a current.   The primer is connected by wires which go back of the scene.   At one of the sides of the stage, out of sight of the spectator, there is a charge which is also ignited by electricity at the same time that the bomb is exploded.   At the proper moment a man throws the shell and touches the button, the bomb bursts, and the spectators, hearing the loud report of the cannon at the same instant, imagine that the harmless paper bomb is the cause of the formidable explosion.

THEATRICAL FIREARMS.

The accidents on the stage caused by firearms have been many and numerous. In melodramas, after great battles, the auditorium becomes filled with dense smoke and a peculiarly disagreeable odor of burnt powder; and, owing to the great precautions which are necessary to prevent danger of fire, the illusion is seriously injured. On account of these drawbacks, a French dramatic author and pyrotechnist, M. Philippi, endeavored to produce a successful imitation of the effects of firing guns, that is to say, the noise, fire, and smoke, while at the same time avoiding the dangers and annoyances that have already been pointed out. The charge consists of a small quantity of fulminate prepared so as to give a red fire and a light smoke which quickly clears away, leaving no disagreeable odor, and not affecting the throat. The preparation is held in a cavity formed in a small cork which is introduced into the extremity

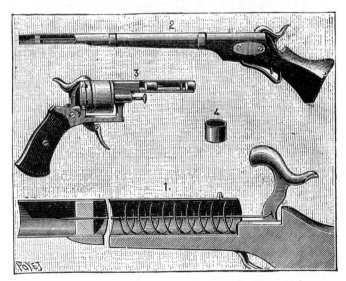

THEATRICAL GUNS AND PISTOLS.

of the gun barrel. The firing pin passes through the barrel, as shown in Fig. 1 in our first engraving, causing the charge to explode through a simple blow. By the very simple contrivance of the spring, as shown in Fig. 1, it is possible to fit almost any gun, wooden or otherwise, which the stage director may wish to use.

Our second engraving represents a mitrailleuse formed by the juxtaposition of a number of short barrels of thin copper arranged in the same manner as in the guns described.

The firing pins are left to the action of the spiral springs, when the hooks, *a*, in which they terminate, are driven from the catches by means of slider, *c*, which moves along a rod, placed back of the barrels, to which it is affixed by a screw, in order to prevent its acting while the apparatus is being carried. A movable bar, *m*, prevents the springs from being set free while the charging is being done, and after they have been set. In order to manipulate, it is only necessary to cause the slider to move along the rod. Firing by platoons is imitated with great exactness. As soon as the cork makes its exit from the barrel, it is thoroughly pulverized, and the discharges received at the end of the muzzle cause no inconvenience.

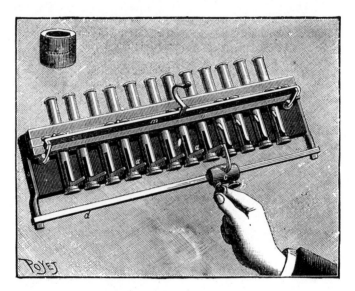

THEATRICAL MITRAILLEUSE.

THE IMITATION OF ODORS.

The imitation of odors upon the stage is not very often attempted. In some plays where a dinner is in progress, more realism is given by introducing such things as a French coffee machine. The penetrating odor of the coffee is soon experienced by the audience, and it adds considerably to the effect. An English impresario adopted a rather novel plan of imitating the salt odor of the ocean for a marine scene. He took a large number of old salt-herring casks and disposed them in the flies and behind the orchestra. There is little doubt that they produced the desired effect, as the persistence of the perfume of this delicacy is well known.

CHAPTER IV.

THEATER SECRETS.

In the present chapter the subject of theater secrets will be taken up, and it will treat of traps, complicated stage settings, properties, and the means of obtaining elaborate effects.

TRAPS.

The trap is one of the oldest and most primitive means of producing stage illusions, and it is in use to-day in most theaters and opera houses. The principle is very simple, and will be understood by reference to the engraving. The actor, singer, or devil who is to make his sudden appearance upon the stage stands on a platform which is hoisted to the stage level by means of winches turned by the stage hands.

We also show another variety of trap which is much used in operatic and ballet performances; it consists of an inclined plane up which the actor or *danseuse* is carried, the inclined plane itself being masked by scenery. The elaborate system of traps used in the "Asphaleia" stage has already been described in Chapter II.

TRAP IN THE STAGE.

FONTANA DESCENDS INTO THE SEA.

THE SWAN IN "LOHENGRIN."

The swan and the swan boat in "Lohengrin" are most interesting properties.   The apparatus which we illustrate is that used at the Metropolitan
Opera House, New York City, and is the result of many experiments.   To
understand the action of the Lohengrin swan it will first be necessary to
describe the setting of the stage.   At the back is a river drop; next come
set water rows, gradating in height to the level of the bank, giving the
effect of water rushes and reeds, and so set that the swan and boat, in passing
through, are enabled to describe a graceful curve.   The foreground is a built-
up bank the width of the scene.   Between the river drop and the first set
water row there is space enough for the miniature figures of Lohengrin and
the swan to pass across the stage before the real Lohengrin and the swan come
into view.   The drop and the set water rows—everything, in fact—give the
idea of the sluggish Scheldt winding in through the weedy meadows.   In
order to produce the effect, two entirely distinct trucks are used—one for the
first act, when Lohengrin and his swan wind their way among the reeds; and
one for the last act, when the swan disappears, and the lost brother of Elsa
takes its place.   The problem which confronted the property master in de-
signing the first swan and car, that is to say, the one which was to bring
Lohengrin, was to devise a method of propelling the truck which carried

the swan and the car so that it could be run in a curved direction, adding greatly to the naturalness of the illusion, and rendering the truck capable of

FIRST SWAN AND CAR IN "LOHENGRIN."

being turned in a short space. A three-wheeled truck was built, the top of which was concealed by draperies painted to match the water rows themselves. The truck is propelled by two men seated within it, who shove the truck along

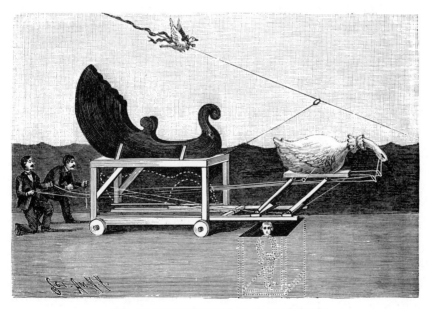

THE DISAPPEARING SWAN IN "LOHENGRIN."

by shuffling with their feet on the floor. The first man steers by means of a handle bar which is secured to the vertical rod which carries the front wheel. The swan is fastened to this vertical bar, so that when the direction of the steering wheel is changed the swan also changes its direction. The neck of the swan is built around a steel spring, and the wings are actuated by levers and strings. The second man has nothing to do with steering the car and the swan. His duties, besides propelling the car, consist in inclining the head of the swan and operating the wings. This is accomplished by means of lines which are invisible to the audience. Lohengrin, on reaching the steps at the bridge, in front, gets out of the boat or car, and sings his farewell song. The swan then takes his departure, drawing away the car.

Now, in the last act an entirely different mechanism is employed, although the change is not perceptible to the audience. In this case it is not necessary for the swan to take a sinuous course, and it proceeds in a straight line across the stage. In this arrangement a truck is mounted on four wheels and is pushed by the men; but in order to transform the swan into Elsa's brother, it is necessary to resort to an entirely different system. The swan, instead of being supported by a couple of rods, is supported on a parallel which is hinged; it is normally held in position by means of cords, so that it shows above the set rows and the bank of the river. When the time has arrived for the transformation to be made, a man at the rear of the truck lets go of the cords which hold the swan in position; the parallel immediately drops, and is drawn back into the truck, carrying the swan with it. At the same instant Elsa's brother is raised by a trap which places him in precisely the same position as that occupied by the swan. Then a clockwork dove descends on a wire, and as the dove drops behind the set piece it takes the place of the swan. Lohengrin steps into the boat, and the dove carries it off from the stage. The changes are so remarkable that the Lohengrin swan must be regarded as one of the most successful effects obtained in Grand Opera.

THE FLOATING RHINE DAUGHTERS IN "RHEINGOLD."

When the curtain rises on the opera of "Rheingold," which is the prelude to the music drama of the "Ring of the Nibelung," the scene represents the bed of the Rhine. In the center rises a high rock which supports the "Rheingold," a great nugget of gold that glimmers on the summit of the rock. The three Rhine daughters, Woglinda, Wellgunda, Flosshilda, suddenly appear upon the scene, swimming with graceful movements about the rock which supports the Rheingold. It may be asked how it is possible for the Rhine daughters to float in space while they sing. A reference to our engraving will explain the mystery.

Each of the singers is supported upon a cradle which is secured to a four-wheeled car by an upright post strongly braced. Each of the cars is pushed around by two attendants, while a third sits in front and steers. They are hidden from view by low scenes which effectually conceal them. We believe that in some opera houses regular tracks have been provided upon which to run them.

At the Metropolitan Opera House, during the German opera season of Mr. Damrosch, in the spring of 1897, an entirely different device was used. The Rhine daughters were suspended from steel cables by means of trolleys. They

THE FLOATING RHINE DAUGHTERS IN THE OPERA "RHEINGOLD."

were drawn back and forth by means of wire ropes which ran to the sides of the stage. Ropes were also run down to the level of the stage, and they were swayed back and forth by men who were hidden from view of the audience by the set rows which masked the lower part of the stage. The arrangement was considered to be very satisfactory.

THE "SUN ROBE."

The illusion which we are about to describe is employed in the " Peau d'Ane " for producing the fairy robes in the story—the color of the sun, the color of the moon, and the color of the sky—required by the play. In the midst of a brilliantly illuminated procession come two porters carrying a large chest by means of handles at the end. Having reached the royal throne they place the chest on the floor and raise the cover. There is immediately seen a fabric the color of the sun, a luminous golden yellow. Afterwards two other porters come with a similar chest, which, when opened, exhibits a bluish-white phosphorescent fabric. The third chest contains a robe of a celestial blue. This robe is also luminous. The fabrics are moved by the porters to make them sparkle. The secret of the illusion is that the bottom of each of these chests is capable of being opened over a trap, and by means of an electric lamp the electric light is directed upon a light and transparent fabric so that it really seems to be on fire. A yellow light suffuses the fabric of the same color and incorporates itself with it. After the cover has been shut down upon the stage, the bottom is closed from beneath, the light is extinguished, the trap is shut

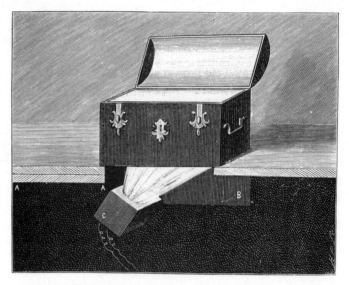

THE SUN ROBE IN THE FAIRY SCENE OF THE "PEAU D'ANE."

up, and the chest is carried away by the porters. The same is done with a slightly bluish-white fabric and a white light, for the moon-colored fabric; and then with blue tarleton and a light with a bluish tinge for the sky-colored fabric.

THE SHIP ON THE STAGE.

An opera or ballet which requires a ship taxes the powers of the stage machinist and the property master to the utmost. The ship which we illustrate was made for the ballet called the "Tempest," at the Paris Opera House, and is superior to most of the ships in the "Corsair" and "L'Africaine." The vessel, starting from the back of the stage, advances majestically, making a graceful curve, and stops in front of the prompter's box. Our illustrations give detailed views of the vessel and the setting of the scenery. The sea is represented by four parallel set rows, the location of which is indicated in our second engraving.

The ship is carried by wheels that roll over the floor of the stage, and is guided in its motion by two grooved bronze wheels, and by a rail formed of a simple reversed T-iron which is bolted to the floor. As the ship advances, the set water rows open in the center to allow it to pass. As the vessel itself is covered up to the water line with painted canvas imitating the sea, it has the appearance of cleaving the wave. When the vessel reaches the first of the

THE SHIP AS SEEN FROM THE STAGE.

water rows the others spread out and increase the extent of the sea. The three strips of water in the rear rise slightly. The shifting of the inclined piece at the front is effected by simply pulling up the carpet which covers it, and

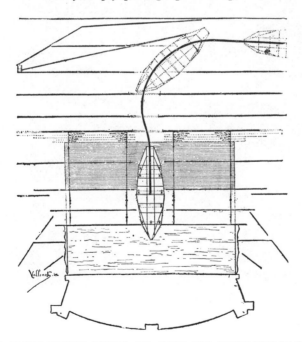

SETTING OF THE SCENERY BEFORE AND AFTER THE APPEARANCE OF THE SHIP.

SHIP OF THE "TEMPEST" IN PROCESS OF CONSTRUCTION.

which enters the groove in the floor in front of the prompter's box. At this
moment the entire stage seems to be in motion, and the effect is very striking.

We now come to the details of the construction of the ship. Our engraving
shows the boat while it was being built. The visible hull of the ship was placed
upon a large and very strong wooden framework formed of twenty-six trusses.
In the center there are two longitudinal trusses about three feet in height and
twenty-five feet in length, upon which are assembled perpendicularly seven other
trusses.   In the interior there are six transverse pieces held by stirrup bolts, and
at the end of each of these is fixed a thirteen-inch iron wheel.   The entire
structure rolls upon these twelve wheels.   There are two bronze wheels which
we have already referred to.   In the rear there are two vertical trusses, sixteen
feet in height, which are joined by ties and descend to the bottom of the frame,
to which they are bolted.   They constitute the skeleton of the immense stern

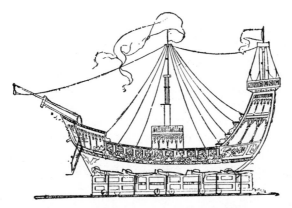

SHIP OF THE NEW BALLET, "THE TEMPEST."

of the vessel. The skeleton of the prow is formed of a vertical truss which is
bolted to the frame.   The rest of the construction of the ship will be readily
understood by reference to the engraving. The large mast consists of a vertical
tube, ten feet high, which is set into the center of the frame, and in the interior of which slides a wooden spar which is capable of being drawn out for
the final apotheosis. The mast carries three foot-boards, and a platform for the
reception of "supers."   It is actuated by a windlass placed upon the frame.
Panels made of canvas, painted, represent the hull; there are nine on each
side; above are placed those that cover the prow and the stern.   The bowsprit
is in two parts, one sliding into the other; the front portion is at first pulled
back in order to hide the vessel entirely in the side scenes.   It begins to make
its appearance before the vessel itself gets under way. Silken cordage connects
the mast, bowsprit, etc. On each side of the vessel there are bolted five iron
frames covered with canvas which reach the level of the water line, as shown
in the above engraving.   Upon these stand the "supers" who represent
the naiads that are supposed to draw the ship from the beach. At the bow

there is fixed a frame which supports a *danseuse* representing the living prow of the vessel. The boat is drawn to the middle of the stage by a cable attached to its right side, passing around a windlass placed in the side scenes to the left. It is at the same time pushed by stage hands placed in the interior of the framework. The trucks or chariots which support the boat are entirely covered with painted canvas resembling water. As the vessel, freighted with harmoniously grouped spirits and naiads, with fairies and graceful genii apparently swimming about it, sails in upon the stage, puts about and advances, and is carried along by the waves to the front of the stage, the effect is really beautiful, and does great credit to the stage machinist's art.

MISCELLANEOUS STAGE EFFECTS.

A rather curious illusion occurs in "Don Juan." The monument of the Gubernator bears the inscription, "Here revenge awaits the murderer." The moment that Don Juan appears in front of the monument, one of the stage hands removes a strip of some opaque substance from behind the transparent inscription, which now appears in brilliant letters on the base of the monument; the letters being lighted by lamps behind the statue.

In ballets the dancers are frequently represented as floating in the air. This movement may be produced by means of a common sea-saw. In aërial

THE GRAVEYARD SCENE IN THE OPERA "DON JUAN."

THE APPARITIONS IN THE OPERA OF "FREISCHÜTZ."

THE ENCHANTED BOOK IN THE OPERA "HANS HEILIG."

21

ballets and in the appearances of angels, etc., special devices are provided in up-to-date theatres, the mechanism usually being in the form of a trolley.

The army of demons and ghosts which pass over the stage in the "Frei-schütz" manage in various ways; in some cases a movable scene is used, and in others the uncanny creatures are painted upon a canvas roll and are projected, by means of a powerful light, upon a scene representing clouds. Hissing, snapping, screeching, and other hideous noises are produced by means of whips, clappers, whistles, rattles, and other like devices behind the scenes.

THE FLOATING WILLIS (BALLET.)

The enchanted book in the opera "Hans Heilig" is operated by means of a black thread which is manipulated by an attendant behind the scenes, as shown in our engraving.

The palm tree in the "Queen of Sheba," which bends in the sirocco, is caused to sway in the same way, by means of a black line which runs back of the stage. The branches of the tree are mounted on steel springs.

THE DESTRUCTION OF THE TEMPLE OF DAGON.

In the production of Grand Opera it is frequently necessary to represent the wholesale destruction of a building or city. This is managed in various ways, as in the destruction of the Temple of Dagon in the third act of "Samson and Delilah." The stage setting is very complicated. The temple appears to be of great size, and is most imposing. The stairs at the center and at the right and the left give access to the various parts of the building. A very

COLUMNS IN THE TEMPLE OF DAGON.

large number of persons are on the stage during this act. Two columns in the middle of the scene are specially noticeable on account of their great size. When the moment has arrived for the destruction of the temple, Samson places himself between the two columns, and with his outstretched arms hurls the columns to the ground. The demolition of the temple quickly follows, each piece of scenery falling in the exact place arranged for in advance, so that there is no danger of injury to the artists or chorus. The two columns are specially interesting, as they are really of great size and weight. In reality the columns are hinged to the stage. To the interior of each column is secured an iron lever which passes down underneath the floor of the stage. This lever is bent like the bascule of a bridge. To the end of this lever is secured a rope which passes over pulleys to a counterweight. From the counterweight another rope runs over the pulley to the windlass. When the columns are to be overthrown, their weight is balanced by the counterweight secured to the end of the rope, so that there is little shock from the fall. The rapidity of the descent of the column is equal to the rapidity of the rise of the counterweight. It will readily be seen that these weights can be adjusted to give any effect desired. The same windlass serves to raise both counterweights.

THE HORSE RACE ON THE STAGE.

When first introduced, the horse race upon the stage was a decided novelty, and it is doubtful if any stage illusion is more ingenious. The two principal plays in which the horse race has been used are Neil[son] Burgess's clever and popular play, "The County Fair," and a French play called "Paris Port de Mer." In both of these plays three horses, each ridden by a jockey, race upon the stage without going out of sight of the spectators. We have here a real effect plus an illusion. The horses are free from all restraint and really gallop, but the ground disappears under their feet, moving in a direction opposite to that of the run; the landscape, as well as the fences, also fly past in a direction contrary to the forward motion of the horses. The illusion in both of the plays we have mentioned is very similiar, but we think the American invention is preferable. At the proper moment the large screw shown in the lower part of our engraving is set in motion by the electric motors. It lifts the mechanism of the horse race up to the level of the floor, which had previously covered it. The lights in the theater are turned out, and after a few moments of inky blackness the flying horses appear at the side of the stage, in a blaze of light, and seem to strain every nerve, fairly flying past the varied landscape. Fences and trees disappear behind them with startling rapidity. When at last the finish is near, one of the horses gradually works forward and becomes the winner by a neck as he approaches the judges' stand. After an instant of darkness a flash of light follows, and the horses are pulled up in front of the judges' pavilion and the race is won.

This result is accomplished by means of three flexible endless platforms passing over rollers at the sides of the stage. These moving platforms enable the horses to be in rapid motion without actually moving forward, and, as a matter of fact, instead of moving forward, they are well secured by wire rope traces. As the race nears the finish, the platform on which the winning horse is stationed is gradually slipped forward on a track provided for the purpose, the actual movement being, of course, only a few feet. The space between the fence and the scenery is fourteen feet, which gives ample space for free action of the horses. The fence in the foreground consists of a number of pickets fastened to an endless belt. The pickets run in guides which hold them rigidly perpendicular during their passage over the stage. The scenery back of the stage is carried by two powerful rollers, and is turned by means of an electric motor so arranged that it may be unwound at any rate of speed.

Much of the effect of the scene is due to the speed with which the electric lights are flashed from extreme darkness to brilliant light. The illusion is further heightened by the way in which the horses' manes are tossed about.

ELECTRICAL DEVICES IN "THE COUNTY FAIR."

This is accomplished in a very novel manner. In the extreme lower right-hand corner of our engraving will be seen a blower actuated by an electric motor. Air from this blower is conducted to a large funnel which discharges the air just out of sight of the audience.   This causes the horses' manes to be blown in all directions.   All of the complicated electrical apparatus is driven from a single switchboard at the right, which is usually manipulated by Mr. Burgess himself.   Our engraving is from "The Electrical World."

Our other engraving shows the arrangement as used in the French play, " Paris Port de Mer."   The tracks are formed of an endless matting of cocoa-nut fibre.   This belt runs over drums at each side of the stage and is made taut by a third drum on a level with the stage floor.   The belt is supported by a series of wooden rollers which are placed very close together and revolve on pivots.   The drum at the left of the stage is driven directly by the motor.   The fence is mounted on an endless belt, as in the Burgess illusion, and is operated by an air motor.   The panorama, which unwinds in a minute and a quarter, is operated by hand.

Mr. Neil[son] Burgess devised another plan for producing the illusion of a horse or other race.   Two or more disks or wheels of appropriate size are secured to a common shaft so that they will rotate independently.   The wheels are of different diameters, so that the larger will afford a clear path for the contestants.   The racers are held back by wires which pass over windlasses, and their relative positions may be governed by paying out or drawing in the wire.   The runners, of course, cause the rotation of the disk as in a horse power, and this gives the illusion of real running.   An appropriate background scene may be used, and the shaft carrying the disks may be moved across the stage by journaling it in a four-wheel truck, the flooring being removed so as to permit of this horizontal movement.

An American, Mr. Frank M. Chapman, invented another scheme for pro-ducing the same illusion.   He devised a circular track, or turntable, somewhat the same as that used in horse powers.   A panorama is carried by rollers, and works across the proscenium opening.   One or more horses are placed upon the turntable at any desired point between the panorama and the front of the stage, and are then started.   They are held back in the same manner as in the ordinary treadmill, and will not advance until the wire is slackened.   In the meantime the panorama is moving in the direction opposite to that in which the horses are supposed to be moving.   This operation is accomplished by means of the gear connection between the rollers of the panorama and the horses acting on the surface of the turntable to turn the same.

HORSE RACING ON THE STAGE—MACHINERY UNDER THE STAGE FOR DRIVING THE ENDLESS BELT.

THE EFFECTS IN "SIEGFRIED."

"Siegfried" is the second drama and the third evening of the "Ring of the Nibelung." It is devoted to the life and adventures of young Siegfried, from his childhood under the care of the dwarf smith Mime, until he wakens Brünnhilde from her long sleep on the fire-guarded rock on which she was put to sleep by Wotan as a punishment for disobedience in sheltering Sieglinde. The first act of "Siegfried" is particularly charming. It is called the "Welding of the Sword." The scene is laid in a large rocky cave with openings leading out to the forest. The forge is built out of rocks, the bellows alone appearing to be artificial. A large anvil and a few tools complete the equipment of the

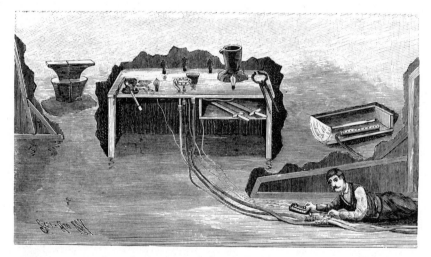

SIEGFRIED'S FORGE.

forge. As the curtain rises, Mime is seen hammering the sword, but the result does not seem to be satisfactory. Suddenly Siegfried enters, clad in a dress of skins, and accompanied by a bear which he captured. Mime retires behind the forge. After Siegfried and Mime have indulged in a dialogue, the former jumps up and goes towards the sword; grasping it, he tries it with his hand, and finally strikes it upon the anvil, whereupon it is broken.

Siegfried forces Mime to tell him the story of his parentage. Mime then brings out the pieces of the broken sword which the dying Sieglinde had left as a legacy to the child. The young hero now begins to set to work to forge the sword, and Mime chuckles with delight when he thinks that after Siegfried has forged the sword and killed the dragon he will poison him. The scene of the welding of the sword is magnificent, and is peculiarly Wagnerian in its conception.

Supported by a square frame of hewn timbers is the bellows, which is composed of hides fastened together with rings. The leather cylinder rises and falls by means of a lever secured to the top. Siegfried goes bravely to work. Going to the forge, he heaps coals upon the open hearth, and gradually fans the fire; it rises and rises until there is a roaring blaze. The light shines fitfully upon Siegfried and upon the walls of the cave. At each stroke of the bellows handle the fire rises higher and higher. Siegfried places a crucible in the midst of the fire, and in it puts the pieces of the broken sword. When the pieces appear to be melted, he takes up the crucible with a pair of tongs and pours the fluid metal into a clay mold. Grasping the mold with a piece of cloth, he carries it to the rough-hewn tempering log trough and throws it in. The heated metal coming in contact with the water causes the steam to rise. When Siegfried judges that the sword has cooled sufficiently, he takes it from the trough and, striking it a smart blow, breaks the mold which surrounds it. He then heats the blade of the sword in the forge and proceeds to the anvil. At each stroke of the hammer the sparks fly, producing a most realistic impression. He now places the sword in a vise, files it, and then rivets on the handle.

At last Siegfried finishes the sword and he says:

" Rescue! Rescue!
Welded anew!
To life once more I have waked thee.
Dead hast lain
In ruins long,
Now flashest thou fiercely and fair.
Blend thou the blatant
Now with thy blaze!
Fell thou the false ones,
Rend thou the rogues!
See, Mime, thou smith—
So smiteth Siegfried's sword! "

—J. P. Jackson's version.

He now wishes to test its temper, and, raising it aloft, he brings it down, giving a tremendous blow to the anvil, which is cleft in twain, sparks following the anvil to the ground. Those who have never seen " Siegfried " can form but a faint idea of the realism of this scene, which taxes the resources of the property master to the utmost. It will now be asked how the very clever illusion of the forge and anvil is produced. Our engraving gives an idea of the rear of the forge. It consists of a rough table, the front of which is covered with canvas to represent rocks. The top of the table is quite well hidden from the spectators by painted work which masks the front of the forge so that the mechanism for obtaining the light effects from the top is disguised. The gas is connected with the forge by means of two pieces of rubber hose, one of which is provided with a small burner which is kept constantly lighted. Before the curtain is raised it is not noticeable, as it is turned down until the flame is blue. When Siegfried goes to the forge and heaps on the coal, the stage hand called the "gas man" turns on the gas so that it flows through the other pipe, which ends in a rose burner at the top of the forge. The instant the gas reaches the rose burner it is ignited by the jet which was kept lighted. By

THE FORGING OF THE SWORD IN "SIEGFRIED."

manipulating the valve, the quantity of gas is regulated so that the flame burns high or low as desired. As soon as the fire is supposed to rise to any height the glare of it is cast upon Siegfried's face. This is accomplished by means of incandescent lamps which are arranged one on each side of the rose burner and

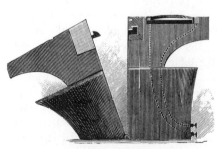

THE DIVIDED ANVIL.

three just in front, in the painted work which masks the front of the forge. The lamps are arranged on two circuits; those in the middle on one circuit, and those on the back of the forge on another circuit. The wires run into the wings, and the electrician lights them and dims them, as required, by means of rheostats. Steam is used to give the effect of smoke. This is admitted by a stage hand in the wings.

The quantity of steam admitted depends upon the height to which the fire is supposed to have risen. It may thus be seen that the effect of the lighting is produced by a clever combination of gas, electricity, and steam, which must be combined with the greatest possible art. In the old forge at the Metropolitan Opera House, which was burned in the fire, the effect was obtained in a slightly different way. A man was placed under the forge, and when the flame was to rise, he blew lycopodium powder into it from a box underneath the top of the forge. A quantity of the powder was blown out at each stroke of the bellows. The particles of the volatile powder caught fire when they came in contact with the gas jet, thus producing the effect of the gaseous flames from blacksmith's coal and its sparks. The new arrangement is considered to be more desirable.

Under the top of the forge will be noticed a shelf on which are kept two swords. This enables Siegfried to substitute the swords as becomes necessary, and here is kept the sword with a firmly riveted hilt which he finally uses to strike the anvil.

The trough is also connected with a steam pipe. When Siegfried throws into the trough the mold which encases the sword, and when he tempers the sword, the steam rises. The steam is supplied from a drilled iron pipe. This pipe is connected with the steam pipes at the side of the stage by means of a hose which is carefully covered from view. The anvil upon which Siegfried strikes in forging the sword has one side covered by a piece of corrugated iron, six by twelve inches, and another piece of iron is over it, as shown in our engraving. It is arranged so that when the bow piece of iron at the top comes in contact with the lower piece a momentary short circuit is produced, so that at each stroke of the hammer a shower of sparks is produced. When Siegfried raises his sword and brings it down upon the anvil, he really strikes a spring which lets one half of the anvil fall, its under and outer side having the corner cut off for the purpose, as will be seen from our engraving.

There are other interesting properties and illusions in "Siegfried." We have just seen how Siegfried has forged his sword "Rescue;" now begin a series of wonderful adventures which only end with his death in the "Götterdämmerung." The second act of "Siegfried" takes place in a forest in which is seen a great linden tree. The whole stage is covered with rocks, and at the left, at the back, is a cave which shelters "Fafner," a giant who has taken the form of a dragon in order to protect the treasures concealed in the cave, which include the mysterious ring and the Tarnhelmet, which gives the possessor unlimited power. Mime and Siegfried approach, Mime showing the way to the cave. Mime then leaves Siegfried alone to his fate. The youthful hero sits down beneath the linden tree and listens to the voice of the bird. He wishes that he could understand its language, and, cutting a reed, he makes a rude musical instrument with which he attempts to imitate the bird's notes, but the result is a failure. He then takes up his silver horn and blows several blasts upon it. He has, however, no comprehension as yet of the song of the birds, but the sound of the horn has awakened Fafner, who appears in the mouth of the cave. The hideous creature moves forward from the cave and says: "Who

FAFNER, THE DRAGON IN "SIEGFRIED."

art thou ? " Then, after a moment's conversation, Fafner opens his tremendous jaws, displaying his teeth. Siegfried seizes his sword and confronts Fafner. The now enraged dragon belches forth a sulphurous breath, while his eyes gleam with a very wicked light. The young Siegfried seems no match for the enormous beast. The dragon has almost seized Siegfried when the latter succeeds in wounding him slightly. The animal rears up on his fore feet, with the intention of hurling himself upon the intruder in order to crush him. In doing this, however, he exposes his breast so that Siegfried is enabled to plunge his sword into the monster's heart. Fafner rears up still higher, and finally sinks upon the ground, and the dying monster sings of the race of the giants and the curse of the dwarfs. At last he dies, and as Siegfried withdraws the sword, his hand becomes sprinkled with blood. He puts his fingers to his mouth to suck off the blood. He now hears the forest bird again, and this time he is able to understand the language.

The fact of the matter is, it would have been much better if Wagner had written the music-drama so that the dragon would have been killed off the stage. Having once been put into the opera, it was, of course, impossible to get along without the ugly beast, but the tendency is now to retire the dragon as far as possible to the rear of the stage. The dragon which we illustrate is the creation of Mr. Siedle, the property master of the Metropolitan Opera House. Fafner is, without doubt, the finest of his race. He gives one the idea of something half snake, half crocodile, and somewhat resembles some of the now extinct animals of bygone geological times. It cannot be said that the dragon is a thing of beauty, unless we can admit there is a beauty of ugliness. Fafner is supremely ugly, but, from a scientific point of view, it is doubtful if there are any properties connected with modern Grand Opera which are more interesting. The problem which presents itself to the property master in building the dragon is an interesting and difficult one. As the dragon must be arranged so that it can be worked by two men, who are inside it, it must be capable of considerable movement and must give the appearance of great size. In the present instance the head of the dragon was modeled in clay, and each line and horny scale and boss was the result of careful calculation. After the head was modeled, a plaster of paris mold was taken from it, and from this another plaster cast was made, upon which the actual head was built up out of *papier maché*. After the *papier maché* work was finished, it was painted dark green; different shades were, of course, used.

The body of the dragon is of cloth; the legs and feet are not attached to it, but are put on by the two men who operate the dragon. The feet and claws of the dragon are pulled on by combination overalls and boots. The man who takes the part of the fore feet wears a heavy belt with hooks on the side to carry the wires which furnish the current for the electric lamps in the eyes, and a rubber hose by which the dragon is enabled to breathe a sulphurous breath. A long lever of iron runs from Fafner's head through his body, and by means of this the man who plays the hind legs moves the head up and down; the shoulders of the first man being the fulcrum. Independently of this, the

WOTAN'S SPEAR.

man in the fore legs moves the upper jaw and the feelers. The painted cloth body might be likened to a camera bellows. The antennæ can be moved by means of cords, adding greatly to the terrible appearance of the monster. The enormous red tongue can also be moved by the first man, and the jaws are freely hinged. The eyes are set in what appear to be enormous saucers; they are covered over with painted silk. Behind this are incandescent lamps which are turned on and off fitfully by one of the stage hands behind the drop scene which represents the mouth of the cave. The wires run to the tail, as does also the steam pipe which furnishes the breath of the monster. The steam is allowed to escape from the mouth and through the nostrils. The tail consists of a number of sections of wood articulated by means of hinges. It is covered with painted cloth. When the first act is about over, the two men who are to act as the legs of the dragon get inside the body and are then elaborately fastened by the stage hands. They then waddle along to the opening of the cave, assisted by several of the stage hands, as the enormous body is very difficult to manage. One man works the steam while the other attends to the lighting of the eyes. After Siegfried kills the dragon, the stage hands go at once to extricate the two men from their uncomfortable position. The singer who takes the part of Fafner may be disposed in two ways; he may be either under the raised bridge upon which the monster stands, or he may be in the wings. In either case he sings through a speaking trumpet, which adds to the effect. The bird which is seen going across the stage and leading Siegfried to Brünnhilde is actuated by clockwork. When it starts, the clockwork is set in motion and makes the wings flap. Another bird, which appears to the audience to be the same, crosses the stage on wire from right to left, further back, and a third one is seen at the left, still further away. This one Siegfried follows to the rock of the Walküre, just as the curtain falls upon the wonderful scene.

The third act of "Siegfried" opens in a wild, rocky path at the foot of a high mountain. The scene is laid at night, and there is considerable thunder and lightning. Before the entrance to a cavern in the rock stands Wotan, who never appears as a greater bore than in this act of "Siegfried." After a seemingly interminable conversation with Erda, she vanishes and Siegfried appears. After considerable conversation between Siegfried and Wotan,

Siegfried advances to the latter, holding his sword, which has once before been shattered on the same shaft, in order that he may reach the summit of the mountain upon which Brünnhilde sleeps, protected by the sea of flames. Siegfried fights with Wotan and hews the spear in pieces. A fearful flash of thunder follows; flames and steam rise in front, and Siegfried's horn is heard as he plunges into the fire. At length the fierce glow pales, the scene changes, and represents the summit of a rocky mountain peak, as in the third act of the Walküre, and Brünnhilde is seen in deep sleep.

The illusion is very clever indeed. Wotan's spear, as shown in our engraving, consists of a divided shaft, one part of which telescopes with the other for a few inches. The upper part of the spear is forced down over the lower, thus compressing a coiled spring. When the spring is compressed sufficiently, it is caught by a catch. Now, when Siegfried strikes the spear with his sword, Wotan presses a button which releases the upper part of the spear. The coiled spring is sufficiently strong to throw it off from the lower part. As the upper part rises, it lights matches secured by holders in the center of the lower part of the spear. A piece of sandpaper is secured to a little door which opens in the shell of the top part of the spear. As the sandpaper passes the matches, it lights them, setting fire to a small quantity of gun cotton, which lights flash paper concealed in the end of the spear. A lightning flash and a flash of thunder usually accompany the breaking of the spear. Formerly an electric spear was used, but it was found that the matches were simpler and more reliable.

Arrangements are provided at the Metropolitan Opera House so that an entire curtain of steam can be made to rise across the whole length of the stage, a narrow section of flooring being taken up, and a perforated section put in instead. A perforated steam pipe is also provided.

THE BED OF TULIPS AND THE ELECTRIC FIREFLY.

A very pretty electrical effect has been introduced in the garden scene in "Faust." Siebel, the would-be lover of Marguerite, advances to a bed of tulips, some red, some white, and some gold, to pluck a bouquet that he would leave upon her window to speak for him. Concealed in the corolla of each flower is an electric lamp. Now Mephistopheles had long before warned Siebel:

> " Every flower that you touch
> Shall rot and shall wither."

But, unheeding, Siebel plucks a golden tulip which shines as he lifts it up to him. A fine wire which carries the current keeps the lamp aglow and is not seen as it trails along the foliage. No sooner does Siebel examine it than

Mephistopheles, partly concealed, raises his hand; the current is cut off, and the flower grows dull and withers perceptibly.

> " What, faded!   Ah me!
> Thus the Sorcerer foretold at the fair:
> That should I touch a blooming flower,
> It shall wither.
> But my hand in holy water I'll bathe—
> See, now, will they wither?"

Then with his other hand he plucks a red tulip, a white and a golden one and holds them up triumphantly, each glowing with a rich light ; for Mephistopheles may not raise his hand against the power of what has been blessed.   Then he changes the flowers from one hand to the other, and instantly they fade ; but they gleam again when, remembering it was with the other hand that he had touched the holy water, he transfers them back again.   This beautiful illusion is easily produced.

THE BED OF ELECTRIC FLOWERS.

The electric firefly which has been used in the play of the " Kaffir Diamond " depends upon a somewhat similar device.   Tiny incandescent lamps are affixed to the reeds and rushes in a swamp, each lamp being connected by means of a fine wire to a storage battery, through the medium of wires in a switch-board.   Our engraving shows the manner of placing the lamp behind the weeds and rushes. The operator, in his hiding place, by pressing upon the keys of the switchboard, alternately lights up one and then another lamp, so that it would appear to be a single firefly darting hither and thither; or, by pressing a number of keys, any number up to a dozen or more could be lighted.

In " Die Walküre," a red incandescent lamp is placed in a tin box which is painted so as to represent a knot in the tree.   When the light is turned on, it causes a red glow on the hilt of the sword, and discovers it to be Siegmund.

ELECTRIC FIREFLIES.

THE ELECTRIC TORCH AND ELECTRIC JEWELS.

We have already given several interesting examples of electricity upon the stage. We now present some engravings of the electric torch and electric jewels for which the theatrical world is indebted to the French inventor M. Trouvé. The electric torch was devised for use in M. Saint-Saëns' " Ascanio." In the mythological ballet, Phœbus appears among the Muses, holding the torch of Genius in his hand; the torch is of moderate size and elegant form, and must be brilliantly illuminated from twelve to fifteen minutes at each performance. An incandescent lamp scarcely concealed under colored glass jewels solves the problem. The principal difficulty was to light this lamp without the use of conductors, which should furnish the electrical current desired. M. Trouvé constructed some portable accumulators which are placed in the torch. The accumulators are six in number; the first three occupy the upper part of the torch, and the three others the lower part. They are of the Planté variety and have lead plates. Each of the elements is placed in the interior of a cylindri-

22

cal piece of thin glass covered with gutta percha. The battery as a whole weighs four hundred and twenty grams (fifteen ounces), and is capable of furnishing electricity to supply the torch for two presentations. A small contact button is placed above two buttons, so that at the least pressure the lamp is lighted, and it is extinguished when the pressure ceases. Our engraving shows Madame Torri in the *rôle* of Phœbus.

FIG. 1.—PHŒBUS HOLDING THE TORCH OF GENIUS.

M. Trouvé also invented what are termed electric jewels, in which glass jewels cut into facets are illuminated by a small electric light placed back of them. The jewels really consist of small lenses whose foci have been accurately determined. The luminous source itself always occupies an invariable position, that is to say in the center of the sphere, which is studded with the glass jewels. The lamp is connected with a small battery through the medium of a flexible conducting cord which is concealed under the garments. The battery is put into the pocket or attached to some part of the dress. Our engraving shows a number of these electric jewels which are used not only for theatrical purposes, but for a novelty in dress.

The jewels are very effective when attached to a ballet costume, and we give on page 341 an illustration of a *danseuse* as she appears when adorned with this glowing electric jewelry.

Another interesting effect which is produced with the aid of a small elec-

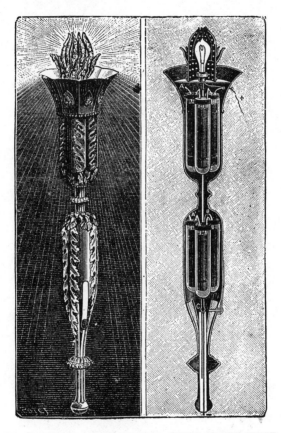

FIG. 2.—EXTERNAL AND INTERNAL VIEWS OF THE TORCH.

tric battery carried upon the person, is used in the duel scene in "Faust," and is also due to M. Trouvé. It is rather simpler than the device which we will show for producing sparks from the sword in the duel. The two swords and the two cuirasses are extremities of the poles of a bichromate battery carried by the combatants. When the two swords come in contact they cause bright sparks to flash, and when one of the swords touches the cuirass of the adversary, a fifteen candle-power lamp is lighted, and remains lighted during the contact of the point of the sword with the cuirass; the lamp

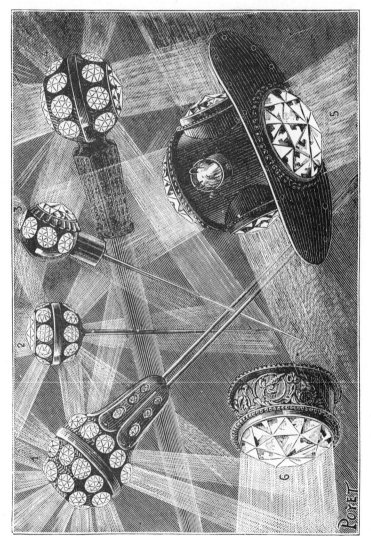

FIG. 3.—TROUVÉ'S ELECTRIC JEWELS.

is, of course, in front of the cuirass.   In furious sword play the two swords touch reciprocally the two opposite cuirasses; both lamps are simultaneously illuminated and give a considerable light around the combatants.   This apparatus is not only useful in the theater, but has been tried in the fencing gallery during an assault; the apparatus shows the location of the blows without the possibility of contesting it.

FIG. 4.—DANSEUSE WEARING ELECTRIC JEWELS.

AN ELECTRICAL DUEL.

In the duel scene in " Faust," a striking effect was obtained a few years ago at the Metropolitan Opera House. It will be remembered that the soldier Valentine, brother of Marguerite, fights with Faust. As Faust is unfamiliar with the use of the sword, the devil, in the guise of Mephistopheles, stands by, sword in hand, ready to aid him, interposing his weapon when Valentine presses the student too closely. In former productions of the opera there was nothing apparent to indicate the possession of supernatural powers by Mephistopheles. The duel takes place at a part of the stage where two plates of copper are sunk into the flooring. These plates are connected with the electric current. Copper nails are driven into one shoe of Valentine and one shoe of Faust, and the wires run up their bodies to the swords. When they draw their swords they insert the wire into the hilts by means of a plug; they are then connected with the copper plate. Every time that Mephistopheles interposes the sword and strikes up the contending weapons, which are in contact, the sparks fly furiously and the weird crackling sounds are heard as in lightning. When Valentine receives his death wound, he throws out the plug connecting his sword with the electric current, and as he falls the sword flies from his hand, and there is nothing to show the presence of any electrical connection.

THE SKIRT DANCE.

The famous skirt dance may be defined as peculiar in the sense that it is not a dance as generally understood in stage parlance. The performer, standing on the stage and dressed in voluminous attire, requiring, it is said, over a hundred yards of material, by slow motions, comprising more arm movements than foot movements, causes the light drapery to wave about in most graceful curves. The variety of shapes and contours that can be produced by a skilled performer is endless. To add to the effect, wands are used to extend the reach in the direction of the lines of the arms, and the greater control thus obtainable adds immensely to the effect. This dance was made famous by Miss Loie Fuller, whose reputation is now world-wide.

Our illustration which forms the frontispiece of the present work is designed to show the methods adopted to produce the wonderfully beautiful effects which have characterized the dance. The performance is executed in a darkened theater. A number of projectors are distributed, four in the wings and one below the stage, so as to be adapted for flooding the figure of the *danseuse* with light. A pane of heavy plate glass set in the floor of the stage permits the projector beneath it to produce its effects. Each projector has mounted in front of it a disc about three feet in diameter, perforated near its periphery with a number of apertures. Colored gelatine is fastened over most of these apertures, a

AN ELECTRICAL DUEL.

different color being used for each opening, except where one may be left for white light. The operators at the projectors follow the movements of the performer, and can produce an almost infinitely extended range of effects by varying the colors thrown by each projector.

The theater being pitch dark, the dancer can be brought slowly into view and can be made to slowly disappear by manipulation of the projectors. She can appear in any color or combination of colors. It is needless to say that it is a composite performance in the sense that the dancer fills only a part of the functions; skilled operators are absolutely essential at the projectors.

One of the prettiest effects is produced by a magic lantern operated from the front of the stage and shown on the left hand in the cut. The operator projects upon the drapery different figures and designs, using regular lantern slides, making the flowing, misty drapery act as the screen for his projections. It is obvious that he must give great attention to his focusing.

The skirt dance has won the attention of artists, and some very beautiful statues have been based upon its cloudlike variations of form. The slight idealization required in representing the soft forms of waving drapery in the solid material of the sculptor's art has given most graceful and characteristic effects.

One of the most startling effects is the flame dance. The filmy veil is pure white, but as the dancer approaches the opening in the stage floor the veil turns to a fiery red, and the flames wave to and fro as if they were being blown by the wind. Shadows are then thrown on the veil and produce an exact reproduction of heavy black smoke, which suddenly changes to an ardent flame again, as if the fire had broken out anew.

CHAPTER V.

THE NAUTICAL ARENA.

The nautical arena, or aquatic theater, was a few years ago one of the sensations of London and Paris. Spectacular entertainments in which water played a prominent part go back to the time of the Romans, when portions of the arena of the amphitheater, or sometimes the entire arena, were flooded, and mimic sea fights took place in galleys carrying gladiators who fought to the death. The Paris aquatic theater is a very handsome building. It is situated in the Rue St. Honoré, and is called the "*Arène Nautique.*" It is intended to fill two distinct *rôles ;* first, it is a circus for equestrian, gymnastic, and aquatic performances, while during the summer it becomes a huge swimming bath. The building was originally used for a cyclorama, but was entirely remodeled when put to its new use. The circular hall is one hundred and ten feet in diameter. In the lower part of this hall is a circular tank seventy-nine feet in diameter, with a gallery running around it. Over this gallery and the water are constructed tiers of seats, as shown in our engraving. In the center is placed a powerful hydraulic cylinder. To the top of the piston rod is affixed a large iron plate forty-four feet in diameter. This plate can be sunk below the level of the water, the tank then being available for aquatic performances. It is the work of a moment to raise the plate. A firm floor is then provided for horses and men.

This arrangement permits of the water being maintained at such a height as to provide a shallow tank for those who cannot swim. The rise of the piston is caused by a compound pump, and the plate is guided in its movement by guide bars fixed vertically around the outer rail. A catch is provided to secure the plate in position. When it has attained a little more than its proper height, it is caused to rotate slightly on its vertical axis by an endless screw. By this means the ends of the radial girders are brought over twenty shoes fixed to the twenty columns; by letting a little of the water escape, the radial girders settle themselves firmly down upon the shoes. The weight of the whole mass is about twenty-five tons. When the arena is to be used for performances in the ring the plate is covered with a mat of esparto weighing about one thousand pounds. It is brought in on two iron trucks. Our engraving represents the removal of the mat before sinking the stage.

THE AQUATIC THEATER—PREPARING TO SINK THE STAGE.

THE NEW AQUATIC THEATER, PARIS.

CHAPTER VI.

A TRIP TO THE MOON.

This is the title of an illustrated lecture which has been very popular in Berlin, and which was also produced in New York a few years ago. The lecture as used in the United States, was rewritten by Mr. Garrett P. Serviss. The first scene is the reproduction of a solar eclipse as seen from the shores of one of the small lakes called Havel, near Berlin, on the morning of August 19, 1887.

On this morning the sun arose with the greater portion of its disc obscured by the moon. As the sun ascended, the crescent diminished, and at the moment of totality a wonderful corona flashed into view. The scene gives the audience an idea of what the astronomers mean when they attempt to describe

SUNRISE ON THE HAVEL, NEAR BERLIN, AUGUST 19, 1887.

THE PRODUCTION OF THE SOLAR ECLIPSE.

this wonderful phenomena. The moon passes slowly before the sun until the earth is fully illuminated and the sky and landscape assume a normal appearance. Interesting as these imitations of celestial and terrestrial phenomena are, the manner in which they are effected is still more so, and our engravings give a peep behind the scenes and explain the means by which the illusion is produced. The trees and foreground are set in front of a transparent scene upon the back of which the opaque parts are silhouetted in black, leaving the sky and water translucent.

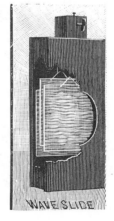

Two optical lanterns are provided, one of which carries the crescent and the other the corona slide. They are mounted upon a box movable along the inclined side of a triangular frame by a drum and cord, and are thus enabled to imitate the appearance and course of the heavenly bodies. The screen immediately below the horizon intercepts the image of the luminary below that line.

The waves that play upon the surface of the lake are

THE PLASTER IMAGE OF THE MOON.

produced by a slide in a third lantern.   This slide consists of glass screens
upon which waves are painted.   These screens are actuated by three eccentrically mounted rods set in motion by clockwork.   The interference with these
waves permits ribbons of light, of constantly varying position and width, to fall
upon the screen and to give the effect of water ruffled by a breeze.   The play
of color and intensity of light produced by the revolutions of the earth and its
passage through the penumbra and umbra of the moon's shadow, and the
development of full sunlight, are perfectly coördinated to the changing condition of their source, the sun.   This part of the illusion is effected by the
management of the foot and border lights.

MT. ARISTARCHUS.

CAPE LAPLACE.

These lights are red, white, and blue incandescent electric lamps arranged in series, and controlled by a rheostat, permitting every possible combination and intensity of tint, and to the intelligent manipulation of which is due much of the success of the scene. Our interest is intensified by a view from a distance of five thousand miles, showing the lunar mountains and other prominent features. The plaster image of the moon, viewed through a circular piece of gauze set in a black drop, is ten feet in diameter. The change of phase is produced from the light thrown from the lanterns, as shown in the illustration.

The splendid scenes of Mt. Aristarchus and Cape Laplace are splendid pictures and are shown from the height of two and one half miles. By trigonometric mensuration of the shadows, and application of their values by perspective, the artist is enabled to represent the general features of the landscape with fidelity. These scenes are lighted from behind by four arc lights, by bunch lights and footlights, and the combined candle power is eight thousand

SUNRISE AND EARTH LIGHT.

BACK OF EARTH WITH GELATINE
ATMOSPHERE.

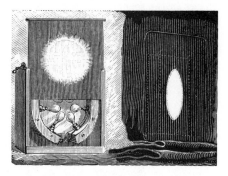

THE SUN BOX INTERIOR AND THE BOX
RISING.

five hundred candles. This brings out the contrast of the landscape in this dead world. From the moon surface, the earth always seems to occupy the same place, and reflects to the moon a part of the light received from the sun. The phenomena of earthlight and sunlight upon the moon are given by transparent

SOLAR ECLIPSE AS VIEWED FROM THE MOON.

places in the scene representing sky, and lit up by a lantern. The mountain on either side has each a lantern, whose light is permitted to fall on the drop by gradually lowering the screen. A modified arc light illuminates the front of the scene and gives the earth light.

Probably the most unique of the cosmic phenomena is a solar eclipse viewed from the moon. The earth is an opaque disc with a red gelatine band attached to its circumference with white muslin, and suspended by two hooks set in a shelf extending across its back. A coat of phosphorescent paint gives the glow. The sun consists of a box with a cover of gelatine on which the sun is painted; a semicircular wooden arm incloses a reflector and supports six incandescent lamps set inwardly. The box hooks into a piece of leather with a circular aperture coincident with the sun's face, and sewed into the drop. Holes in the drop allow the light from an arc light to imitate the stars. The surface of the moon is painted on canvas supported on hinged props having spread feet. A stiff rod joins the hinges and forms the horizon. A footlight is placed within this tent-like cover to illuminate it. The drop curtain carrying the sun box is raised by a windlass, and as the sun rises, accompanied by the stars, the footlight is turned up. In passing behind the earth, the sun imparts a crimson view to the earth's atmosphere, which the footlight transfers to the moon until the extinction of the solar disk. The return to earth is marked by a view of that part of the earth surface most resembling the moon's, the Tyrolean highlands. The afterglow of sunset, moonrise, and a lunar eclipse are depicted with great accuracy. The gradual movement of a deep red gelatine film across the lantern-slide holder causes the moon to appear to enter and emerge from the earth's shadow. A sunset on the Indian Ocean and moonrise on the first scene concludes the lecture. A series of stereopticon views of great beauty are interspersed between the mounted scenes, thus furnishing a continuous performance.

CHAPTER VII.

CYCLORAMAS.

The origin of the cyclorama is traced to the use of scenery by the Italians two or three hundred years ago. They arranged outside of their windows scenes painted on canvas that simulated extensive gardens. Robert Fulton is said to have exhibited a panorama in Paris at the beginning of the present century. It was not, however, a cylindrical painting, as is used in the cyclorama, and the effect was not as illusive. Cycloramas have been on exhibition in many cities of the United States, and they are also very popular abroad.

The cyclorama which we illustrate is the " Battle of Gettysburg," which has been shown in New York, Brooklyn, and other cities of the United States. It was painted by M. Paul Philippoteaux.

The " Battle of Gettysburg " covers an immense sheet of canvas four hundred feet long and fifty feet high. The canvas was imported from Belgium, none being manufactured in the United States which would answer the purpose; it is nine yards wide, and the seams run up and down. The immense canvas is supported from the sides of the building so as to form a cylinder. The building is circular, and a cornice is provided which runs entirely around the building; the upper edge of the canvas is nailed to this cornice. The cloth is first rolled smoothly on an iron roller surfaced with wood, fifty feet long. The roller is held vertically in heavy framework which runs on tracks around the building. From the roller thus carried around, the cloth is gradually paid out, as shown in our engraving. As fast as it comes off the roller it is seized and held by pincers while the edge is being tacked to the cornice. The lower edge is secured to a circle of gas pipes which run entirely around the building. As the pipe would not give sufficient weight to stretch the canvas, a twenty-five-pound weight is hung at every third foot.

The effect of the stretching is that the canvas loses the true cylindrical shape; its sides are no longer parallel, but curve slightly inward, about one foot in amount, at the center. Thus, at the horizon line, the most distant part of the scene, the painting is about a foot nearer the vertical line than in the foreground. In absolute distance from the eye the difference is still greater. Owing to obliquity of the line of sight, the foregound, which seems so near at hand, is really much further off than the horizon.

In a cyclorama of this kind it is necessary to have the scene portrayed with the utmost fidelity. The result is that the landscape is really an artistic tran-

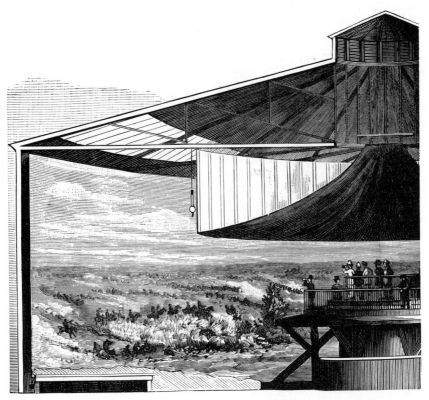

SECTION THROUGH A CYCLORAMA.

script of photographic views of the field. The artist first went to the scene of the great battle of Gettysburg, and selected one point of view, and caused a small stage to be erected at this point, which was of the same height as that upon which the people were to stand in the completed cyclorama. Around the stage a line of pickets was driven in a circle, as shown at the point B. The distance was measured from the top of the stage as a center. From the top of the scaffold three series of ten photographs each were taken, the instrument being sighted by means of the posts. This series of photographs showed the entire field; one series being taken for the foreground, while the other two, by their focusing and exposure, were devoted to the middle distance and background. Each view was divided into squares, as shown in our illustration; the canvas was marked off by corresponding divisions, and the photographs were copied square by square; the blending of the ten views and the aërial perspective was, of course, the critical part of the performance. The painting was done from a scaffold which traveled around on the same tracks which carried the roller frame, as shown in our illustration.

NAILING ON THE CANVAS.

The painting was done in oil, tinsel being occasionally employed. After the circular wall was covered, the foreground next claimed the attention of the painter and his assistants. A wooden platform was built which extended all around the platform upon which the visitors stood, and earth and sod covered these boards. Fences, tufts of grass, wheat, etc., lent their aid to fill up the scene. The continuation of the road was met almost perfectly on the canvas; in fact, it was almost impossible to see the line of demarcation between the real and the painted foreground. We give an interesting engraving of this method of constructing a realistic scene.

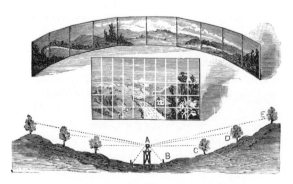

PHOTOGRAPHING THE FIELD.

Two men are seen carrying a litter. The more distant soldier is painted on the canvas; the litter is real, two of its handles passing through holes in the canvas. The figure resting on the litter and the nearer bearer are cut out of boards and painted. Other scenes are similarly painted.

The spectators occupy an elevated stage which they mount by means of staircases running under the scaffolding of the foreground. Once upon the plat-

PAINTING A CYCLORAMA.

form the spectators lose all idea of orientation, and cannot tell the points of the compass or have any conception of the size of the building. Over the stage a circular screen is suspended so that it shades it from the light which enters from the skylight. The sky is thus lighted up, and a peculiar luminous effect favoring the aërial perspective results. At night a number of electric lights, suspended out of sight of the spectators, give about the same effect. Many of the details of the picture were obtained from eye-witnesses of the battle; the uniforms, the modes of carrying the blankets, and the details of harness, and the minor parts of the scenery were studied carefully.   Everything in the building combines to make a wonderful illusion.

HOW THE ILLUSION IS PRODUCED WITH REAL OBJECTS.

THE ELECTRIC CYCLORAMA.

Notwithstanding the fact that cycloramas of the pattern we have just described were the result of the most careful blending of science and art, still their popularity seems to have been limited, and the cyclorama has been, in numerous cases, obliged to bow to the taste of the day.   One has been converted into a circus, others into skating rinks and bicycle academies.   The cyclorama we are about to describe ought to be able to bring panorama once more into fashion.   The idea of Mr. Chase, a resident of Chicago, was to turn to account the most recent discoveries in the way of panorama photography, projection apparatus, electric lighting, and the systems which permit of faithfully representing the phenomena of motion.   The possibility of causing a considerable number of views to pass before the spectator in a limited amount of time, of imparting life to them, gives the cyclorama an animation and diversity which is lacking in the ordinary panorama.

GENERAL VIEW OF THE CHASE ELECTRIC CYCLORAMA.

An ordinary panorama building is used; spectators stand upon the floor of a cylindrical chamber one hundred feet in diameter and thirty feet in height. Upon the walls are thrown photographs placed in a projecting apparatus suspended from the center of the scenery, after the manner of a chandelier.

Our first engraving gives a general view of the panorama as used at the " Chicago Fire " cyclorama. Our second engraving shows the projection apparatus, and our third where a battery of lanterns are used, showing the lantern carriages. Nothing more is required to convert an ordinary cyclorama into an electric cyclorama than to paint the back canvas white and to suspend the platform in the center of the building.

The apparatus is secured in the center of the panorama or cyclorama building by a steel tube and guys of steel wire. The operator stands in the center, upon a circular platform, and is surrounded by an annular table supporting eight carriages, upon which are mounted the lanterns, cinematographs, kineto-

PLATFORM FOR THE OPERATOR AND PROJECTION APPARATUS SUSPENDED IN THE CENTER
OF THE HALL.

THE PROJECTION APPARATUS.

scopes, and all arrangements required for imparting life to the scene and producing the transformation. Each lantern is provided with an arc light, and the wires to furnish the current pass through the suspension tube. The annular table carries the rheostats by which the light is regulated, according to the effects to be produced with iris diaphragms, which permit of obtaining vanishing effects and night, sunrise, or sunset effects. The projecting lanterns, eight in number, are double, one being ranged over the other, thus permitting of the preparation of a view, and focusing it, while the spectators are looking at another. The change of pictures is not effected until everything is in order. The carriages which support the lanterns permit of accurately adjusting views so that the registry is perfect. The eight positive slides produce a panorama three hundred feet in circumference and over thirty feet high. The rays which emanate from each of the projecting lanterns are such that they would overlap did not a frame fixed to the lenses, and carefully regulated, suppress those parts of the views which would encroach upon one another. When the lanterns are properly arranged it is possible to project moving pictures upon any part of the canvas screen.

CHAPTER VIII.

FIREWORKS WITH DRAMATIC ACCESSORIES.

The love of show and the spectacular is inherent in human nature. Games and entertainments on a colossal scale have always appealed to the popular taste. An important factor in such spectacles is the display of fireworks, in the love for which the Americans can sympathize with the Orientals. As far back as 1879, Mr. James Pain of London gave spectacular productions at Manhattan Beach, one of New York's most popular resorts, and since that time their popularity has been increased, so that now entertainments of this class are given in comparatively small cities. It is perhaps more proper to speak of these entertainments as fireworks with dramatic accessories than to

SCENES READY FOR LOWERING.

THE BURNING OF MOSCOW.

call them dramas with fireworks, for the *raison d'être* of the entire performance depends not upon the loosely hung together plot, but on the gigantic display of fireworks, which is accompanied by enough of realistic stage setting and dramatic performance to give a good excuse for the performance. Strange as it may seem, these mammoth plays, as regards the scenery, are as interchangeable as those in any theater, the grounds in which the scenery is installed being of the same general dimensions in all cases. This, of course, greatly simplifies a change of performance. The company which has been prominently identified with these spectacles sometimes has as many as seven in use at one time. They

LOWERING A SCENE.

move about from place to place, so that in the course of a season thirty or forty cities are visited, the stay varying from a week to a whole season. The performance is held in the open air, at either some popular resort or in some place where the grounds are readily accessible.

An amphitheater is provided for the spectators in a rectangular enclosure which may seat as many as ten thousand persons. The seats slope away until the water is reached; here will be found an artificial lake, usually three hundred and eighteen feet long and one hundred and fifty feet wide, and the width of the entire stage being three hundred and fifty feet. Behind the pond is a stage mounted with set scenes. Of course, owing to the distance and darkness, the refinements of acting would be entirely wasted. The management, therefore, depends almost entirely on the spectacular, the cast including companies of clever gymnasts and acrobats.

The performance is so arranged as to lead up to some stirring catastrophe. The climax is generally awful cataclysm, or some blood-curdling war scene, or a conflagration.

We select for the purpose of illustration one of the most successful of these spectacles, the "Burning of Moscow" at the time of the French invasion. The scene is a true representation of the docks and quays of the ancient Russian capital. At each side appear arched stone bridges, and the whole is surrounded by strong fortifications; sentinels walk back and forth upon the walls of the Kremlin. The action of the drama is but brief, and after a gymnastic exhi-

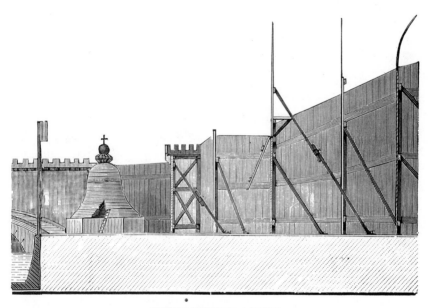

SECTION THROUGH A SCENE.

bition of marching and countermarching by the actors, the band plays the solemn strains of the Russian national hymn, while priests of the Greek Church render classical music of a somber character, which has a striking effect. The army of Napoleon now approaches, shells begin to fly over the doomed city, and, as the bearskins of the French grenadiers appear at the entrances at either side, the terrorized Russians rapidly disappear.

The prisoners in the jails are liberated, and with torches prepare to light the fires. The conflagration now begins, and the pyrotechnic display becomes splendid. The roar of the flames is heard, and, amid explosions, the buildings seem to be licked up by the fire, and collapse, leaving charred remains. The air is full of burning serpents, and the water is alive with incandescent figures. The grand finale is an aërial burst of rockets, as shown in our engraving.

Having seen one of these spectacles the reader will ask how the remarkable effects are obtained. Our illustrations show the scenery as viewed from the rear of the stage. The scenery is hinged and braced, some parts turning on pivots, and all arranged so as to be quickly thrown down into such semblance of ruin as shall best carry out the idea the piece is intended to represent. It is, however, only the work of a few hours to rehabilitate the entire scenery for use the next night.

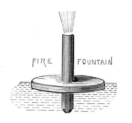

FIRE FOUNTAIN

In the performance which we have described, some of the best effects of the art of pyrotechnics are shown in the brilliancy and sustaining power of the various lights and colors given out by the rockets, wheels, stars, Roman candles, gold and silver rain, etc. Of course, vast quantities of colored fire are also required to light the scene.

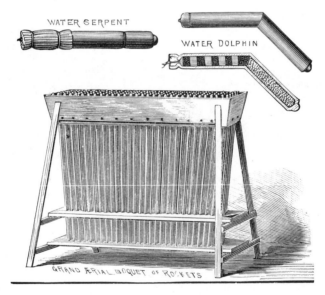

WATER SERPENT

WATER DOLPHIN

GRAND AËRIAL BOUQUET OF ROCKETS

FIREWORKS.

Our last engraving shows how some of the firework effects are obtained. The grand aërial bouquet of rockets consists of a battery of rockets which are discharged simultaneously from the stand, as shown in the engraving. Our other engravings show water serpents, water dolphins, and the floating fire fountains. As they float around in the water, they produce fine effects.

BOOK IV.

AUTOMATA AND CURIOUS TOYS.

CHAPTER I.

AUTOMATA.

The present division of the work deals with interesting automata, curious toys, and miscellaneous tricks of an amusing nature. A very large number of devices and tricks of this kind have been published in the "Scientific American" and the "Scientific American Supplement," and the ones which we select are among those which have been considered as the best. The subject of curious toys and science in toys is very fully treated in the excellent work of Mr. George M. Hopkins, entitled "Experimental Science," which is published by the publishers of the present work.

AUTOMATON CHESS PLAYERS.

For a very long time the automaton chess player, or "Psycho," has been celebrated as *the* automaton, and quite a literature is centered about it. We present two forms of the "Psycho," one of which depends upon compressed air, and the other upon a small individual who is secreted in the cabinet. We will first describe the one which operates by compressed air.

Let us explain to those who have not seen "Psycho" that it consists of a small figure, dressed as a Turk, sitting cross-legged (as shown by dotted lines) on a chest; this chest is in turn supported on a glass tube, about twelve inches diameter and three feet long, which rests on a four-legged stool. The bottom of chest and top of stool are covered with green cloth so as to make a tolerably air-tight joint. The right arm is extended as in the drawing, and a semi-circular rack, in which are placed the thirteen cards dealt to "Psycho," is fixed by means of a bracket (not shown) in such a position that the edges come between the finger and thumb. The arm turning horizontally on the pivot, A, the hand can be brought over any part, and by closing the finger and thumb and raising the arm, the card will be withdrawn from the pack and held in the air.

In Figs. 1*a* and 1*b* (elevation and plan), the wheels E and M have each a train of clockwork (left out for the sake of clearness) which would cause them to spin round if unchecked. M, however, has two pins, $p\ p'$, which catch on a projection on the lever, N. E′ is a crown-wheel escapement—like that in a bottle roasting-jack—which turns A alternately to the left and right, thus causing the hand to traverse the thirteen cards. A little higher on A will be seen

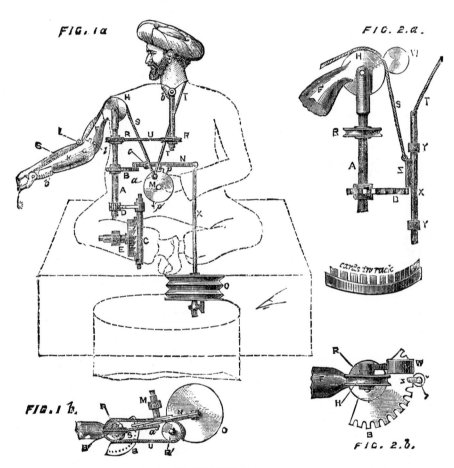

AN IMPROVED PSYCHO.

a quadrant, B (see plan), near the edge of which are set thirteen little pins. The end of the lever, N, drops between any two of them, thus causing the hand to stop at any desired card. The lever being pivoted at *c*, it is obvious that, by depressing the end, N, B will be set at liberty, and the hand will move along the cards; by slightly raising it this motion will be arrested; by raising it still more the pin, p, is released, and M begins to revolve; and by again depressing N this wheel will, in its turn, be stopped. Near the bottom of the apparatus is a bellows, O, which contains a spring tending to keep the lever, N, with which it is connected by a rod, X, in the position shown. This is connected with the tubular support, which may be connected by a tube through the leg of the stool, and another tube beneath the stage, with an assistant behind the scenes. By compressing or exhausting air through this tube it is obvious that the lever, N, will be raised or depressed, and the clockwork set going accordingly; *a* is a crankpin set in M, and connected with the head by catgut, T, and with the thumb by S.

At R and R' are two pulleys connected by gut. Thus, if the hand moves round, the head appears to follow its motions, and when raised by pulling S, the head also rises, by means of T. Further explanation seems almost unnecessary; *l* is a stop to prevent the elbow moving too far, and *b b*, spiral springs to keep thumb open and head forward respectively. When N is raised, M pulls T and S, the latter closing thumb, and then raising arm by pulley, H. If the lever is allowed to drop, *p'* will catch and keep arm up. On again raising N, the arm will descend.

Figs. 2*a* and 2*b* show another and simpler arrangement, in which only one train of clockwork is used. On the same axle as H is fixed a lever and weight, W, to balance the arm. A vertical rod, X, having a projection, Z, slides up and down in guides, Y Y, and carries the catgut, S and T. The quadrant, B', has cogs cut, between which Z slides, and stops the motion of A, which is moved, as before, by clockwork. The lower part of X is connected direct with O. When X is slightly raised, as shown, A is free to move; but on exhausting air and drawing X down, Z enters the cogs and stops the hand over a card; continuing to exhaust, the thumb closes and the card is lifted up. The details of the clockwork we leave to the ingenuity of the reader. There should be a fan on each train to regulate the speed. The figure should be so placed that the assistant can see the cards in the semicircular rack.

THE AUTOMATON CHESS PLAYER.

The newspapers announced some time ago that the police of Bordeaux had forbidden the exhibition of the automaton Az Rah, one of the attractions of the Exhibition Theater, because it had been discovered that the manikin was set in motion, not by mechanical arrangements, but by a youth of eighteen years, inclosed within a cavity behind the wheelwork, and whose health was gravely compromised by this daily torture.

This automaton recalls the famous Turkish chess player that was constructed in Hungary by Baron Kempelen in 1769, and exhibited in Germany, Russia, France, England, and America, without the public succeeding in ascertaining its mechanism. In 1819 and 1820 a man named Melzer showed it anew in England. Robert-Houdin saw it in 1844 at the house of a mechanician of Belleville, named

Cronior.   Since then its fate has been unknown, and it is very probable the Az Rah of Bordeaux is nothing else than the Turk of Vienna.   Our readers who have seen it at the Exhibition will be enabled to decide the question after reading the description that we shall give.   Baron Kempelen, a Hungarian nobleman and an Aulic Councilor of the Royal Chamber of the Domains of Hungary, being at Vienna, was called to the court to be present at a séance of magnetism that a Frenchman named Pelletier was to hold before the empress. Kempelen was known as an ingenious amateur of mechanics, and the persons present having asked his opinion in regard to the experiments which he had witnessed, he said that he believed he could make a machine that would be much more astonishing than anything that he had just seen.   The empress took him at his word and expressed a desire that he should begin the work. M. De Kempelen returned to Presbourg, in his own country, and in six months produced an automaton which played a game of chess against any one who offered himself, and nearly always won it.

This automaton was a human figure of natural size, which was dressed in the Turkish style, seated on a chair, and placed behind a wooden chest on which was laid the chessboard.   He took the pieces up with his hand in order to play them, turned his head to the right and left in order to see them better, and nodded his head three times when he checkmated the king, and twice on attacking the queen.   If his adversary made a mistake, he shook his head, removed the wrongly-played piece, deposited it outside of the chessboard, and played his own.   The showman, who stood near the automaton, wound up the mechanism after every ten or twelve moves, and occasionally replaced certain wheels; and at every motion of the Turk were heard noises of moving wheelwork.   To show that there was nothing within but mechanism, doors were opened in the chest and body.   There was also a magnet lying on the table to make believe that magnetism, then in great vogue, and as yet full of mystery, played a preponderating *rôle* in the affair.   M. De Kempelen was accustomed to say: "The machine is very simple, and the mechanism appears wonderful only because all has been combined with great patience in order to produce the illusion."

Many hypotheses were put forth on the subject, and two books, one published in 1785, and the other in 1789, were devoted to a discussion of them.   Those that appeared to be most likely were, on the one hand, that the Turk's body contained an extraordinarily small dwarf; and, on the other, that the showman acted upon the automaton from a distance by the aid of magnetic influences. These two explanations gave a very imperfect account of the facts, and it was not until some years ago that the trick was unveiled in an anonymous book.

The following is an exact description of the apparatus and the successive operations performed by the exhibitor:

The chest was three and one-half feet long, two feet wide, and two and one-half feet high, and was provided with doors and drawers whose use will presently be seen.   The front part of the chair seat was affixed to the chest, and the back part rested on the floor by two legs which, as well as the four legs of

THE AUTOMATON CHESS PLAYER.

E. MOREU Sc.

the chest, were provided with casters.   The right hand of the manikin was movable on the upper part of the chest that formed a table, and, at the beginning of operations, held a pipe, which was afterward removed, and it rested upon a cushion lying in a certain definite position.   The chessboard in front of the player was eighteen inches square.   The exhibitor, provided with a light, begins by allowing the interior of the apparatus to be examined by the spectators.   He opens the door A (Fig. 1), and allows to be seen a series of gearings that occupy the whole width of the chest.   Then he passes behind and opens the door B (Figs. 2 and 8), opposite the door A, and introduces a light into the interior to show that it is empty.   The spectators standing on the other side can, in fact, see the light shine through the different pieces of mechanism through the door, A, that remains open.   He afterward locks the door B, and comes in front of the chest and opens the drawer G, from which he removes the chessmen, and a cushion which he slides under the left arm of the automaton.   This drawer seems to serve no other purpose than the preservation of these objects.   He then opens the two doors, C C, in front of the chest, and shows a large closet lined at the sides with dark drapery, and containing two boxes, L and M, of unequal size, and a few belts and pulleys that seem to be designed for putting in motion the mechanism contained in the boxes. Passing behind again, he opens the door D, and introduces a light into the interior of the chest to show that it has not a false bottom.   Then he closes this door again, and also the doors A and C, by means of the same key.   Next he turns the apparatus around so as to show the public the other side (shown in Fig. 2), and raises the clothing of the Turk, and opens the apertures, E and F, in the back and thigh, to show that no one is hidden within.   These doors remain constantly open afterward.   Finally the showman turns the Turk back to his former position, facing the spectator, removes the cushion and pipe, and then the game may begin.

We shall explain as clearly as possible how the game was directed by a man who succeeded in hiding himself by a series of movements when the different doors of the apparatus were successively opened:

The drawer G G, when closed, does not reach the back side of the chest, but leaves between it and its back an empty space, O, measuring fourteen inches in breadth, eight in height, and two feet eleven inches in length (Figs. 9, 10, and 11).   This space is never shown to the spectator.   The little closet extending from A to B is separated into two parts by a dark hanging, S (Fig. 8), which is raised when the door, B, is opened, and lowered when it is shut.   The front part of the closet is entirely filled with the wheels that are thought to move the automaton.   The back part is empty and is separated from the large closet that the doors C form, by a thick curtain, R, which hangs freely, being only fixed at its upper part.   A part, Q, of the bottom partition of the large closet C C—the part in front of the Turk—is movable around a horizontal axis, and is provided with a weight toward the interior of the closet sufficient to cause it to fall always in a vertical position.   The box L is movable, and serves to hide an aperture in the floor of the closet; and the box M is stationary, but has no bottom, and covers likewise a corresponding hole in the lower floor over the space O. The interior of the Turk is arranged as indicated in Figs. 8, 10, and 11. The end of the chest to the right of the Turk slides in horizontal grooves (properly hidden) in such a way as to give access to the space K. It will now be seen that if a man of small stature introduces himself into the chest on this side, he will be able to thrust his legs into the empty space hidden behind the drawer, and to place the rest of his body in the space K, as may be seen in Fig. 5, and by pushing the curtain before him and removing the movable box, L, he will be able to assume the position shown in Figs. 3 and 4. It is in such position that he awaits the beginning of the exhibition. The box M serves for receiving his feet.

It will be remembered that the first operation of the exhibitor consists in opening the door A, at which time the public sees only the mechanism, and, behind it, the dark curtain, S, whose distance cannot be estimated. The exhibitor next passes behind the chest, and, opening the door B, introduces a light behind the mechanism, which is believed to occupy the whole width of it. The curtain, S, being raised, it is seen by the light that shines through the different pieces that they cannot serve to hide any one. He then closes and locks the door B, and, returning to the front, opens the drawer and performs the operations already described, in order to give his confederate time to take the position shown in Fig. 5. The box L having been put back in place, as well as the curtain R, the public sees only an empty space when the doors C are opened. The curtain S, which has fallen, hides the back of the confederate, although the door A remains open; and it is then that on introducing the light through the door D, the exhibitor shows that the large closet has not a double bottom. The doors C being again closed with the same key, so as to make believe that these different closings are due to the necessity of removing this key at every operation, the chest is turned around, the two doors, E and F, are opened before the public to show that the body of the Turk is empty, and finally the machine is wound up slowly, the wheelwork making considerable noise the while. During this time the confederate raises the movable partition Q, takes his legs from behind the drawer, introduces the upper part of his body into a portion of the manikin, which is so arranged as to give his loins a convenient support, and seats himself on the box L, as shown in Figs. 6 and 7. The game may then begin, the hidden player following his moves through the sufficiently transparent fabric that forms the Turk's clothing. In order that the confederate may easily introduce his arm into that of the manikin, it is necessary to give the latter a certain position, this being the reason for the addition of a pipe in the hand and a cushion under the elbow, both of which are removed when the game begins. A simple cord permits of moving one of the manikin's fingers so as to pick up or drop the chessmen. The left arm of the confederate, which remains in the machine, is employed in moving the head and in producing the noise of wheelwork at every motion.

In reality, in M. De Kempelen's automaton, it was the left arm that moved the pieces. It is said that this peculiarity was due to the fact that the chess player who operated the automaton was left-handed. There has even been a touching romance related on this subject, to the effect that the hidden chess player was a Polish officer who, having been compromised in the revolt against Catharine the Great, and having lost his legs in fighting, was received by Kempelen, who thus hid him so well from the searches of the Russian police that he could go to conquer his sovereign in the game in the midst of her court.

A CURIOUS AUTOMATON.

The automaton which we illustrate has a peculiarity of being actuated by a simple flow of sand. It is curious that it was made in the first half of the eighteenth century. The image, clad in Oriental costume of bright colors, is seated behind a little table which is located in front of what appears to be a brick and stone structure; it is made of pasteboard. All of the details are executed with great care. When the automaton is in motion it acts as a juggler. The arms rise alternately or in unison, and lift the cups, and at every motion expose upon the table first to the right a white ball, then to the left a red ball, which passes to the right and disappears. Then two white balls make their appearance on a new motion of the cups, and these are changed into red ones

FIG. 1.—AUTOMATON REPRESENTING A JUGGLER PLAYING WITH BALLS.

at the next motion. The house forms a receptacle for fine sand which falls upon the wheel, G, through the hopper, F. The sand flows in a continuous stream, and causes the wheel, G, to revolve with great rapidity. To this wheel are fixed six tappets which engage with the toothed wheel, J, and thus diminish the rapidity. The wheel itself communicates through the medium of teeth with the cylinder, H, which is thus given a slow motion, which causes the automaton to act as follows: Opposite the cylinder there are two series of levers of four each, the extremities of which we suppose to be marked A, B, C, D, and A′, B′, C′, D′. The two levers, D and D′, lift the arms, L L, and the

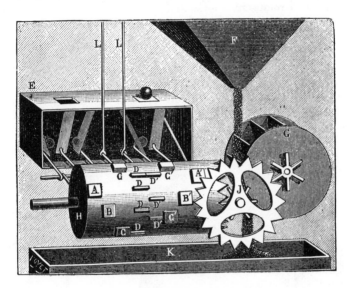

FIG. 2.—INTERNAL MECHANISM OF THE AUTOMATON.

extremity of each of the six others is placed under a small strip of cardboard. Each of these strips is hinged by one of its extremities to the table; the other end, on rising, places itself just beneath the small aperture in the table, E. If now we examine the cylinder, B, we shall see that it is provided with a series of cams, A, B, C, and A′, B′, C′, and opposite these, other and smaller ones, D and D′. Each cam, when the cylinder revolves, strikes in turn one of the levers. The larger cams lift the levers and consequently the hinged cards, with the balls of different colors, and keep them lifted for some time, and during this period the smaller cams act upon the levers of the arms that hold the cups. In this way the balls are in place when the arms rise, and do not disappear, in order to be replaced by others, until the arms have descended. The cams, A and A′, cause the red balls to act, and the white balls are raised by the cams, C and C′. As for the cams, B and B′, they act upon strips of cardboard that merely support obturators for the apertures in the table.

THE TOY ARTIST.

The mechanical toy shown in the accompanying illustration is one of the most original and ingenious things of its kind that have recently appeared. Within the base upon which the "artist" and his easel are placed, and immediately below the figure, is a small pinion which is operated by a worm at the end of the crankshaft which is seen projecting through the side of the base. The pinion, which rotates in a horizontal plane, is provided with a couple of pins upon which is placed one of the sets of removable cams which accompany the toy. The cams are double, being provided with two separate peripheral edges, and each edge is engaged by the short arm of a pair of levers, as shown in the engraving. The upper lever attaches at the end of its long arm to a vertical shaft which passes up through the body of the figure, and is pivotally attached to its right arm at the shoulder. By this means the rotation of the cam causes a vertical up and down movement of the arm and the drawing pencil which it carries. The lower cam operates a system of levers by which the arm is given a series of right and left movements. It is evident that by giving the proper relative contours to the two edges of the cam, the arm, with the pencil which it carries, may be made to trace any desired line upon the

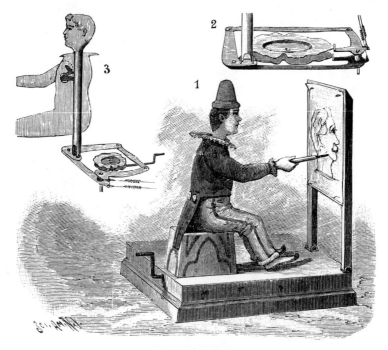

THE TOY ARTIST.

paper, either vertical or horizontal, by the action of the first or second cam; or diagonal or curved, by the joint operation of the two. Each of the double cams which are provided with the toy is cut so that its operation will cause the figure to draw some well-known object. The levers are kept in snug contact with the cams by a pair of spiral springs.

The easel is hinged to the base and is pressed against the pencil by means of a coil spring. It is provided with four projecting pins upon which the sheet of paper is held while the sketch artist is at work. The model from which our engraving was made produced an easily recognized likeness of the Emperor William of Germany (the device is "made in Germany"), and a drawing which bore a strong resemblance to the familiar barnyard fowl.

A STEAM MAN.

A good many years ago what was supposed to be a steam man was exhibited all over the country, but finally the "steam man" presumably died, as his remains were seen quite recently in one of the downtown New York junk stores. The steam man which we illustrate was invented by Prof. George Moore, who exhibited him very widely in the United States.

In our illustration we show the section and general view of the steam man. In the body is the boiler, containing a very large heating surface which is supplied with a gasoline fire. Below the boiler is situated the engine. While this steam engine is not at all large, it runs at a very high speed and is of high power, the combination of boiler and engine giving about one-half horse-power. From the engine the exhaust pipe leads to the nose of the figure, whence the steam escapes when the machine is in motion. Through the head the smoke flue is carried, and the products of combustion escape from the top of the helmet. The steam gauge is placed by the side of the neck. The skirts of the armor open like doors, so as to give free access to the engine. The main body of the figure is made of heavy tin. By reducing gear the engine is made to drive the walking mechanism of the figure at reasonable speed.

In our sectional view we show the combination of levers by which the figure is made to walk. The engine imparts a swinging to the whole length of the leg from the hip; a second swinging motion, from the knee downward, is accomplished by a similar system of levers and connections; and, finally, a true ankle motion is given to the foot by the rod running down through the lower leg. The heels of the figure are armed with calks, or spurs, which catch on the surface on which it is walking and give it its power. As exhibited, the steam man is connected to the end of a horizontal bar about waist high, which is fastened to a vertical standard in the center of the track. Thus supported, the man walks round in a circle at quite a rapid rate of progress.

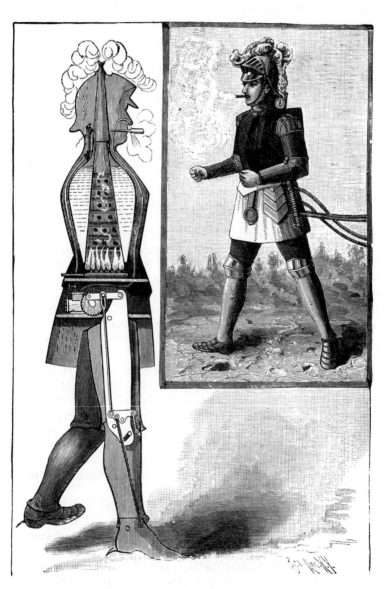

THE STEAM MAN.

For the last eight years the inventor has been at work on a larger steam man which he hopes to have in operation sometime. The new one is designed for use on the open streets, and is to draw a wagon containing a band. In the upper figure we indicate the method of attachment to the wagon which has been adopted. By the long spring at the side of the figure an elastic connection is secured, so that the figure shall always have its weight supported by the ground. The present man, which is about six feet high, when in full operation, cannot, it is said, be held back by two men pulling against it. The larger man, built for heavier work, is expected to pull as many as ten musicians in his wagon. Our cuts show the general appearance of the figure, which is attired in armor like a knight of old, and which appears to be thoroughly operative. The action is quite natural, and the hip, knee, and ankle motion of the human leg have been very faithfully imitated. The figure moves at a brisk walk and can cover about four or five miles an hour.

CHAPTER II.

CURIOUS TOYS.

AN OPTICAL ILLUSION.

The simple toy illustrated in the engraving has printed on the underside the rather high-sounding title, "X-Ray Machine. Wonder of the age!" But it is neither an X-ray machine nor a wonder. It is simply a reduced copy of an ancient trick. The two cylinders mounted on the base, with a space between them, are perforated axially and are supposed to represent coils. When the eye is applied to the end of one of these cylinders, objects may be clearly seen through them; and when a coin is slipped between the ends of the cylinders, as shown in the cut, it offers no obstruction to the light. Objects can appar-

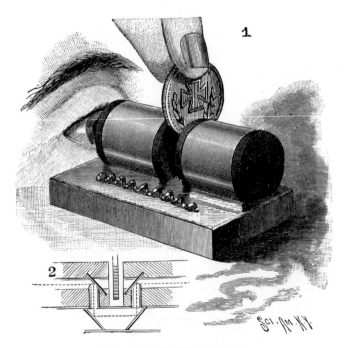

X-RAY MACHINE WITH NO X RAY.

ently be seen through the coin. Fig. 2 affords an explanation. The hole in each cylinder is intercepted by a mirror arranged at an angle of forty-five degrees with the axis of the cylinder, and in the base are two mirrors arranged parallel with the first two, as shown. A hole extends downward from the central hole of each cylinder, so that light entering at one end of the machine is reflected downward at right angles by the first mirror, thence forward by the second mirror to the third, which throws it up to the fourth mirror, by which it is reflected to the eye. It will thus be seen that the light never passes entirely through the cylinders, and the observer does not see through, but around, the coin.

The old device which preceded this was on a much larger scale, and was generally used in connection with a brick, which, of course, had the same transparency as the coin.

THE MONEY MAKER.

A few years ago a familiar sight on Broadway was the toy vender who sells the little machine called the "Money Maker," the machine consisting of a pair of rollers in one side of which are inserted plain sheets of paper of the size of a bank note, and as the rollers revolve, a bright new bill rolls out from the opposite side; then another blank sheet is inserted, and another bill rolls out, and so on. To the uninitiated this operation is a mystery, and to the

FIG. 1. THE MONEY MAKER.

unprincipled it is apparently the device long looked for.   This machine is certainly as good as any device calculated to make something out of nothing, but in this, as in other things, what you get you must pay for.

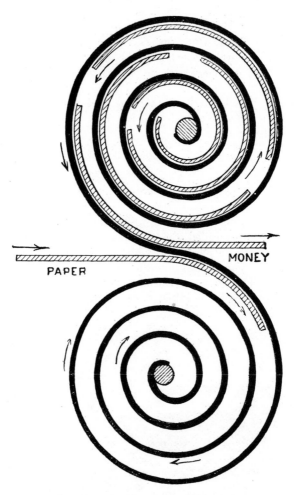

FIG. 2.—CROSS SECTION OF THE MONEY MAKER.

The explanation of the device is made simple by the enlarged cross section. To the two rollers journaled in the standards are attached the ends of a strip of black cloth which is wound around both rollers in opposite directions, so as to about evenly divide the cloth between the rollers.   The gudgeons of the rollers are squared to receive an ordinary clock key, by means of which either may be turned.   To prepare the machine for operation, the cloth is wound upon one of the rollers while it is partly unwound from the other; then the key is transferred to the gudgeon of the partly filled roller, and as it is turned, crisp new bank bills are fed into the machine and are wrapped with the black cloth upon the roller between the convolutions of the cloth; one bill after another is thus inserted until three, four, or more bills are hidden in the roll, and the rollers present about the same appearance as to size. This preparation, of course, takes place aside, and is not seen by the persons to whom the trick is to be shown. The key is shifted from the roller containing the bills (the upper one in the present case) to the lower one. Now, as the lower roller is turned so as to unwind the cloth from the upper roll, a piece of plain paper of the width and length of a bank note is inserted at the moment the first bill is about to emerge from the layers of cloth on the upper roll. The paper begins to be rolled upon the lower roll under the outer layer of cloth, so that while the paper appears to be simply rolled through between the rollers, coming out upon the opposite side a complete bill, it is in reality only hidden by the cloth on the lower roller. After the first bill is discharged from the rollers another piece of paper must be supplied in such a manner that it will begin to enter the machine as the next bill emerges, and so on.

EXPERIMENTS IN CENTRIFUGAL FORCE AND GRAVITY.

The elasticity of torsion and tension, the storage of energy, centrifugal force, momentum, and friction are all concerned in the movement of the simple toy illustrated in Fig. 1; and yet, perhaps, not one in a thousand of the people who see the toy realizes the composite nature of its action. Barring the well-known return ball, nothing can be simpler than this toy, which consists of two wooden balls of the same diameter connected by a slender rubber band attached by staples, as shown in the lower figure.

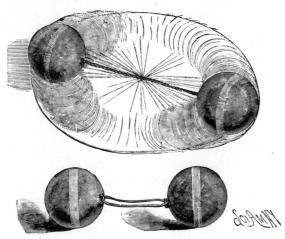

FIG. 1.—GYRATING BALLS.

To prepare the toy for operation, it is only necessary to twist the rubber band by holding one of the balls in the hand and rolling the other round in a circular path upon the floor by giving to the hand a gyratory motion. As soon as the band is twisted, the free ball is grasped in the hand, then both are released at once.

The untwisting of the rubber band causes the balls to roll in opposite directions in a circular path, and centrifugal force causes the balls to fly outward. By virtue of the acquired momentum, the balls continue to rotate after the rubber band is untwisted, so that the band is again twisted, but in the opposite direction. As soon as the resistance of the band overcomes the momentum of the balls, the rotation ceases for an instant, when the band again untwisting

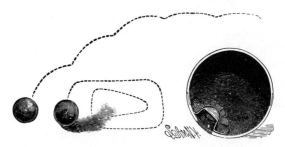

FIG. 2.—UNBALANCED BALL.

revolves the balls in the opposite direction, and the operation is repeated until the stored energy is exhausted.

In Fig. 2 is illustrated another ball in which the center of gravity is located near the periphery. The ball, which is hollow, is made of paper. To the inner surface of the ball is attached a weight which is secured in place by a piece of cloth glued over it. When this ball is thrown through the air with a whirling motion, it describes a curve like that indicated by dotted lines in the upper part of the engraving, so that it is difficult, if not impossible, to catch it. When the ball is rolled on a plane surface, it does not take a straight-forward course, as would be expected from a well-balanced ball, but its course is very erratic, as indicated by dotted lines in the lower part of the figure.

THE MAGIC ROSE.

An artificial rose, which is of paper, is traversed by a metallic tube that forms its stalk. One end of this tube extends slightly beyond the petals of the flower, and the other is prolonged in such a way that it can be held in the mouth, the flower being at a distance of about ten inches from the eyes.

If the tube be blown into regularly, and a small elder-pith ball. to which two artificial butterflies are affixed by slender wires, be placed over the flower,

THE MAGIC ROSE.

the ball, when well centered in the current of air, will remain suspended therein at an inch or so from the flower. As the current of air is invisible, the effect produced is very surprising, and the butterflies, incessantly in motion, appear to be engaged in rifling the flower of sweets, after the manner of living ones. It sometimes happens that the ball revolves in the current and carries along the butterflies, which thus describe a circle around an axis. It is unnecessary to say that the blowing must be done with great regularity.

ELECTRICAL TOYS.

The vulcanite electrophorus shown in our first engraving consists of a plate of vulcanite about one-third of an inch in thickness; one or more small pieces of tin foil about the size of a playing card are pasted on one side of the plate. The electrophorus is then placed on a table, and the surfaces are successively rubbed with the palm of the hand. If the plate is raised from the table and the tin foil is approached by the other hand, a spark is produced. A number of figures of elder pith complete the toy and show the phenomena of electrical attraction and repulsion in the most comical manner. The plate being excited, the small elder-pith figures are placed on the tin foil, and the plate is lifted from the table. The figures raise their arms, and the hair of the one in the center stands out like the bristles of a porcupine.

Our second engraving shows some electrical bottle imps. A glass vessel is mounted on a hollow base containing an electro-magnet provided with battery

FIG. 1.—ELECTROPHORUS WITH ELDER-PITH FIGURES.

FIG. 2.—ELECTRIC BOTTLE IMPS.

connections. One or two small figures surmounted by a hollow glass bulb have a small piece of wire attached to the feet and are placed in the vessel. The air in the hollow glass bulb will draw them up to the surface of the water, as shown in the engraving, but as soon as the current is turned on, the figures will be drawn irresistibly to the bottom of the vessel; as soon as the current is interrupted the figures will rise rapidly.

The magic fishes shown in our third engraving depend upon a similar trick. The electro-magnet is replaced by a small electro-motor which rotates from right to left, or from left to right, and causes a corresponding movement in the fishes, as the shaft carries a magnet which, of course, attracts the fishes and causes them to make a circular course around the small fish tank.

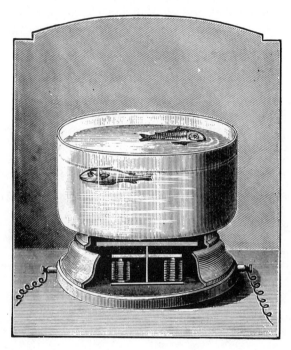

FIG. 3.—MAGIC FISHES.

THE ELECTRIC RACE COURSE.

Whatever may be the opinion that is held as to horse races and their moral influence, it is none the less certain that they offer an irresistible attraction to a large number of persons, and that this growing passion prevails equally in all degrees of the social scale.   Bold innovators have seen a vein to be exploited in the racing mania, and the game of the miniature horse race, an always popular pastime at bathing resorts, is only one of the more happy forms given to true races with a view of prolonging the excitement of betting, of the unexpected, and of chance, at times when genuine racing could be done only with difficulty and would attract too small a number of persons.   The electric race course that we are now going to present to our readers occupies a place just between genuine races and the miniature horse race.   It is, in fact, a happy alliance of genuine races, the game just mentioned, hobby horses, and electricity.   Taken as a whole, it consists of a certain number of hobby horses,

FIG. 1.—ELECTRIC RACE COURSE AT NICE.

half natural size, each moving over a circular track, under the influence of an individual motor, and receiving the current of a single generator, but in an independent manner; thus securing a perfect autonomy to each courser, qualified, moreover, by the surveillance of the electrician who acts as a sort of despotic monarch over them. The horses are ridden by children and even by grown persons, and it is in this that they resemble hobby horses, although the possibility of imparting different speeds to them permits of their being passed by competitors and of passing the latter in turn, thus increasing the excitement of the riders. Bets may be made, of which the chances are just as certain as those of the play of odd and even upon the numbers of the hacks traversing the boulevards of Paris.

FIG. 2.—MECHANICAL HORSE.

M. Salle's race course constitutes an interesting application of the carriage and of the distribution of motive power by continuous currents. The installation erected in Nice (shown in Fig. 1) comprises a twelve-horse-power gas engine that actuates a Rechniewsky dynamo with double winding, which sends the current into six electric motors.

About the motor and dynamo there is nothing peculiar. An electric motor is arranged behind each horse (Fig. 2). When the circuit of the dynamo is closed, all the horses start at once and take on relative speeds that are so much the greater in proportion as the circle upon which they are placed has a greater radius. The speed of each horse, moreover, can be regulated at will by means of a rheostat interposed in its particular circuit. An interrupter permits of stopping any horse whatever without stopping the movement of all the others.   All the motions are controlled from the post of the electrician, who, standing upon a lateral stage, overlooks the entire track, and can watch and regulate what takes place upon it, for upon a horizontally arranged board he has all the maneuvering pieces necessary for the play.   These pieces are, in the first place, a main commutator that cuts the circuit from all the horses at once ; then six individual commutators for each of the horses, six rheostats interposed in the respective circuits of the six motors and permitting of regulating the angular speeds of each horse, and finally an exciting rheostat of the dynamo machine that permits of varying the speeds of all the motors at once, in the same ratio.

It is therefore possible, by maneuvering these different pieces, to regulate the general or particular gait of each horse, and to stop any one of the horses almost instantly if an obstacle falls upon the track, or if one of the riders becomes suddenly indisposed.

The driving of the motive wheel by the motor is done by direct contact. To this effect the large wheel is provided with a rubber tire, against which the pulley of the motor bears.   The friction thus obtained is sufficient to carry along the vehicle, which, with the rider, weighs a little less than six hundred and fifty pounds.   The mean speed is thirteen feet per second, but the horses placed at the circumference can obtain a speed of sixteen or eighteen feet, a velocity that it is not prudent to exceed, or even reach, on account of the difficulty the rider would have in holding himself in equilibrium, and the feeling of dizziness that he might experience.

The vehicle upon which each horse is mounted merits special mention, because of the arrangements made to prevent upsetting.   Each of the four wheels has a different diameter.   Their two axles converge toward the center of the circular track upon which each horse moves, and the axis inclines toward the center.

Each pair of wheels, therefore, constitutes a true rolling cone, whose apex passes through the central point of the track situated upon the horizontal rolling plane.   The inequality of the wheels naturally makes it necessary to employ but a single driving wheel, and to mount the four wheels loose upon the axles.   Owing to these arrangements no tendency to derailment has shown itself, even with speeds of from sixteen to twenty-two feet per second upon curves of thirteen feet radius.

Two small rollers placed upon the track tend to prevent an upsetting under the action of a lateral thrust or a strong impulsion.   The track consists of a single tram rail, with which engage the two external wheels.   This rail serves as a guide and suffices to prevent derailment.   The current is led to each motor by two rollers moving over two circular metallic bands in direct communication with the poles of the dynamo, through the intermedium of the maneuvering board, thus permitting of varying the speed of each of the horses, and even of stopping the latter by interrupting the circuit.

MAGNETIC ORACLE.

The toy shown in the subjoined figure, taken from "*La Nature*," although far from new, is, nevertheless, ingenious, and cleverly modernized by the constructor. This is the way to make the oracle speak; we will afterward give the secret of its accurate answers. We write upon twelve prepared cards a series of questions relating to history, geography, science, customs, etc. One of the company takes one of these cards at random and reads one of the questions;

FIG. 1.—THE MAGNETIC ORACLE.

then the card is placed under the magician's feet, in a groove made to receive it. Immediately the oracle turns on its axis, and after some oscillations becomes fixed in a certain position, its magic wand pointing to one of the numbers by which it is surrounded. On referring to the corresponding number on a list, we read an admirably exact and accurate answer.

We may see that by varying at will the cards of questions and answers we may obtain from the oracle an indefinite number of replies. Nothing could be simpler than the process by which this result is obtained. The base of the toy, into which the cards slip, bears a vertical pivot on which rests the body of the magician, whose robe conceals a vertical U-shaped magnet, having its two poles near the base, as shown in Fig. 2.

FIG. 2.—DETAILS OF THE MAGNETIC ORACLE.

In each of the cards there is another magnet concealed, a straight rod, occupying a different position for each of the twelve cards. We see that, in virtue of the well-known laws of the attraction of magnets for each other, each time that a card is placed with its magnet in the base, the figure will turn round this axis and effect a series of oscillations round its own axis until the poles of the U-shaped magnet holder under its robe are opposite the contrary poles of the straight rod hidden in the card. If the base has been correctly marked previously, the divining rod will indicate the corresponding number of the answer. Any boy with a little genius and a few tools can make an oracle similar to our engraving.

THE DANCERS.

We present an illustration of one of the toys of the year. It consists of a nickel-plated box some three inches in diameter. In the center of the top projects the end of a spindle, and at one side is a lever. To operate the toy this side projecting piece is pulled out, and one of the triangular pieces of tin, to which paper figures are attached, is placed in contact with the spindle in the top of the box. The dancers then begin a lively waltz on the top of the box. The secret of operation is not at first apparent, though it is evident that magnetism has something to do with it. On opening the box the mystery is solved. The spindle is of magnetized steel and extends through the top of the box, forming a slight projection. It turns freely and carries a pinion and a metal disk. The pinion is actuated by the projecting side piece through the medium of a toothed sector. Motion is transmitted to the triangular piece of tin carrying the dancers by the magnetized spindle, causing a horizontal move-

THE DANCERS.

ment, and giving it a movement around its own axis. Curved wires and a spiral, one side of which is colored, are also provided, and they all move around the pin at a lively rate, producing novel effects.

AN ANCIENT COUNTERPART OF A MODERN TOY.

The very curious engraving which we reproduce herewith (Fig. 1) shows once again that, as regards manners and the details of life, there is nothing new under the sun. Every one has seen in the show windows of toy-dealers a plaything called the "wrestlers," and which consists of two little weighted and jointed figures that are set in motion by a taut string. At every tension of the latter these two little figures move about, go through the motions of wrestling, and sometimes fall on top of one another, much to the amusement of the spectator. Now, it is seven hundred years ago that Herrade de Lansberg, abbess of Hohenbourg, in a sort of encyclopædic compilation entitled "*Hortus Deliciarum*," drew the little combatants that are reproduced

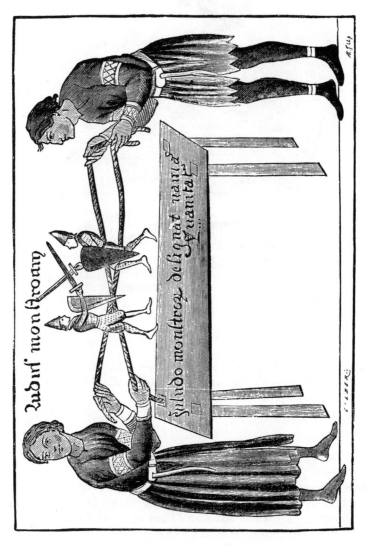

FIG. 1.—A TOY OF THE TWELFTH CENTURY.

in Fig. 1. This valuable MS., which was destroyed by Prussian shells in 1870, has been happily saved from absolute annihilation by the copies of M. De Bastard, that are at present preserved in the Cabinet of Prints of the National Museum. This book is a sort of abstract, in figures, of Alsatian life in the twelfth century, and games have not been forgotten therein. Herrade de Lansberg's little combatants are clad after the manner of the warriors of those times, just as in our toy—the wrestlers—the figures preserve the traditional

FIG. 2.—A TOY OF 1897—THE WRESTLERS.

costume of wrestlers at fairs. The two little warriors wear a helmet with nasal; and a coat of mail, a buckler, and a sword complete their equipment. Their feet, which were probably weighted with lead, kept the puppets in a vertical position, and upon maneuvering the strings an imitation of a sword contest was obtained.

It is probable that this toy was not a recent invention in the time of Herrade, and that the abbess of Hohenbourg only put into her drawings a costume that was already ancient.

NOVEL TOYS.

On any pleasant day may be found on lower Broadway and other down-town thoroughfares venders who sell almost anything in the way of novelties. Among these may be seen culinary implements, toilet articles, cheap microscopes, magnifying glasses, and various toys. Nothing takes better in the way of articles for this kind of trade than some new toy. Whether a toy will probably have a good run can be determined by these venders in a very short time. If it takes well, crowds gather around him, and he does a thriving business, making money for himself as well as for the inventor. If, however, the article is not wanted, the vender very soon finds it out, and looks for other wares.

FIG. 1.—ACROBAT WITH MERCURY WEIGHT.

Some of the toys are scientific, others are not. We give two examples of scientific toys which have sold very well. They are similar in character, and illustrate what shifting the center of gravity can do. They are both acrobats. The one shown in Fig. 1, and designated " McGinty," and sometimes " Little Tommy," consists of a paper figure attached to a tube closed at both ends and inserted in paper disks which are bent down on the tube, forming semicircular end pieces on which the device may roll. A drop of mercury placed in the tube completes the toy. When placed on a slightly inclined plane, with the tube parallel with the surface, the mercury rolls to the lower end of the tube, causing that end to preponderate. The lighter end, actuated by gravity, then moves forward until it strikes the inclined surface, when the mercury again rolls to the lower end and causes another half revolution, and so on. This toy moves down the incline with a slow and stately movement.

FIG. 2.—TUMBLER.

The toy shown in Fig. 2 is made upon the principle just described, but the round ends of the figure furnish the rolling surfaces, and a bullet is used for the weight instead of a globule of mercury, the body being simply a straight paper tube with convex ends.

COLUMBUS'S EGG.

The accompanying engravings represent an object sold in the London bazars. It is made of tin, is painted red, and is called " Christopher Colum-

FIG. 1.—COLUMBUS'S EGG,

bus's Egg,'' because those who do not know how it is constructed cannot make it stand up on the projecting part situated at the base. This egg, which it is impossible to open, is hollow, and contains a leaden ball which causes it to fall over on its side, unless it (the ball) is in the longer axis.

The sections in Figs. 2 and 3 explain the construction, and show how the ball is brought into the desired position to cause equilibrium.

Corresponding to the point where the halves of the egg are soldered together, there is internally a partition that has the form of a channel, of semicircular section, which runs around the tube, T. The ball, B, when the egg is held vertically, is capable of revolving around this tube, T, and as long as it remains in the channel will cause the egg to fall every time the operator endeavors to make it stand on its base, *c*. The egg can stand upright only on condition that the ball be made to pass from the upper to the lower compartment, in which case it will take the position, B''', at the base of the egg. This result is reached as follows: The central tube contains, just beneath its upper extremity, an aperture, B'', that forms a communication between the two compartments, and that is sufficiently large to allow the ball to pass through. Two small guides start from the side of the egg, and follow the contours of the partition up to the orifice in the central tube. On a line with the orifice, and on the outside of the egg, there is a

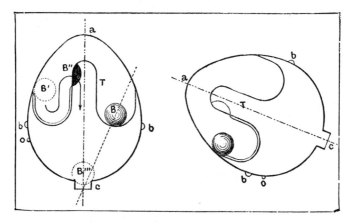

FIGS. 2 AND 3.—DETAILS OF CONSTRUCTION.

small and scarcely visible point, *o*. If the egg be sufficiently inclined toward this latter, as in Fig. 3, the ball will take the position, B', at the beginning of the guides leading to the orifice, B''. If at this moment the egg be gently turned back in the opposite direction, the ball, being kept in the plane formed by the point, *o*, and the egg's axis, will run along the guides and drop through the orifice into the lower compartment. When the egg is righted, the ball will take the position, B''', at its base, and the egg will then stand upright. By turning the egg upside down, the ball may be made to enter the upper compartment again, and things will then be as before.

With a little practice and skill, it is not even necessary to look for the position of the point, *o*, and thus run the risk of showing the uninitiated how the trick is done. On giving the egg a slight angular motion, the hand will feel the passage of the ball over the slight projection formed by the guides; the ball will naturally seat itself upon the latter, and the double motion above mentioned will accomplish the desired result. Effected in this way, and the hand being covered with a handkerchief, the mode of operating will not be perceived by the uninitiated spectator.

JACOB'S LADDER.

The simple toy illustrated in the annexed engraving is very illusive in action. When the upper block is grasped by the edges, as shown in Fig. 1, and turned so as to lift the second block in the series to the same height, the upper end of the second block falls into an inverted position, and appears to pass downward on the other members of the series, first upon one side of the ladder and then upon the other, until it reaches the bottom. This effect is only apparent, as the second block in reality only falls back to its original position in the series, but in the operation it becomes reversed; what was before the lower end

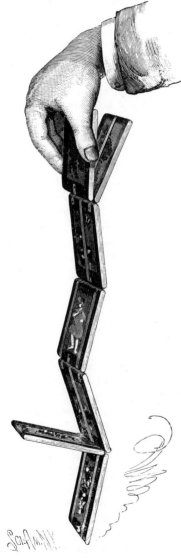

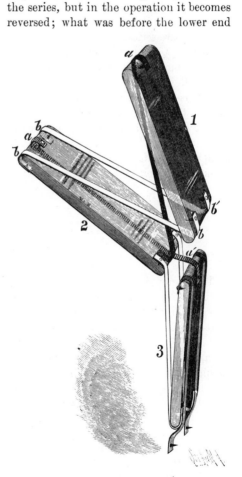

FIG. 1.—JACOB'S LADDER.   FIG. 2.—CONNECTIONS OF JACOB'S LADDER.

becoming the upper end, the front having exchanged places with the back. This change of position of the second member brings it parallel with the third block, which is then released, and the third member drops over on the fourth, when the fifth block is released, and so on throughout the entire series.

In Fig. 2 are shown the three upper blocks of the series, 1, 2, and 3, and their connecting tapes, the blocks being represented as transparent and separated from each other a short distance to show the arrangement of the connections. Block 1 has attached to it three tapes, *a, b, b.* The tape, *a,* is attached to the face of the block at the center, at the upper end, and extends over the rounded end of this block and under the rounded end of block 2. The tapes, *b, b,* are attached to the face of block 1, extending downward, under the lower end of this block, and upward, over the upper end of block 2. The tape, *a,* which is attached to the center of the upper face of block 2, extends over the end of this block, downward underneath the block, and over the upper end of block 3, where it is secured. This arrangement of tapes is observed throughout the entire series.

In Fig. 2, block 2 is represented as falling away from block 1. When block 2 reaches block 3, the tape, *a,* will be parallel with the face of block 3, and the latter will be free to fall in a right-handed direction, in the same manner as block 2 is falling in a left-handed direction. When block 3 is parallel with block 4, the fourth block will fall over in the left-handed direction.

The blocks, which are of pine, are each $3\frac{5}{8}$ inches long, $2\frac{3}{8}$ inches wide, and $\frac{1}{4}$ inch thick. The tapes, which are each $4\frac{3}{4}$ inches long and $\frac{3}{16}$ wide, are fastened at the ends to the blocks by means of glue and by a small tack driven through each end of the tape, as shown.

A NOVEL TOY.

The annexed engraving represents an amusing toy recently sold on the streets of New York. It is not particularly scientific, but it shows how a device having little novelty finds sale in places traversed by the multitude.

It consists of the figure of a Japanese in sitting posture, representing the "Mikado." In his right hand he holds a Japanese umbrella, and in his left a fan. The umbrella is provided with a little reel at the top. The stick of the umbrella in this case is formed of a tube which is held by the hand of the Mikado, and a spindle attached to the umbrella top and passing through the tube, with its lower end resting upon a beveled wheel journaled within the figure. The beveled wheel carries a crank pin working in a slotted arm that extends through the side of the figure and grasps a fan, as shown in Fig. 2. When a cord is wound around the reel at the top of the umbrella, and drawn off after the manner of top spinning, the umbrella spins, giving a rotary motion to the beveled wheel, and the crank pin projecting from the wheel

THE " MIKADO," A NEW TOY.

imparts an oscillating motion to the arm carrying the fan. The umbrella, being slightly out of balance, gives a vibratory motion to the figure, which causes it to rock slightly and turn upon its support.

A TOY CART.

This simple toy for the diversion of children has been patented by Mr. Paxton Pollard, a deaf-mute printer, of No. 89 Main Street, Norfolk, Va. When the cart is drawn along, either forward or backward, the figures are caused to bend or bow simultaneously ; and at the same time, by the compression and escape of air through drum-like pedestals beneath the figures in the cart body, a whistling or squawking noise is made. The

POLLARD'S TOY CART.

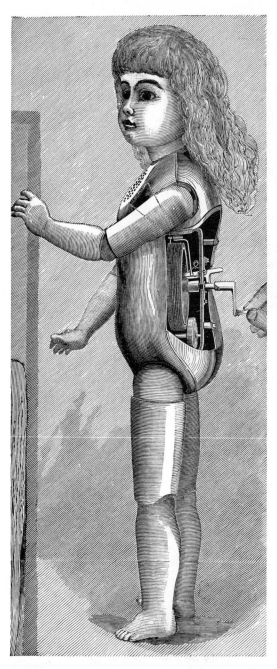

THE PHONOGRAPHIC DOLL.

figures may be of any desired grotesque shape, formed of paper or other suitable material, and in each is a spiral spring normally holding the images upright. The pedestals, of which a sectional view is shown in the small figure, have each an upper and lower head and a covering of thin skin or something similar, and in each is a coil spring, while in each upper head is a small opening covered by a thin metallic tongue arranged to vibrate rapidly on the passage of air through the opening. The upper portions of the two figures are connected by a transverse rod, and this rod is centrally connected by cord or rod with a crank in the central portion of the axle, whereby the figures are made to bend or bow as the cart is drawn along.

THE PHONOGRAPHIC DOLL.

One of the novelties which were introduced a few years ago was the talking doll. This interesting toy consisted of a good-sized doll which secreted a working phonograph. The doll's body is made of tin, and the interior thereof is filled with mechanism very much like that of the commercial phonograph, but, of course, much more simple and inexpensive. The cylinder of the phonograph of the talking doll is mounted on a sleeve which slides upon the shaft, the sleeve being screw-threaded so as to cause the cylinder to move lengthwise of the shaft. A key is provided by which the cylinder may be thrown out of

MECHANISM OF THE PHONOGRAPHIC DOLL.

engagement with the segmental nut, and a spiral spring is provided for returning the cylinder to the point of starting. The cylinder carries a ring of wax-like material upon which is recorded the speech or song to be repeated by the doll. Upon the same shaft with the record cylinder there is a large pulley which carries a belt for driving the flywheel shaft at the lower part of the phonographic apparatus. The key is fitted to the main shaft, by which the phonographic cylinder is rotated, and the flywheel tends to maintain a uniform speed.

Above the record cylinder is arranged a diaphragm such as is used in the regular phonograph, carrying a reproducing stylus, which is mounted on a lever in the same manner as the regular phonograph.   The funnel at the top of the phonographic apparatus opens underneath the breast of the doll, which is perforated to permit the sound to escape.   By the simple operation of turning the crank any child can make the doll say " Mary had a little lamb," " Jack and Jill," or whatever it was, so to speak, taught to say in the phonograph factory.

MAKING PHONOGRAPHIC RECORDS.

Our last engraving shows the manner of preparing the wax-like records for the phonographic dolls. They are placed upon an instrument very much like an ordinary phonograph, and into the mouth of which a girl speaks the words to be repeated by the doll. A large number of these girls are continually doing this work. Each one has a stall to herself, and the jangle produced by a number of girls simultaneously repeating "Mary had a little lamb," "Jack and Jill," "Little Bo-peep," and other interesting stories, is beyond description. These sounds united with the sounds of the phonographs themselves when reproducing the stories make a veritable pandemonium.

In passing through the works it is noticeable that order and system reign in every department. Everything is done upon the American, or "piece," system. The tools and machinery here used are the finest procurable. Every piece, without regard to its size or importance, is carefully inspected by aid of standard gauges, so that when the parts are brought together, no additional work is required to cause them to act properly.

The works of the doll are to some extent adjustable, and any adjustment necessary is effected in an extensive department in which the little phonographs are received from the assembling-rooms. Here they receive the finishing touches, and are passed on to another room where they are placed in the bodies of the dolls. From this department the finished dolls pass on to the packing-room, where they are carefully stored away in boxes having on their labels the name of the story the doll is able to repeat.

CHAPTER III.

MISCELLANEOUS TRICKS OF AN AMUSING NATURE.

INTERESTING TRICKS IN ELASTICITY.

The clever trick with billiard balls shown in Figs. 1 and 2 depends for its success on a truly scientific principle. A number of billiard balls are placed in a row against the cushion of the table. The player asks one of the spectators to name a certain number of balls to be pocketed without any apparent disturbance of the others. Suppose the number to be three. Then at the will of the player three balls separate from the others and roll into the pocket. The number is perfectly controllable, and when the hand of the player and one

SCIENTIFIC TRICKS WITH BILLIARD BALLS AND COINS.

end of the row of balls is covered, the trick appears mysterious. It is hardly less so when the entire experiment is visible. The feat is accomplished by removing from one end of the series as many balls as are to be projected from the opposite end, and rolling them forward against the end of the row remaining. An equal number of balls fly off from the opposite end of the row and roll into the pocket. Three balls driven against one end of the series will cause three to roll off, two will drive off two, one will drive off one, and so on.

The principle of this trick is illustrated in the well-known classroom experiment in which a series of contacting suspended balls of highly elastic material are made to transmit a blow delivered on the first of the series to the last ball of the series, so that the last ball will fly off without any apparent disturbance of the other balls. In this experiment, the first ball of the series is drawn back and allowed to fall against the first one of those remaining in contact. The impact of this ball will slightly flatten the ball with which it comes in contact, and each ball in turn transmits its momentum to the next, and so on through the entire series, the last of the series being thrown out as indicated.

In the case of the experiment with the billiard balls it is found by careful observation that separate blows are given to the series, corresponding in number to the number of balls removed, so that while the separation of the three balls at the end of the series is apparently simultaneous, in reality they are separated one at a time.

In Fig. 3 is illustrated a method of repeating the experiment with coins in lieu of balls. Dollars or half dollars may be used, and the effect is produced by sliding the coins.

NOVEL PUZZLE.

Our engraving shows a single perforated piece of wood having the form of a conventional heart, and in the perforation is inserted an arrow, also formed of a single piece of wood, the barb and head being much larger than the perforation in which the shank of the arrow is received. The heart is made of one kind of wood and the arrow of another. The question is, How did the arrow get into the heart? We have heard of the philosopher who was unable to rightly place a horse collar; and we have seen philosophers who could readily harness a horse, but who could not explain how the arrow got into the heart.

The puzzle illustrated is one of many thousands distributed gratuitously upon the streets of New York as an advertisement. The heart is of black walnut and the arrow is of basswood. Now we fear that the secret is out; for any one familiar with the properties of basswood knows that it may be enormously compressed, after which it may be steamed and expanded to its original volume. One end of the arrow was thus compressed, and in its compressed state was passed through the aperture of the heart, after which it was expanded.

A NOVEL PUZZLE.

Advantage has been taken of this principle in the manufacture of certain kinds of moldings. The portions of the wood to be left in relief are first compressed or pushed down by suitable dies below the general level of the board, then the board is planed down to a level surface, and afterward steamed. The compressed portions of the board are expanded by the steam, so that they stand out in relief.

SIMPLE MATCH TRICK.

To lift three matches by means of one, it is necessary to make an incision in the end of a match and insert the pointed end of a second match into this incision. Place them on the table, with a third match resting against them

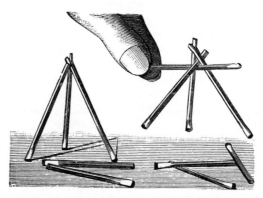

A SIMPLE MATCH TRICK.

for a support, as shown at the left of the figure. Then present a match to any one who may be looking on, and ask him to raise the three together by means of the match in his hand.

The solution is given at the right of the figure.

Bear lightly against the two matches that are joined until the third falls against the one held in the hand. Then raise it, and all three will be lifted together. Although this trick, which we find described in a French paper, "*Le Chercheur*," is probably as ancient as the art of making matches, our juvenile readers may find it of interest, and possibly it may afford them a half hour's amusement at recess time.

CRYSTALLIZED ORNAMENTS.

A beautiful ornament, which is very easily made, consists of a wooden cross covered with canton flannel, with the nap side out, and crystallized by immersion in a solution of alum. The nap retains the crystals so that they are

FIG. 1.—GROTTO.

not readily loosened or detached. The flannel should be attached to the wood by means of brass wire nails, and the cross should be suspended in a solution formed by dissolving a pound of alum in a gallon of warm water. The cross should be suspended in the solution while it is still warm and allowed to remain in until the solution cools, when it will be found covered with bright crystals.

Fig. 1 is a perspective view, and Fig. 2 a longitudinal section, of a grotto formed by crystallizing alum in a box containing jagged points covered with canton flannel, or wrapped about in various directions with coarse thread or twine. The box may be of wood or metal. It should have apertures in the top, ends, and sides. These apertures are stopped with corks while the box is filled with solution. After the crystallization the corks are removed, and the holes in the top, sides, and one end are covered with colored glass, and over the

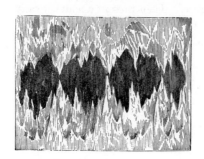

FIG. 2.—SECTION OF GROTTO.

front aperture is secured a convex spectacle lens, having a focus about equal to the length of the box. When the interior of the box is illuminated by a strong light passing through the colored windows, the effect is fine.

The solution used in this case is the same as that given for the cross. After the crystals are formed and the liquid is poured from the box, the interior should be allowed to dry thoroughly before closing the apertures.

FIG. 2.—SECTION OF GROTTO.

MAGICAL APPARITION OF A DRAWING ON WHITE PAPER.

It is well known that the vapors of mercury are very diffusive in their nature, and some quite singular experiments have been devised, based upon this knowledge, and upon the fact that the salts of silver and the chlorides of gold, platinum, iridium, and palladium are affected by these mercurial vapors.

If any one, for instance, should write upon a sheet of white paper with platinum chloride, no mark would be visible, as the liquid is quite colorless. If, however, the same sheet of paper should be held over a little mercury, the metal will be brought out on the paper in dark tints. This magical apparition of a figure or drawing on a sheet of paper which appears to be perfectly white is very astonishing to the spectator.

MAGICAL APPARITION OF A DRAWING ON WHITE PAPER.

Reversing the experiment, a no less marvelous result is obtained. At first expose the drawing or writing to the gases of mercury ; the lines will become charged with mercury, and then by simply bringing the drawing in contact with a sheet of paper previously sensitized with a solution of platinum, the drawing will be reproduced, line for line, on the white paper.

Drawings made in this way give a charming effect, the tones being very soft and the lines distinct and clear.

MAGIC PORTRAITS.

An able chemist, C. Wideman, has recently devised a curiosity in the way of engraving. It is a square piece of transparent glass in which absolutely nothing can be seen, even on the closest examination. If the glass be breathed

MAGIC PORTRAITS.

upon, so as to cover its surface with moisture, a face like that shown in the cut makes its appearance. As soon as the moisture leaves the glass, the image disappears.

A piece of glass is obtained similar to that used for making mirrors. The glass may be transparent, tinned, or silvered; that makes no difference as to the final result. Then a small quantity of fluorspar is placed in a porcelain capsule and moistened with sufficient sulphuric acid to make the proper chemi-

cal reaction to write with.   With this liquid and a quill pen the desired drawing or writing is executed on the previously well-cleaned glass.   In about five
minutes, or ten at the most, the glass is to be washed in common water and
dried with a cloth.   The plate will then be ready, and it will only be necessary
to breathe upon it to see the figures that have thus been traced make their
appearance.

A little practice will show the exact time necessary to leave the fluid lines
on the glass.   Too long a biting of the acid would be accompanied by so deep
an engraving of the glass that the lines would always be perceptible, even on
the dry glass.

A TRICK OPERA GLASS.

We present an engraving of a trick opera glass which may be new to some
of our readers, although the principle involved is very old.   One tube of the
opera glass is constructed in the ordinary manner, being provided with lenses,
while the other tube is arranged to give a view of any object at right angles to
the line of vision of the normal tube, or considerably to the rear of it.   The
trick tube has no eyepiece, and the objective is done away with, a piece of
japanned wood taking its place.   A portion of the tube and its leather cover is

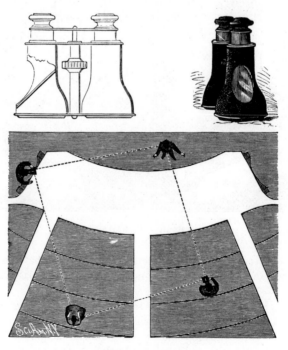

A TRICK OPERA GLASS.

cut away, and a mirror is inserted at an angle in the tube. When the observer wishes to use the trick glass at short range, he covers up a portion of the opening in the tube with his fingers, but at longer range this precaution would not be necessary. The practical uses of the glass are apparent. Our engraving shows a plan view of a theater, with the stage, boxes, and seats. The gentleman in the box and the one on the right of the center aisle both appear to be observing the actor on the stage, but in reality they are observing the lady on the left of the center aisle. Of course each of the gentlemen has his glasses turned a different way around.

A TOY BIRD THAT FLIES.

The naturalness and the easy movement of the wings of the little toy bird shown in the accompanying illustration, as the operator pulls gently on the end of the supporting string over which the bird moves, in accordance with the movement of the wings, always attracts observers when this toy is shown on the streets, as it has been by numerous venders within a short time. The toy is one of the latest of the many novelties which are constantly being exhibited by the wide-awake salesmen in the streets of New York and other large cities, and in the construction of some of which a surprising degree of skill and ingenuity are displayed. The cord leading from the aperture below the mouth

A TOY BIRD THAT EFFECTIVELY SIMULATES A BIRD FLYING.

of the bird is attached at its outer end to a hook in the wall or other support, while its inner portion passes over an idler and around a pulley, to which it is attached. This pulley is a little smaller than another at its side, as shown in Fig. 2, both pulleys being fast on the same shaft, and a cord from the larger pulley passes over an idler and out rearwardly, having at its end a finger-piece, on which the operator pulls in manipulating the toy. The cords are wound in opposite directions on their pulleys, so that the unwinding of the cord from the larger pulley, and the rotation of the same, winds up the cord on the smaller pulley, and causes the bird to move forward on what seems to be only a single length of cord, the backward movement taking place by gravity when the pull on the string is released. The movement of the wings is effected by a crank on each outer end of the pulley shaft, the crank being pivotally connected with an extension of a member of the inner one of two pairs of lazy tongs, and this member having also a pivotal bearing on a crossbar which turns in bearings on the outer side of the toy, just under where the wings are hinged to the body. The larger pair of lazy tongs is pivotally connected to the outer portion of the wing, giving a longer sweep thereto than to the inner portion, with which the smaller lazy tongs are connected; and the pivotal connection of the lazy tongs with the bearing in the crossbar gives an oscillatory movement to the wings, which constitutes a very good simulation of the natural movement of the wings of a bird in flight. A high degree of mechanical skill is shown in the putting together of this little toy.

THE PLANCHETTE TABLE.

This curious toy was popular as far back as 1867. Marvelous tales were told by the credulous about it, and even as distinguished scientists as Professor Tyndall and Professor Faraday were drawn into controversies concerning it. Many think there is some hidden secret in the construction of the planchette table. All that is necessary is that it should stand firmly and move readily on its legs. All that is needful is a heart-shaped cedar board with two nicely turned metal legs carrying well-oiled casters, and in the point of the board an aperture of suitable size for the insertion of a lead pencil, which serves as the third leg, and rests upon the paper. Many believe that humbug was stamped over every movement of the planchette board, and that one or the other of those whose hands bore upon it conspired with the little board in the formulation of its reply. Certain it is that planchette has performed some curious feats and has made for itself a position in the world of mysteries.

Probably the most generally accepted explanation is that advanced by Lewes and others, that although there is no intentional movement of the hands of those who are subjecting planchette to the influence, still there is, in spite of this, an unconscious pressure of the finger tips upon the board, which directs the movement of the pencil. Nor does it seem that such can be at all unlikely, for unconscious movement is by no means an unusual phase of our existence. The somnambulist who nightly takes a promenade from cellar to garret, or whose steps by chance have led him to the border of a precipice, has as little knowledge of the peril he has escaped, when the morning beams have awakened him, as planchette is conscious of its movements. How often also in mercantile pursuits do those who are accustomed to a certain routine perform it unconsciously, and after the work has been finished would be unable to tell you of many of the details of the work which custom has taught them to perform correctly, even while in a state of abstraction. Much has been said at times of

PLANCHETTE.

planchette's prophetic nature. Under the influence of certain people of a highly nervous temperament, or having to a certain extent the qualities of mediums, future events are said to be foretold. Secrets of which the person touching planchette is in ignorance have been divulged in a remarkable way, and many anecdotes shrouding planchette in mystery are repeated and believed.

Were the testimony, however, more universal, were planchette more consistent, and were it more generally truthful and less given to uttering remarkable sayings only occasionally, there would be more reason for according it a place for thorough and systematic investigation. Perhaps the day will come, when mesmerism is understood and mind reading is more satisfactorily explained, in which there will be occasion for looking upon planchette more seriously, and of regarding it as a wonderful means of displaying a rational nervous action independent of conscious mental cerebration.

JAPANESE MAGIC MIRRORS.

Mr. R. W. Atkinson, of the University of Tokio, Japan, communicates to "Nature" the following interesting account of these curious mirrors:

"A short time ago a friend showed me a curious effect, which I had previously heard of, but had never seen. The ladies of Japan use, in making their toilet, a small round mirror about one-twelfth to one-eighth of an inch in thickness, made of a kind of speculum metal, brightly polished, and coated with mercury. At the back there are usually various devices, Japanese or Chinese written characters, badges, etc., standing out in strong relief, and brightly polished like the front surface. Now, if the direct rays of the sun are allowed to fall upon the front of the mirror, and are then reflected on a screen, in a great many cases, though not in all, the figures at the back will appear to shine through the substance of the mirror as bright lines upon a moderately bright ground.

"I have since tried several mirrors as sold in the shops, and in most cases the appearance described has been observed with more or less distinctness.

JAPANESE MAGIC MIRROR.

"I have been unable to find a satisfactory explanation of this fact, but on considering the mode of manufacture I was led to suppose that the pressure to which the mirror was subjected during polishing, and which is greatest on the parts in relief, was concerned in the production of the figures. On putting this to the test by rubbing the back of the mirror with a blunt-pointed instrument, and permitting the rays of the sun to be reflected from the front surface, a bright line appeared in the image corresponding to the position of the part rubbed. This experiment is quite easy to repeat; a scratch with a knife or with any other hard body is sufficient. It would seem as if the pressure upon the back during polishing caused some change in the reflecting surface corresponding to the raised parts whereby the amount of light reflected was greater; or supposing that of the light which falls upon the surface, a part is absorbed and the rest reflected, those parts corresponding to the raised portions on the back are altered by the pressure in such a way that less is absorbed, and therefore a bright image appears. This, of course, is not an explanation of the phenomenon, but I put it forward as perhaps indicating the direction in which a true explanation may be looked for."

The following account of the manufacture of the Japanese mirrors is taken from a paper by Dr. Geerts, read before the Asiatic Society of Japan, and appearing in their "Transactions" for 1875–76, p. 39:

"For preparing the mold, which consists of two parts put together with their concave surfaces, the workman first powders a kind of rough plastic clay, and mixes this with levigated powder of a blackish 'tuff-stone' and a little charcoal powder and water, till the paste is plastic and suitable for being molded. It is then roughly formed by the aid of a wooden frame into square or round cakes; the surface of the latter is covered with a levigated half-liquid mixture of powdered 'chamotte' (old crucibles which have served for melting bronze or copper) and water. Thus well prepared, the blackish paste in the frame receives the concave designs by the aid of woodcuts, cut in relief. The parts of the mold are put together in the frame and dried. Several of these flat molds are then placed in a melting box made of clay and 'chamotte.' This box has on the top an opening into which the liquid bronze is poured after it has been melted in small fireproof clay crucibles. The liquid metal naturally fills all openings inside the box, and consequently also the cavities of the moulds. For mirrors of first quality the following metal mixture is used in one of the largest mirror foundries in Kioto:

Lead .... 5 parts.
Tin .... 15 "
Copper .... 80 "
                                                            ——
                                                            100

"For mirrors of inferior quality are taken:

Lead .... 10 parts.
Natural sulphide of lead and antimony .... 10 "
Copper .... 80 "
                                                            ——
                                                            100

"After being cooled, the melting box and molds are crushed and the mirrors taken away. These are then cut, scoured, and filed until they are roughly finished. They are then first polished with a polishing powder called *to-no-ki*, which consists of the levigated powder of a soft kind of whetstone (*to-ishi*) found in Yamato and many other places. Secondly, they are polished with a piece of charcoal and water, the charcoal of the wood *ho-no-ki* (*Magnolia hypoleuca*) being preferred as the best for the purpose. When the surfaces of the mirrors are well polished they are covered with a layer of mercury amalgam consisting of quicksilver, tin, and a little lead. The amalgam is rubbed vigorously with a piece of soft leather, which manipulation must be continued for a long time, until the excess of mercury is expelled and the mirrors have a fine, bright reflecting surface."

MAGIC MIRRORS.

The following article on magic mirrors by MM. Bertin and Dubosq outlines several interesting experiments.

"The people of the Far East, the Chinese and the Japanese, in bygone times were acquainted with metallic mirrors only; and even to-day they make only these. They are made of speculum metal, of various forms and sizes, but always portable. One of the faces is polished and always slightly convex, so that its reflection gives images which are reduced in size; the other face is plane or slightly concave, and always has cast on it ornaments which are in relief. Among the many mirrors thus constructed there are a few which possess a wonderful property: when a beam of the sun's light falls upon the polished surface and is reflected on a white screen, we see in the disk of light thus formed the image of the ornamentation which is on the back of the mirror. The Chinese have long known of these mirrors and value them highly; they call them by a name which signifies 'mirrors which are permeable to the light.' We, of the West, call them 'magic mirrors.'

"Very few persons had seen magic mirrors till Mr. Ayrton, professor of the Polytechnic School at Yeddo, exhibited several which he had brought with him from Japan, and he experimented with them as already mentioned.

"In the meantime I received a visit from M. Dybowski, my former pupil, who had returned from Japan, where for two years he had been the colleague of Professor Ayrton. He brought back with him as objects of curiosity four *temple mirrors*, that is to say, antique mirrors; these are far superior to those of modern production, for their manufacture has been nearly abandoned by reason of the introduction of the silvered mirrors of Europe. We tried them together; three were circular, and the thinnest of them, which is a disk of 15.3 centimeters in diameter, was found to be slightly magic.

"To try such a mirror we reflect a sunbeam from its polished surface to a white cardboard about one meter distant. But to obtain the very best effects we must illuminate the mirror with a diverging pencil of light; this pencil is made still further divergent by reflection from the mirror, because its reflecting surface is convex. We can now receive the reflected rays on a screen at a greater distance, and we at once see distinctly the magnified image of the ornamentation on the back of the mirror. These raised designs appear on the screen in white on a dark ground. The image thus made by our mirror was confused, because it was not a good one; had it been properly made, the image would have been sharply defined. I then knew of no means by which I could make it give better effects.

"The means by which the mirror could have been improved were first pointed out by M. Govi in the second of his two papers. It is a consequence of the true theory of magic mirrors. The theory was not reached at once. I proposed to M. Dubosq to associate himself with me in order, first, to repeat the experiments of the learned Italian, Govi, and then to study generally the interesting phenomena of magic mirrors, in the hope of being able eventually to reproduce them in his workshops. At first we had only at our disposal the mirror

THE MAGIC MIRROR.

brought from Japan by M. Dybowski, and which gave confused images with the reflected solar rays. These images became very sharply defined when we had heated the back of the mirror with a gas lamp, and it gave very magic effects.

"We then made a mold and reproduced this mirror, not in Japanese bronze, but in ordinary gun metal. The first copy was roughly worked on the lathe, after the Japanese manner, in order to render it magical, but this was broken. The second was worked carefully on an optical grinding tool; the surface was then polished and nickel plated, but it was not magical; it acquired this property in a high degree when it was heated, and even retained traces of it after it had been repeatedly heated. Several Japanese mirrors which we have procured have given analogous results.

"We then engraved letters on the back of little rectangular Japanese mirrors. On heating these the letters appeared in black in the reflected image. When we cut lines around the design on the back of the mirror, heat rendered them very magical, for the design stood out, framed in the black lines which bordered the figures.

"Thus it is seen that heat is very efficacious in rendering mirrors magical, but it is not without its inconveniences. First of all, it injures the mirrors, which thus lose their polish, especially when they have been amalgamated; also, the mirror is often not heated equally, and the images are deformed. It occurred to us that the change of curvature which was required could be obtained more uniformly by means of pressure. M. Dubosq therefore constructed a shallow cylinder of metal, closed at one end by the metallic mirror, and at the other by a flat plate of brass, having in its center a stopcock which we could attach, by means of a rubber tube, to a little hand pump. This pump could be made either to condense or rarefy air. If the rubber tube was attached to the pump, arranged as a condenser, a few strokes of the piston sufficed to compress sufficiently the air in the shallow cylinder; the mirror became more and more convex, the cone of reflected rays became more and more open, and in the image on the screen the design on the back of the mirror became more and more distinct. Our Japanese mirror when thus treated gave very fine images, and the copy which we had made, and which gave no result as ordinarily experimented with, now became a magic mirror as perfect as any of those which Professor Ayrton had exhibited before us. A mirror in brass, nickel plated, on whose back was soldered tin-plate figures, around whose borders were cut lines, became very magical by pressure, and gave the design on its back in light surrounded by dark borders.

"This is what I call the *positive image.* We can also obtain the *negative image,* or the inverse of the preceding one, by rarefying the air in the shallow box. To do this we have only to attach the rubber tube to the pump arranged as an ordinary air pump. On now working the piston the air in the shallow box is rarefied; the mirror becomes concave; the cone of the diverging reflected rays closes up; the image of the design is reduced in size, changes its appearance, and becomes an image of the design on the back of the mirror; but this now shows in shade edged with bright borders.

"These experiments require an intense light. A jet of coal gas is insufficient, but the oxyhydrogen light is sufficiently intense. We intercept it with a screen perforated with a small hole, so that the diverging pencil which falls on the mirror may not spread too much. The mirror is mounted on the top of a column so that it can be made to face in any required direction. The effects are most brilliant and the best defined when we experiment with the rays of the sun. When we expose the mirror to the beam of the *porte-lumière* it is generally not entirely covered by the light; in this case it is best to use a diverging beam, obtained by means of a lens placed between the *porte-lumière* and the mirror.

"Thus we have seen that we can now make copies of the Japanese mirrors, some of which may be magical, but all may be rendered so by making them covers of the shallow box containing either compressed or rarefied air. This pressure box and its mirror, made in the Japanese style, certainly forms one of the most curious pieces of apparatus which is to be found in the cabinet of physics.

"We shall not, however, stop here. One of these days, while our mirror is magical under the influence of pressure, we will take a cast of its surface, and then reproduce this by means of galvano-deposition. This surface will have all the irregularities of that of the magic mirror, and will produce by its reflected rays the image of a design which no longer exists on its back."

BOOK V.

PHOTOGRAPHIC DIVERSIONS.

CHAPTER I.

TRICK PHOTOGRAPHY.

LAVATER'S APPARATUS FOR TAKING SILHOUETTES.

This is not a photographic diversion, but it is so interesting and so much of a historical curiosity that we reproduce it here. When first introduced, the silhouette attracted the attention of the learned, and was regarded as one of the wonders of the age. Lavater, in his celebrated work on physiognomy, describes an accurate and convenient machine for drawing silhouettes. The engraving is almost self-explanatory. "The shadow," says Lavater, "is projected upon a fine paper, well oiled and dried, and placed behind a piece of plate glass supported in a frame secured to the back of the chair. Behind this glass the artist stands, and holding the frame with one hand, draws with the other." A candle was used to furnish the necessary light. The proportions of the silhouette must be judged principally from the length and breadth of the face; a correct and well-proportioned profile should be equal in breadth and height. A horizontal line drawn from the point of the nose to the back of the head (provided the head be erect) should not exceed in length a perpendicular line which extends from the top of the head to the junction of the chin and head. All of the forms which deviate sensibly from this rule are so many anomalies.

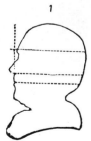
1

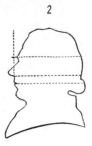
2

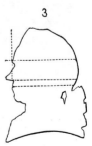
3

SPECIMENS OF SILHOUETTES OBTAINED BY LAVATER.

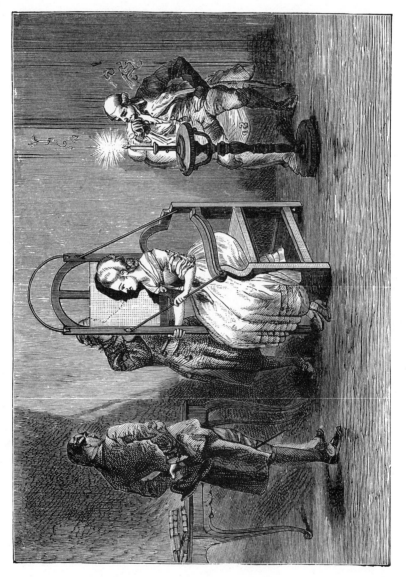

LAVATER'S APPARATUS FOR TAKING SILHOUETTES.

In support of these observations Lavater gives a number of specimens of silhouettes, and insists upon the conclusion which he deduces from their study. We take a few examples of them. In No. 1 Lavater sees an upright soul, an even temper, taste, and frankness; in No. 2 the contour of the nose carries the infallible mark of a good temper; in No. 3 we have clearness of judgment.

PHOTOGRAPHY UPON A BLACK GROUND.

Some of the most interesting trick photographs are obtained by the use of a black background. In brief, the process consists in limiting the field of an objective so as to preserve intact for subsequent exposures the unused portion of the sensitized plate, and to be able to obtain upon the latter such combinations as may be desired of any number whatever of successive poses. The annexed diagram shows the arrangements which may be used. Nos. I. to III. are the ones most frequently used, and No. IV. permits of taking a number of photographs analogous to the one that we reproduce in our second engraving.

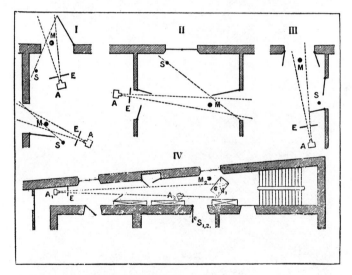

FIG. 1.—EXPLANATORY DIAGRAM.

Where a kneeling girl is represented as a statuette upon a table, the operator is seen in the rear, manipulating the rubber bulb which controls the shutter. In Fig. 3 is shown a picture taken in open daylight, using as a black background the opening of a large coach house; as a screen, a piece of blackened cardboard was used, as is shown, supported by a violin stand to the right of the figures. Now, if we closely examine the child who, in front of the cart, is assisting in

FIG. 2.—COMPOSITE PHOTOGRAPH IN TWO POSES, AT DIFFERENT DISTANCES, ON THE SAME
PLATE.

FIG. 3.—GROUP IN OPEN AIR, IN TWO DIFFERENT POSES ON ONE PLATE.

FIG. 4.—FACSIMILE OF A COMPOSITE PHOTOGRAPH.

FIG. 5.—A DECAPITATION.

the delivery of his own head, we shall find that it is traversed vertically by a line of shadows, indicating that a slight veil was produced at the first exposure upon all that portion of plate that was exposed by the incompletely drawn shutter of the frame. If the plate had been entirely exposed it would be difficult to suspect anything.

The apparatus for producing the composite photographs upon a black background is very simple. A blackened piece of cardboard is provided with an aperture nearly corresponding to the place preserved in the definitive picture for the object, head, bust, etc., that one desires to isolate. This screen is slid into the first fold of the bellows of the camera, that is to say, very close to the

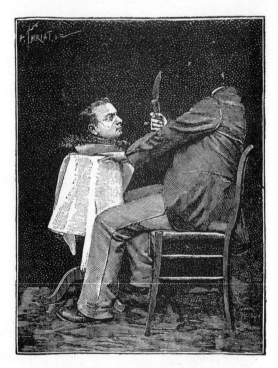

FIG. 6.—ANOTHER DECAPITATION.

sensitized plate, and at the moment of focusing, the position of the apparatus is so regulated as to make the image of the subject appear through the apertures in the screen and in the proper position. This process is the most rapid and is the surest. No reflection is any longer possible, and the preservation of the plate is absolute. What is no less advantageous is the sharpness of the outline, which permits of the most delicate junctions; such sharpness is inversely proportioned to the distance that separates the screen from the sensitized plate. We present a number of engravings of photographs taken upon a black background.

FIG. 7.—THE HEAD IN THE WHEELBARROW.

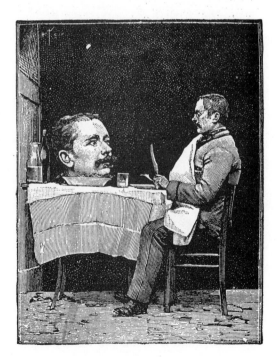

FIG. 8.—THE HEAD UPON A PLATE.

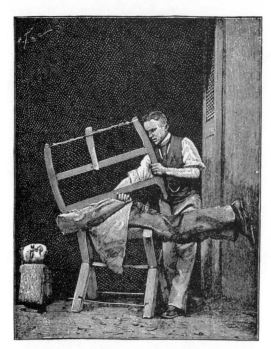

FIG. 9.—THE SAWED-OFF HEAD.

FIG. 10.—THE REDUCTION.

Our next engraving represents a decapitation by means of a saber, and it is taken by means of an exposure in which the head was placed upon a block, the subject inclining forward upon his knees, and the diaphragm occupying about two-thirds of the plate, completely masking the body up to the neck. Then, without changing the position of the apparatus, the diaphragm is placed on the other side in order to conceal the head, and the body is photographed in the second position along with the person representing the executioner. It would have been possible by a third exposure to so arrange things as to make the executioner the decapitated person. By the same process the following trick photographs are made.

FIG. 11.—MAN IN A BOTTLE.

The sawed-off head is one of the best of these photographs. Fig. 10 gives the same individual photographed twice on two different scales. This kind of reduction gives very astonishing results.

The most curious illusion of all is the one in which a man is seen inside of a bottle. The individual represented was first photographed on a sufficiently reduced scale to allow him to appear to enter the bottle. The diaphragm was arranged around the subject. The bottle was then photographed on a large scale, and the result is, the man is seen in the bottle.

SPIRIT PHOTOGRAPHY.*

Many years ago, in the old wet-collodion days, a well-known photographer was one day surprised by the visitation of a spirit. The apparition did not make its appearance during the nocturnal hours, as is, we have been given to understand, the custom of these ladies and gentlemen from the other world, but, strangely enough, in broad daylight; and not by his bedside to disturb his peaceful slumber, but upon the photograph he was in the act of producing. Had this gentleman been of that soft-brained kind, so easily gulled by the professional spiritualist, it is possible that he would not have done what he did, which was to make a thorough and scientific examination as to the probable cause of the phenomenon. The case was this: A gentleman sitter had been taken in the usual manner upon a collodion plate. Upon taking a positive print from the negative, he was surprised to find a dim white figure of a lady apparently hovering over the unconscious sitter. Upon examination of the negative, the image of the figure was also visible, but not so plainly as in the positive. The explanation of the whole matter was soon made easy. In those days glass was not so cheap as at present, and all new or spoiled negatives were cleaned off and freshly prepared with collodion for further use. In this case the glass had previously supported the negative image of a lady dressed in white. Some chemical action had evidently taken place between the image and the glass itself, turning the latter slightly yellow in some parts. This faint yellow image, although hardly visible in the negative, had, being of a non-actinic color, given quite a distinct image in the positive. The case was not an isolated one, as these spirit photographs, as they were called, often made their appearance when old negatives were cleaned and the glass used again. The precise action producing the image has never, we think, been satisfactorily explained. It could often be made more distinct by breathing on the glass. We do not know if any enterprising humbug ever took advantage of this method of producing spirit photographs to extort money from the unwary, but about ten years ago a work was published, entitled "Chronicles of the Photographs of Spiritual Beings and Phenomena Invisible to the Material Eye," by a Miss Houghton. In this a number of reproductions of photographs of "spirits" were given with a detailed explanation of how they were obtained and the difficulties attending their production, the "spirits" being apparently of very independent natures, only making their appearance when they felt so inclined. It is quite possible that a person entirely ignorant of photographic methods might be led into the belief that they were actually photographic images of the dead, but we fear that the book is hardly well enough written to deceive the experienced photographer. At certain and most unfortunate periods in the process employed, some of the plates had a conven-

---

* From "Photographic Amusements," by Walter E. Woodbury. New York, 1896. The Scovill & Adams Co., publishers.

ient habit of slipping into the washing tank and there, according to the author, becoming utterly ruined; also we learn that many were ruined by being accidentally smudged by the photographer's fingers. We should not, we fear, have a very high opinion of an operator who was in the constant habit of "smudging" negatives with his fingers so as to entirely spoil them, nor can we quite understand what brand of plates was used that "got spoiled by falling into the water."

A " SPIRIT " PHOTOGRAPH.

It is not difficult to explain how these pictures were produced. There are quite a number of methods. With a weak-minded sitter, over whom the operator had complete control, the matter would be in no wise a difficult one. It would then only be necessary for the "spirit," suitably attired for the occasion, to appear for a few seconds behind the sitter during the exposure and be taken slightly out of focus, so as not to appear too corporeal.

If, however, the sitter be of another kind, anxious to discover how it was done and on the alert for any deceptive practices, the method described would be rather a risky one, as he might turn round suddenly at an inconvenient moment and detect the *modus operandi*. In such a case it sometimes becomes necessary to find some other method where it would not be requisite for the "spirit" to make its appearance during the presence of the sitter.

The ghostly image can be prepared upon the plate either before or after the exposure of the sitter. The method is this: In a darkened room the draped figure to represent the spirit is posed in a spirit-like attitude (whatever that may be) in front of a dark background with a suitable magnesium or other light arrangement thrown upon the figure, which is then focused in the "naturalistic" style; or, better still, a fine piece of muslin gauze is placed close to the lens, which gives a hazy, indistinct appearance to the image. The exposure is made and the latent image remains upon the sensitized plate, which is again used to photograph the sitter. Upon developing we get the two

SPIRIT PICTURE.

images, the "spirit" mixed up with the figure. The "spirit" should be as indistinct as possible, as it will then be less easy for the subject to dispute the statement that it is the spirit-form of his dead and gone relative. Some amount of discretion in this part of the performance must be used, we fancy, otherwise the same disaster might happen as did to a spiritualist some little time ago.

An elderly gentleman had come for a séance, and, after some mysterious maneuvers, the gentleman was informed that the spirit of his mother was there. "Indeed!" replied the gentleman, somewhat astonished. "What does she say?" "She says she will see you soon," informed the medium. "You are getting old now and must soon join her." "Quite right," replied the old gentleman; "I'm going round to her house to tea to-night."—Total collapse of spiritualist.

Fluorescent substances, such as bisulphate of quinine, can also be employed. This compound, although almost invisible to the eye, photographs

SPIRIT PICTURE.

nearly black. If a white piece of paper be painted with the substance, except on certain parts, the latter only will appear white in the picture.

We hope that it will not be inferred that we desire to explain how to deceive persons with regard to photographs of "spirits," for this is not so; we only hope that they will be made merely for amusement, and, if possible, to expose persons who practice on the gullibility of inexperienced persons.

The engraving on page 436 is a reproduction of a "spirit" photograph made by a photographer claiming to be a "spirit photographer," and to have

PHOTOGRAPH OF "SPIRITS."

the power to call these ladies and gentlemen from the " vasty deep " and make them impress their image upon the sensitized plate by the side of the portraits of their living relatives.

Fortunately, however, we were in this case able to expose the fraud. Mr. W. M. Murray, a prominent member of the Society of Amateur Photographers of New York, called our attention to the similarity between one of the " spirit " images and a portrait painting by Sichel the artist.

PAINTING BY N. SICHEL.

A reproduction of the picture is given herewith, and it will be seen at once that the " spirit " image is copied from it.

In a recent number of " The Australian Photographic Journal " we read of the following novel method of making so-called " spirit " photographs: " Take a negative of any supposed 'spirit' that is to be represented, put it in the printing frame with the film side out; lay on the glass side a piece of platino-type paper with the sensitive side up; clamp in place the back of the printing frame and expose to the sun for half a minute. Now place in the printing frame the negative of another person to whom the ' spirit ' is to appear, and over it put the previously exposed sheet, film side down; expose to the sun for two minutes until the image is faintly seen, then develop in the usual way, and the blurred ' spirit ' photograph will appear faintly to one side or directly behind the distinct image.   Sheets of paper with different ghost exposures can be prepared beforehand.''

" Spirit " photographs might easily be made by means of Professor Roentgen's newly discovered process of impressing an image upon a photographic dry-plate without uncovering the shutter.   The process would, however, entail considerable expense, and would necessitate the use of so much costly apparatus that we will content ourselves with the simple mention of the possibility.

ARTIFICIAL MIRAGE.

The mirage is a well-known natural phenomenon, especially in tropical countries.   Our engraving shows an interesting experiment which permits of reproducing a mirage by photography.   A very even plate of sheet iron is taken and placed horizontally upon two supports.   The plate is heated very uniformly and sprinkled with sand.   A small, painted Egyptian landscape is arranged at one end of the plate, and the " eye " of the photographic instrument is so placed that the visual ray may be said to graze the plate.   The mirage can be photographed as shown in our engraving.

DUPLEX PHOTOGRAPHY.

The following very ingenious method is pointed out by M. H. Duc, of Grenoble.   It consists in making use of a special frame which, instead of having a sliding shutter, is provided with two shutters that operate like the leaves of a door.   These shutters, B B (Fig. 1), pivot upon two vertical axes, A A, whose upper extremities project from the frame so that they can be maneuvered from the exterior.   As the shutters must join very accurately, M. Duc affixes asbestos paper to their edges.   A sliding steel plate, E D, permits of keeping the two shutters closed before and after exposure.   This is removed when the frame is in the camera.

The ground glass is divided into two parts by a pencil line that exactly tallies with the junction line of the shutters.   The subject is focused on one of the halves of the glass, and then the

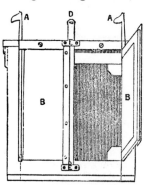

FIG. 1.—PLATE FRAME.

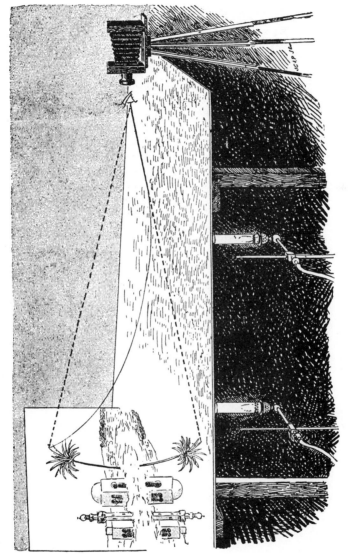

ARTIFICIAL REPRODUCTION AND PHOTOGRAPHING OF A MIRAGE.

corresponding side of the frame is unmasked.   After exposure the model changes place, and then the other side of the frame is opened.

The photograph reproduced in Fig. 2 was taken in this manner.   It contains three representations of the same person.   The easel, stool, and artist having

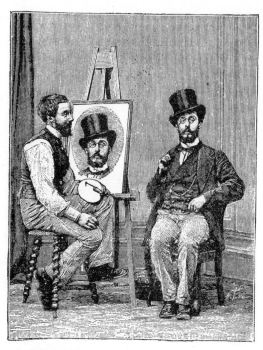

FIG. 2.—COPY OF A PHOTOGRAPH SHOWING THE SAME PERSON THRICE REPEATED.

been arranged, an image is taken on the left side of the plate, then the painter moves his position to the right and a second exposure is made.   The portrait on the easel is that of the same person, but was taken afterward on the positive by means of the negative and a vignetter (Fig. 3).

The other photograph (Fig. 4) is likewise very curious, and was taken with the same apparatus.   A hat was fixed firmly to a head rest, and the same person then glided under it and presented his two profiles.

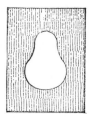

FIG. 3.—VIGNETTER.

FIG. 4.—COPY OF A PHOTOGRAPH GIVING TWO PROFILES OF THE SAME PERSON.

ILLUSIVE PHOTOGRAPHY.

The amusing examples of illusive photography which we show herewith are due to Mr. Frank A. Gilmore, of Auburn, R. I. The camera is so arranged that the pictures which are reproduced suggest the story of Dr. Jekyll and Mr. Hyde. The porter with the sack and the gentleman who is about to give him some money are one and the same person. The pedestrian is walking with himself, and the fighter is prepared to annihilate himself.

The method of producing the illusion is very simple. A black-lined box is fitted to the back of a "kodak" or any other camera; the front of the box is closed by two doors. On opening one door a picture may be taken on one side of the plate; on closing this door and opening the other, the other half of the plate is ready for exposure. The subject poses in one position and his photograph is taken with one door open, care being taken to bring the figure within half of the area of the sensitized plate. A good finder enables this detail to be attended to. Then one door is closed and the other is opened, and the exposure of the other half of the plate is accomplished. The plate holder is not removed during the dual exposure. If possible, instantaneous pictures

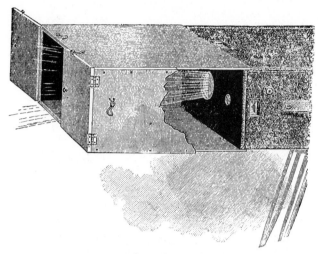

ATTACHMENT TO KODAK FOR DUPLEX PHOTOGRAPHY.

should be taken, as time exposures are rather risky, involving danger of shaking the camera, and the length of exposure may not be the same for both sides of the plate.   Our engravings were taken with an ordinary four by five "kodak," and the box was an ordinary cigar box cut down to fit, and blackened inside.

SHOWING TWO PHOTOGRAPHS OF SAME PERSON ON A SINGLE NEGATIVE.

OTHER ILLUSTRATIONS OF DUPLEX PHOTOGRAPHY.

PHOTOGRAPHING A HUMAN HEAD UPON A TABLE.

The picture is made in the following way: A table is provided with a top having a portion of it movable at B.   The person whose head is to be photographed sits in a chair underneath the table.   The board is removed to allow the person's head to pass above the table.   The board is again placed in position on the table, and the closer the person's neck fits the hole in the table the better.   The camera is arranged with a box, as in the illusion we have just described; but in this case the camera is turned so that the two doors, C and D, open up and down instead of sideways.   The camera is raised or lowered until the crack between the two doors of the box is on a level with the edge of the table.   The upper door, C, in the box is opened wide, so as to expose to the sensitized plate, when the shutter is worked, the head above the table, and all of the objects within the range of the lens above the edge of the table.

PHOTOGRAPHING A HUMAN HEAD UPON A TABLE.

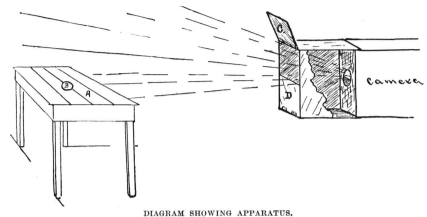

DIAGRAM SHOWING APPARATUS.

After making these arrangements an exposure is made, then the person whose head has been photographed is no longer required. The top door, C, is now closed, and the bottom door, D, is opened wide. By this means the upper part of the plate is protected from a second exposure and leaves the way clear to expose the lower, and as yet unexposed, part of the plate. The shutter is again opened, and this time everything in range of the lens below the edge of the table is photographed, and, of course, does not show the person under the table. The illustration which we give, as well as the diagram showing how it may be produced, are the work of Mr. James Burt Smalley, of Bay City, Mich.

PHOTOGRAPHING A HEAD ON A PLATTER.

We have already shown how a photograph may be made upon a table, and we now show how one can easily take pictures of the same person in different attitudes on one plate. This trick is performed by Mr. Frank Gilmore, of Auburn, R. I. Pictures made in this manner seem extremely puzzling, when in

HEAD OF LADY PHOTOGRAPHED ON A PLATTER.

PAN CUT AWAY TO REPRESENT PLATTER.

reality they are very simple to make. An ordinary extension dining-table is used, the person to be photographed being seated in an opening between the two ends of the table, caused by the removal of a leaf. The tablecloth is then arranged so as to cover the gap. If necessary, the table may be built up with boards so as to support the cloth and other articles. To make the illusion complete, a pan, cut away so that it may be conveniently placed around the neck, as shown in our engraving, may be used. This gives the appearance in the photograph of being an ordinary platter bearing the head of a living person.

HOW THE PHOTOGRAPH IS MADE.

PHOTOGRAPHING A CATASTROPHE.*

On this page we reproduce a curious photograph by M. Bracq, which appeared some time ago in the "Photo Gazette."

Despite all the terrible catastrophe which it represents, carrying pictures along with him in his fall, the subject has not experienced the least uneasiness, not even so much as will certainly be felt by our readers at the sight of the tumble represented.

FIG. 1.—A CATASTROPHE.

The mode of operating in this case is very simple, and we are indebted to "*La Nature*" for the description of the method employed by M. Bracq. The photographic apparatus being suspended at a few yards from the floor of the room, in such a way as to render the ground-glass horizontal (say, between the two sides of a double ladder—a combination that permits of easy focusing and putting the plates in place), there is spread upon the floor a piece of wall-

* From "Photographic Amusements," by Walter E. Woodbury.

FIG. 2.—ARRANGEMENT OF
CAMERA.

paper, about six feet in length by five feet in width, at the bottom of which a wainscot has been drawn. A ladder, a few pictures, a statuette, and a bottle are so arranged as to give an observer the illusion of the wall of a room—that of a dining-room, for instance. A hammer, some nails, etc., are placed at the proper points. Finally a five by two and one-half foot board, to which a piece of carpet, a cardboard plate, etc., have been attached, is placed under the foot of a chair, which then seems to rest upon this false floor at right angles with that of the room.

Everything being ready, the operator lies down quietly in the midst of these objects, assumes a frightened expression, and waits until the shutter announces to him that he may leave his not very painful position. This, evidently, is merely an example that our readers will be able to modify and vary at their will.

NEW TYPE OF PHOTOGRAPHIC PORTRAIT.

Our engraving shows a new type of photographic portrait which gives the effect of a marble bust. The model is placed behind a hollow column or thin pedestal of painted wood. If it is desired to represent a man in classic costume, a helmet of white cardboard is placed upon the model's head, his hair and face is whitened with rice powder, and those portions of the body it is desired to render visible are surrounded with white flannel. The background should be formed of black velvet. After the negative is developed, the figure that it is desired to preserve is cut around with a penknife, and the arms and all the portions that are not wanted are scratched out. The glass thus becomes transparent when the scratching has been done, and in the positive the bust stands out from the background.

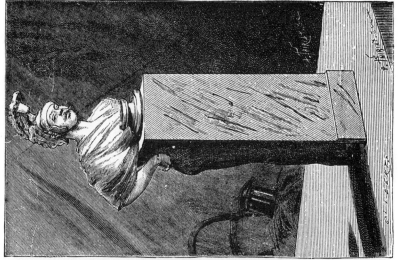

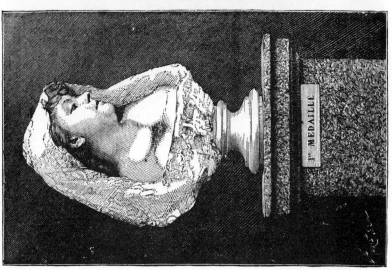

FIG. 2.—HOW THE BUST IS MADE.

FIG. 1.—A PHOTO BUST.

A MULTIPLE PORTRAIT.

The portrait which we reproduce was taken by a photographer of Constantinople, Mr. Baboudjian. The subject of the photograph is represented a

FIG. 1.—REPRODUCTION OF A PHOTOGRAPH OF A MULTIPLE PLATE.

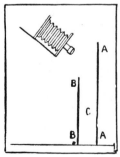

FIG. 2.—DIAGRAM SHOWING THE ARRANGEMENT OF THE APPARATUS.

number of times, so that the whole presents the aspect of a number of persons standing in a line. Two mirrors, A and B, are placed parallel to each other, and are separated by an interval of about two feet. In the narrow corridor thus formed he places the subject to be photographed. One of the mirrors must be a little taller than the other, and the apparatus is turned toward the shorter one and is slightly inclined toward the floor. The mirrors are without frames. The result of this arrangement is shown in our engraving, the same person being represented a number of times. There is considerable difficulty in lighting the subject properly.

MULTIPHOTOGRAPHY.

The system of photography which we illustrate gives an excellent opportunity for a great range in the art of posing; the instrument is called the "multiphotograph." If an image is placed in front of two mirrors inclined

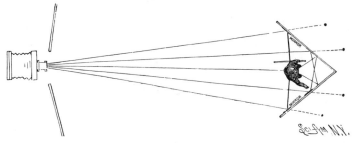

DIAGRAM OF THE PRODUCTION OF FIVE VIEWS OF ONE SUBJECT BY MULTIPHOTOGRAPHY.

to each other at an angle of ninety degrees, three images will be produced in the mirror; at sixty degrees, five images will be produced; at forty-five degrees, seven images; and if the mirrors are parallel, theoretically, an infinite number

GALLERY ARRANGED FOR MULTIPHOTOGRAPHY.

REPRODUCTION OF A MULTIPHOTOGRAPH.

of images will result. In the process of the photography which we illustrate, advantage is taken of this to produce at one exposure a number of different views of the same subject. The person to be photographed sits with the back to the instrument, while in front of the face are two mirrors set at the desired angles to each other, the inner edges touching.

In the case illustrated, these mirrors are inclined at an angle of seventy-two degrees; four images are produced. The exposure is made, and on the negative appears not only the back view of the subject, but also the four reflected images in profile and different three-quarter positions.

The courses taken by the rays of light are determined by the law that the angle of incidence is equal to the angle of reflection. In the diagram the rays of light are traced in their course from the subject to the mirror, and back and forth, giving a good idea of the relation of the images to the subject and of the five images to the focal plane, the virtual position of the images being further from the instrument than the subject proper. We also give an engraving showing images of a full-length figure.

IMAGES OF A FULL-LENGTH PORTRAIT.

PINHOLE CAMERA.

We illustrate in the cut a camera for photography in which the *ne plus ultra* of simplicity may fairly be said to be attained. It is a little tin box two inches in diameter and three-quarters deep from cover to bottom. A hole was punched in the center of the cover, and over this a piece of foil was secured by varnish. The foil was taken from a button card. Small mother-of-pearl buttons are generally mounted on pieces of pasteboard with this foil under them. Through the foil, where it extended across the hole in the box cover, a hole was made with a No. 10 needle. The needle was pressed through until

PINHOLE CAMERA.

its point could be just felt by the finger held against the opposite side of the foil. This made an aperture one-sixtieth inch in diameter. The interior of the box was blackened. A piece of Eastman's "A" bromide paper, cut circular so as to fit in the box, was placed in it against the bottom, and the cover put on. This, of course, was done in the absence of actinic light. Then, with an exposure of four minutes, at a distance of about ten feet from the object, the negative shown in the sketch was taken. It was developed with oxalate developer. Castor oil or vaseline was used to make it transparent, so as to adapt it for printing from. The subject of the negative was the old armory at Summit Hill, Mt. Jefferson, Pa.

As nothing special, neither paper, glass negative, nor developer, was used, this process of pinhole photography deserves special mention. It might often be of considerable use in emergencies that sometimes will present themselves to the photographer.

The special novelty that presents itself is the use of paper instead of glass for the negative, as paper can be cut to fit any size or shape of box. The brand of paper employed is slow paper.

A PHOTOGRAPHIC NECKTIE.

This ingenious apparatus is a French invention. The general appearance of the necktie is seen in our second engraving, the first figure showing the back of it. The metallic camera is flat and very light, and is hidden under the

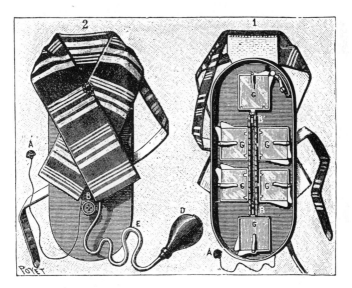

FIGS. 1 AND 2.—PHOTOGRAPHIC NECKTIE—FRONT AND BACK VIEW.

vest. The interior mechanism comprises six small frames which are capable of passing in succession before the objective. These frames each hold a sensitized plate or film. The necktie having been adjusted, the shutter is set by a pull upon the button, A, which passes under the vest. In order to change the plate it is necessary to turn from left to right the button, B, which has been introduced into the buttonhole of the vest and which simulates a button of that garment. The frames are attached to a link chain, something like an ordinary bicycle chain, which is operated by the button. In order to open the shutter it is only necessary to press the rubber bulb, which may be placed in the pocket. The shutter is tripped pneumatically by means of the bulb and tube. In order to change the plates it is only necessary to turn the small springs,

G G G. The sensitized plates or films are put in the frames, and the springs are turned back to their former position. The lens is, of course, concealed in the scarf pin.

MAGIC PHOTOGRAPHS.

A recent novelty is a cigar or cigarette holder accompanied by a small package of photographic paper about the size of a postage stamp. One of these papers is placed in the interior of the holder, before an orifice arranged for the

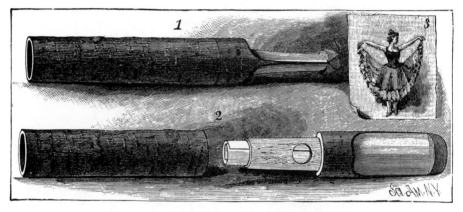

PHOTOGRAPHIC CIGAR HOLDER.

purpose. The smoke of the tobacco, coming in contact with it, develops a portrait or other subject. The process employed is very simple and consists in preparing a small photograph on chloride of silver paper. The paper can be purchased ready prepared. The prints are fixed in a bath of sodium hyposul-

DEVELOPING THE PHOTO.

phite (eight to ten per cent.), without having been toned with gold. They are then washed with great care in order to free the fibres of the paper from every trace of the salt, which would cause a yellowing of the print after it was finished. The print is now taken and floated on a five per cent. bath of bichloride of mercury. The images at first gradually fade and finally disappear altogether. After the prints are thoroughly bleached, they are washed in water and allowed to dry. In order to make the latent image appear, it is only necessary to immerse the print in a weak five-per-cent. solution of sulphite or hyposulphite of sodium. When the prints are to be developed photographically, they are placed in the cigar holder so that the lateral orifice in the holder will admit the smoke to the print. The ammoniacal vapors contained in tobacco smoke possess, like sodium hyposulphite, the property of coloring black the chloride of mercury contained in the prepared paper.

AN ELECTRO-PHOTO DETECTIVE THIEF CATCHER.

The device which we illustrate has been very successful in securing photographs which have led to the identification of the perpetrators of petty thefts. A cigar dealer of Toledo, Ohio, had for some time lost cigars from his showcase, and the detectives were foiled in their attempts to discover these thieves, so he had recourse to the proprietor of the photographic apparatus shown in

FIG. 1.—THE PHOTO DETECTIVE.

our engravings. The apparatus was set up and arranged in working order. It was then left to do its work.   Early one morning two boys entered the place, opened the showcase, and, in so doing, set in operation the apparatus, which made a permanent record of their deed, and upon the evidence thus obtained they were sent to prison.   As the boys opened the case they closed an electric circuit which released the camera shutter, and at the same instant operated the flashlight apparatus.   Our first engraving shows the photograph being taken, and our second shows the mechanism.   The side and end of the camera are removed so as to show the mechanism.   The camera is placed in a box which is provided with a shutter operated by the spring seen at the front of the box.   The shutter is tripped by an electro-magnet.   On the top

FIG. 2.—DETAILS OF THE PHOTO DETECTIVE APPARATUS.

of the camera box is arranged another electro-magnet, and a vertical spindle carrying at the top a roughened disk; the electro-magnet being connected with a detent which engages an arm on the vertical spindle. A match is placed in a spring-pressed holder which rests against the roughened disk, and above the disc is supported a flashlight. When the circuit is closed by tampering with the showcase, the shutter of the camera is opened by the action of the magnet connected with the escapement, and the detent magnet at the top of the box is operated with the shutter. The detent is then released and allows the vertical spindle to revolve, the power for the purpose being stored in a volute spring connected with the spindle. The match is ignited, and as the disk completes its revolution, the match projects through the aperture and ignites the flashlight powder. All this occurs in a fraction of a second, and as soon as the shutter is opened and closed the image on the sensitive plate is prevented from being further acted upon. To secure the closing of the shutter, the current which lets off the igniting mechanism is taken through a fusible wire or strip located in the flashlight chamber. When the flashlight powder burns, the wire or coil is melted, the circuit is broken, and the shutter is released, so as to close automatically. The effectiveness of the apparatus is clearly proved by the work it has done. At the same time there seems to be no good reason why the burglar could not smash the whole apparatus, thus destroying all photographic record of the crime.

COMPOSITE PHOTOGRAPHY.

Composite photography consists in the fusion of a certain number of individual portraits into a single one. This is effected by making the objects which are to be photographed pass in succession before the photographic apparatus, giving each of them a fraction of the long exposure, equal to such exposure expressed in seconds and divided by the number of the objects which are to be photographed. Composite photography is interesting when applied to photographs of persons. Theoretically this is what occurs: Features peculiar to each of the portraits, not having been sufficiently exposed, do not take; and the features common to all, having been given a proper exposure, alone leave a visible trace along the sensitized plate. Therefore, the result obtained may be considered as the type of the race or the family, but, of course, is only of limited value. Our engraving shows twelve portraits, six men and six women, some of whom are quite young and some middle-aged, as may be readily seen. An exposure was made in succession of No. 1 to No. 12, that is to say, beginning with the youngest woman and ending with the oldest man; and then from No. 12 to No. 1, that is to say, in inverse order. A man and a woman were interposed, and the experiment was renewed, preserving the same arrangement, but changing the order of the subjects. The result remained constantly the same, as may be readily seen by glancing at the four composites, A, B, C, and

D, of the engraving.   Upon one side the type of six men (composite E) was made, and on the other, of six women (composite F).   Here the change produced is very perceptible.   It is always the same head; but while before we had a being of indeterminate sex, we find here, with perfect distinctness, a man on one side and a woman on the other.   The experimenter wished to see whether twelve other persons (six men and six women), taken from the same population, would give a type analogous to the first.   As may be seen (composite G), there is a slight difference, but the character of the head is the same, the difference existing especially in the physiognomy.   The same remark may be made as to the composite H obtained from the six women of the preceding group joined with the six women figured Nos. 1, 2, 3, 4, 5, 6, which alone gave the composite F.   This observation proves (what was to be foreseen) that the more the number of subjects for each experiment is increased, the greater will be the probability of obtaining the true type of the population studied.   On the contrary, when but three are taken, a great risk will be run of generalizing too much. In this case, moreover, each exposure is necessarily too long, since it consists of a third of the normal exposure and is no longer the resultant of the three heads, but their superposition.   Hence the slightest increase in the length of one of the three exposures assumes considerable importance.

COMPOSITE PHOTOGRAPHS.

CHAPTER II.

CHRONOPHOTOGRAPHY.

Instantaneous photography has been of the greatest possible use to science, especially that branch of it which has been termed "chronophotography." It is to the investigations of Mr. Muybridge and M. Marey that we are indebted for the most valuable researches on the subject. Chronophotography consists in taking a number of photographs of any object at short and regular intervals of time. This is accomplished in many ways, and results obtained are useful for many purposes. The graphic method has been of great service in almost every branch of science, and laborious statistics obtained by computation have been replaced by diagrams in which the variation of a curve expresses in the most striking manner the various phases of some patiently observed phenomena. Furthermore, by the methods of modern science, a recording apparatus has been devised which, working automatically, traces the curves of such physical or physiological events which, by reason of their slowness, feebleness, or their speed, would otherwise be inaccessible to observation. The development of these methods of analyzing movement by photography have enabled the researches of physiological laboratories to become of the greatest possible value. The matter in this chapter is very largely an abstract of M. Marey's researches, which were originally published in "La Nature," and their publication in the "Scientific American Supplement" extended over a period of several years. Subsequent to this publication M. Marey wrote a book called "Le Mouvement," which has been translated by Mr. Eric Pritchard under the title of "Movement." It is published in the International Scientific Series; and for a more extensive and scientific treatment of the subject than we are able to give here, we refer our readers to this excellent work. M. Marey describes the rudiments of chronography by supposing we take a strip of paper which is made to travel by clockwork at a uniform rate. A pen affixed above the paper marks, as it rises and falls alternately, the various periods and intervals. When the pen comes in contact with the paper it leaves a record in the form of dashes of different lengths at varying intervals. If the dashes should be equidistant it shows that the periods of contact follow one another at equal intervals of time. Now, as it is known that the speed at which the paper travels is so many inches or feet per second, it is an easy matter to obtain an accurate measurement of the duration of contact and of the intervals between. In brief, this is the principle of chronography. Chronophotography is simply an amplification of this system and has many advantages, rendering measurements possible where the moving body is inaccessible. In ᴏther words, there need be no material limit between the visible point and the sensitized plate.

Mr. Muybridge's experiments on the gaits of the horse are famous. He used a battery of cameras as shown in our first engraving. Some of the results obtained are shown in Fig. 2.

FIG. 1.—ARRANGEMENTS ADOPTED BY MR. MUYBRIDGE IN HIS EXPERIMENTS ON THE GAITS OF A HORSE.

On the left is the reflecting screen against which the animal appeared *en silhouette*. On the right is the series of photographic apparatus, of which each one took an image.

In Mr. Muybridge's arrangement, photographic instruments faced a white screen before which passed an animal walking, trotting, or galloping. As fast as the animal advanced, the shutters of the lenses opened and permitted the taking of negatives of the animal. These were, of course, different from each other, because they were taken in succession. They therefore showed the animal in the various attitudes he assumed at different instants during his passage across the field covered by the instruments. The dazzling white light

FIG. 2.—TWELVE SUCCESSIVE PHOTOGRAPHS, BY MR. MUYBRIDGE, OF A HORSE IN FULL GALLOP.

In the last figure the horse is shown standing still. The speed of the horse was about 1,142 meters (3,746 feet) per minute.

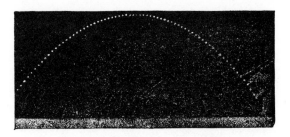

FIG. 3.—CHRONOPHOTOGRAPHIC TRAJECTORY OF A BRILLIANT BALL THROWN ACROSS
THE BLACK SCREEN.

brought out *en silhouette* the body of the animal. Each shutter is actuated by
a powerful spring; the shutter is opened as the animal advances. Threads may
be observed across the road; the animal, breaking these threads one after the
other, opens the shutters. Mr. Muybridge varied his experiments most successfully. He studied the gaits of different animals, and those of men in jumping, vaulting, and in the handling of various utensils. But since this time the

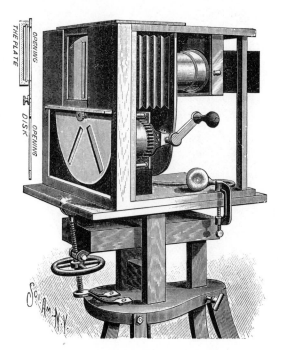

FIG. 4.—CHRONOPHOTOGRAPHIC APPARATUS PRODUCING UPON ONE PLATE A SERIES OF
PHOTOGRAPHS AT EQUAL INTERVALS OF TIME.

The apparatus is open and shows the position of the disk, with its openings moving in front
of the plate.

FIG. 5.—GENERAL VIEW OF THE PHYSIOLOGICAL STATION AT PARIS.

progress of photographic chemistry has wonderfully increased the sensibility of the plates, and at the present day more than mere silhouettes of moving animals and men can be obtained. In a good light full images with all desired relief can be obtained. For example, if an athlete in motion is photographed, all of the muscles of the body are perfectly traced in relief, indicating the parts taken by each of them in the movement executed. The methods

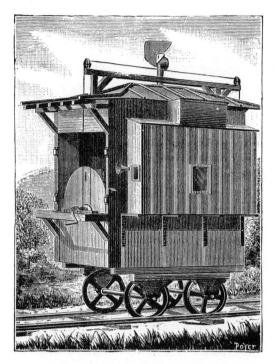

FIG. 6.—DARK CHAMBER ON WHEELS.

used by Mr. Muybridge would always suffice to illustrate the successive phases of the displacement of the members if they were taken at equal intervals of time, but the arrangements adapted for bringing about the formation of the successive phases cause irregularity in the extent of these intervals. The threads give more or less before breaking; moreover, the progress of the horse is not at an even rate of speed. Nevertheless, Mr. Muybridge endeavored to develop from a series of images the trajectory of each leg of a horse, but the curves obtained in these laborious attempts had not sufficient precision. A very simple method enables us to obtain, with perfect fidelity, the trajectory of a body in movement; it is the photographing of this body in front of a black surface. If the photographic apparatus is directed against a black screen, the objective can be uncovered without effect on a sensitized plate, as it will receive no light; but if a white ball strongly illuminated by the sun is thrown across the plane of this screen, and parallel with it, its image will be reproduced upon the plate, which will show the track of the ball in its trajectory, just as the eye receives a momentary impression of lines of fire when a lighted piece of charcoal is waved through the air at night.

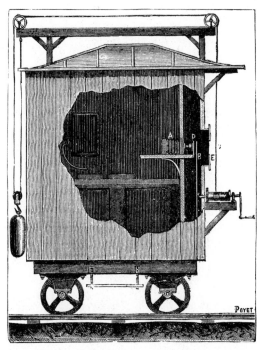

FIG. 7.—INTERIOR ARRANGEMENT OF THE DARK CHAMBER.

Fig. 3 shows the parabolic trajectory of a brilliant ball thrown across the face of a dark screen; but it is discontinuous, as exposures were only produced each fiftieth of a second on account of the number of the openings and the speed of the rotation of the disk. This is only an example which shows the almost limitless number of varieties of movement which may be analyzed by chronophotography.

With ordinary shutters it would be difficult to obtain this quickness, but the perforated disk which is used in chronophotography gradually acquires a speed of rotation that may be very great. Fig. 4 shows the arrangement of this disk by which a rotary movement is imparted by a powerful gearing controlled by a regulator. As soon as the disk obtains a speed of ten turns a second, the regulator maintains this speed with perfect uniformity. The disk moves in front of the sensitized plate a few millimeters only; then, knowing the angular value of each of the openings, the period of exposure is easily deduced therefrom.

The condition most difficult of fulfillment is the absolute darkness of the screen before which the photographs are taken. Little light as there is, the

FIG. 8.—WALKING MAN, CLOTHED IN WHITE, PASSING ACROSS THE FIELD.

screen might reflect upon this sensitized plate, during a single exposure, small quantities of light, which would tend to fog the plate. A wall painted with any black pigment, or even covered with black velvet, exposed to the sun, reflects too much light for a plate to withstand. The term "black screen" is used in a metaphorical sense. In reality the work is done before a dark cavity, being in truth what is known as "Chevreul's black." To obtain these favorable conditions, a chamber nearly thirty-three feet deep and of equal breadth was constructed; one face of this chamber was open, and restricted by movable frames to the exact height necessary. The interior of the chamber was completely blackened, the ground was coated with pitch, and the back hung with black velvet.

FIG. 9.—INSTANTANEOUS PHOTOGRAPH OF A MAN JUMPING OVER AN OBSTACLE.

Before entering into a detail of the experiments, we shall point out the general arrangement of the Physiological Station of Paris. Fig. 5 gives a general view of the grounds and buildings.

On these grounds, which were laid out by the city of Paris as a nursery, there is a circular road, thirteen feet wide, designed for the exercise of horses, and, outside of this, a footpath for men. All around this road there runs a telegraph line whose poles are spaced 164 feet apart. Every time that a person walks in front of a pole a telegraphic signal is given, and this is inscribed in one of the rooms of the principal building. Further on we shall speak of this sort of automatic inscription, by means of which we ascertain at every instant the speed of the walker, the variations therein, and even the frequency of his steps. In the center of the track there is a high post that carries a mechanical drum which regulates the rhythm of the gait, and which is actuated by a special telegraph line running from one of the rooms in the large building, wherein the rhythm is regulated by a mechanical interrupter.

From the center of the circle, likewise, there starts a small railway upon which runs a car that forms a photographic chamber, from the interior of which is taken a series of instantaneous images of the horses or men whose gait we desire to analyze.

Fig. 6 represents the photographic chamber in which the experimenter places himself. This chamber is mounted upon wheels, and runs upon a railway in such a way that it can approach or move away from the screen according to the objectives that are being used and to the size of the images that it is desired to obtain. As a general thing, it is advantageous to place the photographic apparatus quite far from the screen, say about 164 feet. From this distance the angle at which the subject whose image is being taken does not change much during the time it takes to pass before the black screen. From the exterior of this chamber are seen the red windows through which the operator can follow the different motions that he is studying. To have the different acts performed he gives his orders through a speaking trumpet. The front of the chamber is removed in Fig. 6 in order to show a revolving disk provided with a small window through which the light enters the photographic objective intermittently. This disk is of large dimensions (four and three-quarters feet in diameter), and the window in it represents only one hundredth of its circumference. It follows from this that if the disk makes ten revolutions per second, the duration of lighting will be but *one thousandth of a second*. Motion is communicated to the disk by a train of wheels which is wound up with a winch and which is actuated by a weight of one hundred and fifty kilograms placed behind the chamber. The motion of the disk is arrested by a brake, and a bell maneuvered from the interior serves to give orders to an aid either to set the disk in operation or to stop it.

Fig. 7 shows the inner arrangement of the chamber, a portion of one of the sides being removed to show the photographic apparatus, A, placed upon a bracket before the screen. This apparatus receives long and narrow sensitized plates that exactly hold an entire image of the screen. At B is the revolving disk which produces the intermittent illuminations, and at D is a cut-off which is raised vertically at the beginning of the experiment, and which is allowed to fall at the end so as to allow light to enter only during the time that is strictly necessary. E is a wide slit in front of the objective, for allowing the latter to take in the field in which are occurring the motions that are being studied.

The darkness that reigns in the rolling chamber permits of manipulating the sensitized plates therein at ease, and of changing them at every new experiment.

Against the dark field just described, a man placed in full light, naked, or clothed in white, gives a sharp image on the sensitized plate. The results in running and jumping which are obtained by this means are very satisfactory. For scientific purposes it is found that the results are better if, instead of

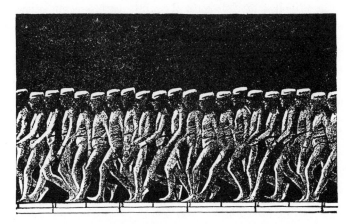

FIG. 10.—INSTANTANEOUS PHOTOGRAPH OF A MAN WALKING.

FIG. 11.—MAN CLOTHED IN BLACK VELVET.

The axes of the limbs are traced by white cords ; the joints carry white buttons placed at the point of rotation. The head is covered by a helmet of black velvet which completely hides it, and to which is affixed a bright ball at the level of the ear.

white clothing, the runner is clothed in black velvet. By this means he becomes nearly invisible before the black area. If white cords are attached to this costume, following the direction of the axes of his limbs, and white buttons used for the principal articulations, the white parts are reproduced and re-obtained on the sensitized plate in an almost unlimited number of positions.

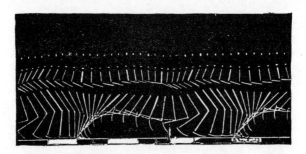

FIG. 12.—CHRONOPHOTOGRAPHIC IMAGES OF A RUNNER.

Below the figure is a scale whose divisions are 0.50 meter (19$\frac{7}{10}$ inches) long, and serve to give the extent of the movements.

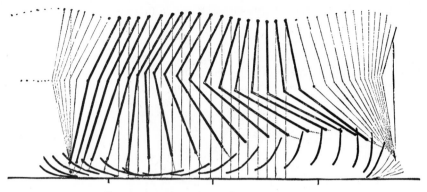

FIG. 13.—OSCILLATIONS OF THE LEG OF A WALKING MAN.

Using a disk pierced with five holes, which gives twenty-five images per second, the result shown in Fig. 12, which shows in full detail the movements of the left half of the body, head, arm, and leg, was obtained by this method for the action of running. Every fifth image is a little stronger than the others. This is effected by making one of the apertures in the disk larger than the others. The time of exposure is thus increased, and the intensity of the image

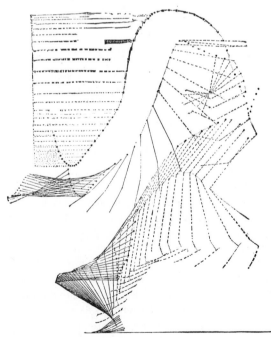

FIG. 14.—SUCCESSIVE POSITIONS OF THE LIMBS IN AN ELASTIC JUMP UPON THE BALL OF THE FOOT.

is greater. The object of this disposition is to furnish base marks, by means of which it is always easy to recognize traces corresponding to the same image, that is to say, to a given attitude of the runner. For detailed studies a part of the image is screened, as shown in Fig. 13. These diagrams are very well adapted for the comparison of two sorts of movements whose difference cannot be discerned by the eye. Thus, in jumping from an elevation the shock

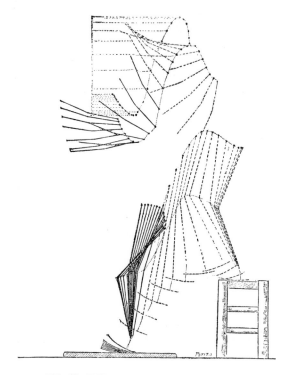

FIG. 15.--INELASTIC JUMP UPON THE HEELS.

caused by the feet striking the ground is reduced in intensity by bending the legs, while the extensor muscles operate to sustain the weight of the falling body. Our next two engravings show two kinds of jumps: the first, the flexure of the legs and the reduction of the shock; the second, with the leg almost straight, which implies a severe shock by the feet striking the ground.

The practical applications of chronophotography are soon seen. Just as machines are driven so as to obtain a useful effect at the smallest expenditure of power, so a man can govern his movements so as to produce the wished-for effects with the least waste of energy, and, consequently, with the least possible fatigue. Of two gaits which can carry us over a definite space in a given time, the one should be preferred which costs the least possible fatigue. Chronophotography furnishes the missing elements of the problem, giving exactly the velocity of the different parts of the body, by the balancing of which we can determine the masses in movement. From a long series of comparisons, important conclusions can be drawn, as, for example, the following: in walking, the most favorable gait is one where step succeeds step at the rate of about one hundred and twenty a minute; for running, the step should be nearly two hundred and forty a minute. Fewer or more numerous steps will give less effect at a greater expenditure of the work. The applications are therefore obvious;

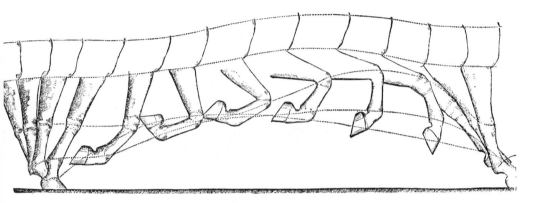

FIG. 16.—OSCILLATION OF THE FORE LEG IN A GALLOP. INTERVAL BETWEEN EXPOSURES ONE TWENTY-FIFTH OF A SECOND.

they enable us to fix the rate of steps of soldiers to economize as much as possible their strength in the severe trials to which they are subjected. These studies have been followed out at great length, under varying conditions, using a considerable number of subjects; and the results, while not final, have shown that the true method has been found. Experiments have confirmed that which the laws of mechanics could not foretell when the dynamic conditions of the work of man were incompletely known.

M. Marey's studies of the legs of the horse are particularly interesting. We give one engraving showing the oscillation of the fore leg of a horse in a gallop.

The analysis of the flight of birds presents special difficulty. Owing to the extreme rapidity of the movements of the wings, an extremely short exposure is required. The direction, often capricious, of the flight of the bird, and the length of the path which must be followed, to include on the sensitized plate sufficiently sharp images, add to the difficulty. Several repetitions of the same experiment are generally required before success.

The photographic gun is particularly valuable for taking photographs of birds. Our engravings show the mechanism of the photographic gun and the method of using it.

We present a photograph of a gull taken during its flight and an enlargement of the same.

The photographic gun will be understood by reference to the engraving, and is fully described in the "Scientific American Supplement," No. 386, to which the reader is referred.

We also give photographs of a pigeon rising in flight and the successive attitudes of a gull.

Space forbids us to more than state that the analysis of the flight of birds is a most interesting and important subject, and the results obtained by chronophotography are most gratifying.

FIG. 17.—MODE OF USING THE PHOTOGRAPHIC GUN.

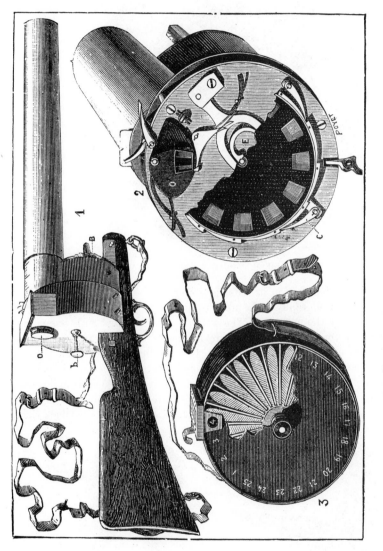

FIG. 18.—MECHANISM OF THE PHOTOGRAPHIC GUN.

1.—General View of the Apparatus.
2.—The Shutter and Perforated Disk.
3.—Box containing Twenty-five Sensitized Plates.

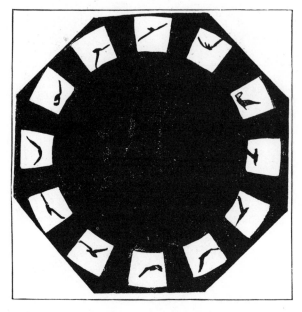

FIG. 19.—PHOTOGRAPH OF A GULL TAKEN DURING ITS FLIGHT.

The analysis of locomotion in water is one of the most interesting developments of chronophotography. In order to study locomotion in water it was necessary to modify the method. The animals experimented with swam in a glass-sided aquarium fitted in an aperture in a wall, as shown in our engraving. The aquarium was directly illuminated by the light of the horizon, forming a very clear field upon which the animals were outlined as silhouettes. Sometimes the external glass of the aquarium was covered by letting down an opaque shutter; then, upon opening another shutter, placed above the water, the brightly illuminated animals were seen standing out from the black field.

FIG. 20.—ENLARGEMENT OF AN IMAGE TAKEN BY THE PHOTOGRAPHIC GUN.

FIG. 21.—ENLARGEMENT OF ANOTHER IMAGE OF A BIRD TAKEN BY THE SAME APPARATUS.

FIG. 22.—PIGEON RISING IN FLIGHT.

The successive images correspond to less and less advanced phases of the wing's revolution.

In most cases it was found necessary to operate before the luminous ground, so it was not possible to receive several successive images upon a removable plate, but it was necessary to cause the sensitized surface to move by starts, so as to bring before the objective points which were always new for each new image that is to be formed. A flexible gelatino-bromide-of-silver film was used. The film was cut into a long and narrow strip which in the camera passed along at the focus of the objective, and unwound from a supply bobbin, and wound around a receiving one.

The objective turned toward the right has a slit in the center for the passage of the diaphragm which, in revolving, allows the light to pass intermittingly. When the small diaphragm makes one revolution the large one makes five revolutions, and it is then only that the apertures meet and the light passes. The bellows behind the objective allows the light to reach the sensitized film. The box is, of course, tightly closed. The focusing is done by means of a small telescope or spy glass. It is necessary at each new experiment to use a new band of film, and the substitution of rolls of films is effected in the light by means of bobbins upon which the film is rolled.

FIG. 23.—ELEVEN SUCCESSIVE ATTITUDES OF A FLYING GULL.

In this series of images, traced from the originals, the distances representing the positions of the bird in space are exaggerated to avoid confusion.

At the extremity of each band of film are glued paper bands of the same width. One of these prolongations is red and the other is black. Each of them is about twenty inches in length. Having the two colors makes it almost impossible to reëxpose a film, as one is not liable to confound a bobbin which has been used with one that has not, the color of the roll being different. Special devices are employed in the camera to render the film immovable for an instant while it receives the impression from the object. Arrangements

FIG. 24.—ARRANGEMENT OF THE AQUARIUM FOR THE STUDY OF AQUATIC LOCOMOTION.

are also provided for obtaining a uniform velocity. The use of the apparatus which we have just described permitted of seeing with what a variety of means of locomotion the various kinds of aquatic animals—fishes, mollusks, crustaceans, etc.—propel themselves. The motion of the medusa is particularly interesting, and the phases of the movement of the umbrella are shown in Fig. 26. The propulsion of this mollusk is effected through the alternate contraction and dilation of its umbrella. Ten images per second were sufficient to obtain a pretty complete series of the phases of this motion. These images gain much by being examined in the zoetrope, wherein they reproduce with absolute perfection the aspect of the animal in motion.

The hippocampus, which is otherwise known as the "sea-horse," affords another interesting example of aquatic locomotion. The principal propeller of this animal is a dorsal fin which vibrates with such rapidity that it is almost invisible, and has an appearance analogous to that of the branches of a tuning fork in motion. With twenty images per second it is seen that this vibration is undulatory. We have before us the successive deviations of the lower, middle, and upper rays of the film. In the present case the undulation takes place from the bottom upwards.

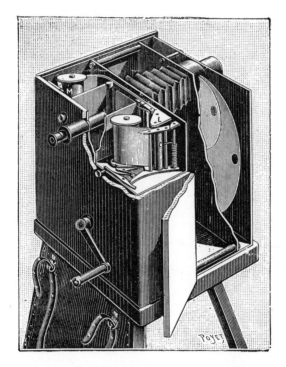

FIG. 25.—PHOTOCHRONOGRAPHIC APPARATUS.

The comatula is habitually fixed to the bottom of the aquarium, just as a plant is fixed to the earth by its roots. It therefore makes nothing but vague motions of the arm, which it rolls up and unrolls; but if the animal be excited by the means of a rod, it will be observed to begin a strange motion which carries it quite a distance. In this kind of locomotion the ten arms move alternately; five of them rise and keep tightly pressed against the calyx, and the other five descend and separate from it. Upon the arms that rise, the cirri are invisible, and while upon those that descend, they diverge in order to obtain a purchase upon the water. These motions of the cirri seem passive, like those of a valve that obeys the thrust of a liquid.

M. Marey says: "I have obtained images of a certain number of other aquatic species, the swimming of the eel, the skate, etc. These types of locomotion ought to be studied methodically, compared with each other, and considered in their relations with the conformation of the different species. It will, I hope, be a new element for the interpretation of the laws of animal morphology, which are very obscure."

M. Marey has also investigated the flight of insects by means of chronophotography. These experiments are most delicate and interesting, and the results obtained go a long way towards making up a satisfactory theory of insect life. M. Marey says that the wing in its to-and-fro movements is bent in various directions by the resistance of the air. Its action is always that of an

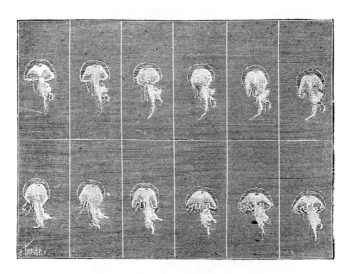

FIG. 26.—MOTIONS OF THE UMBRELLA OF THE MEDUSA.

inclined plane striking against the fluid, and utilizing that part of the resistance which is favorable to its onward progression. This mechanism is the same as that of a waterman's scull (reference of course being to "sea sculling" and not to "river sculling"), which, as it moves backward and forward, is obliquely inclined in opposite directions, each time communicating an impulse to the boat. There is, however, a difference between these two methods of propulsion. The scull used by the waterman offers a rigid resistance to the water, and the operator has to impart alternate rotary movements to the scull by his hand—at the same time taking care that the scull strikes the water at a favorable slant. The mechanism in the case of the insect's wing is far simpler. The flexible membrane which constitutes the anterior part of the wing presents a rigid border which enables the wing to incline itself at the most favorable angle. The muscles only maintain a to-and-fro movement. The resistance to the air does the rest, namely, effects those changes in surface obliquity which determine the formation of an 8-shaped trajectory by the extremity of the wing.

M. Marey states that he succeeded in obtaining a photograph of the gilded wing of an insect, which, though not absolutely at liberty, could fly at a comparatively high rate of speed. The photographs of the trajectory of the wing of an insect are very interesting. A wooden box was lined throughout with black velvet. The bottom of the box, a simple disk supported by a foot piece, was placed in position; the periphery of the space was covered with a white material, leaving between it and the central disk an annular track covered with black velvet. It was around this annular track the insect was made to fly. A needle stuck in the middle of the disk served as an axis for a revolving beam and its counterbalance. This beam consisted of a straw, and at the end of it was fixed a light pair of forceps to hold the insect. The dragon fly commenced flying around the track at a very rapid rate, drawing the straw after it. The gold spangles passing through his wings described a trajectory which was easily photographed.

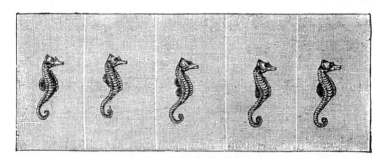

FIG. 27.—MOTIONS OF THE DORSAL FIN OF THE SEA-HORSE.

The chronophotography of insects by the use of a moving film has been also accomplished by means of very ingenious apparatus. In some cases the insects were held in forceps, and in other cases they were allowed free flight in a cardboard box.

" Comparative locomotion," which is rendered possible by chronophotography, might almost be called a new science. It is, at any rate, an important adjunct to the studies of the zoölogist. The researches of M. Marey upon the different terrestrial mammals, birds, tortoises, lizards, frogs, toads, tadpoles, snails, eels, fish, insects, and arachnids are of the greatest possible value and interest. The applications of chronophotography to experimental physiology are numerous. It supplements the information obtained by the graphic methods. It has rendered possible the photography of the successive phases of cardiac action in a tortoise under condition of artificial circulation. The mechanism of cardiac pulsation has also been studied by its means, as well as the determination of the centers of movements in joints.

It has been found that chronophotography could be applied not only to

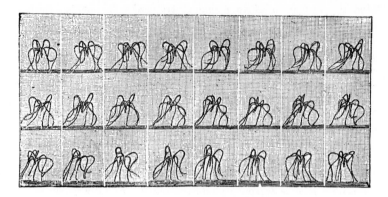

FIG. 28.—MOTIONS OF THE COMATULA.

objects of considerable size, but to those of microscopic size as well. Special arrangements of apparatus are necessary for this purpose. By its means the retraction of the spiral stalks in vorticellæ, the movement of the blood in capillary vessels, and the movements of the zoöspores in the cells of conferva have been determined.

The great value of chronophotography is unquestionable for use in every case where the body whose rapid changes of position or form we wish to know is inaccessible to us, or its movements cannot be mechanically traced.

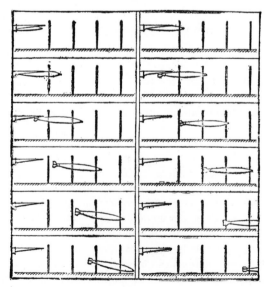

FIG. 29.

TORPEDO BADLY FIRED.   TORPEDO PROPERLY FIRED.

Chronophotography has been used in France for studies touching the military art, being employed for registering the firing of projectiles having a relatively slow motion, such as the explosion of stationary torpedoes, the recoil of guns, the motion of automobile torpedoes, etc.   Special arrangements are provided to permit of electrically controlling the phenomenon to be photographed. The apparatus is described in detail in the "Scientific American Supplement," No. 743.

We present a diagram showing the results obtained by photographing the firing of torpedoes.   Although the velocity of these projectiles is not very great, about sixty feet per second, it is yet very difficult for the eye to take exact account of what is occurring during the launching.   As the net cost of a torpedo is considerable, it is essential that the conditions which influence the regularity of its submarine flight shall be known with precision.   If it inclines in front more or less in plunging, the regularity of its running will be put to hazard; if, on the contrary, it falls flat upon the water, the results will be very different.   Our engraving shows the torpedo starting from the tube and traversing the different panels in the field of firing.   In the first half the torpedo, gradually inclining, falls point foremost; it has been badly fired.   In the second series, on the contrary, the torpedo is maintaining itself horizontally, and, in a manner, moving always parallel with itself.   Under such circumstances it falls flat and starts off normally and regularly to the object to be reached.   This shows the great utility of chronophotography.

AN AMATEUR CHRONOPHOTOGRAPHIC APPARATUS.

The experiments which we have been describing necessitate apparatus of the most expensive kind, and they are unadapted for the use of the amateur. The apparatus of M. Georges Demeny, which we illustrate, is, however, very simple.   The reader needs to be reminded that there are three types of chronophotographic machinery in use, in two of which a single objective, with a disk shutter revolving at great speed, is employed.   In one the object shifts, and gives several images from an immovable plate, while in the other the object is stationary, and the movable sensitized surface gives well-separated images.   The third method, which is the least interesting, consists in taking as many objectives and plates as it is desired to have images, and in freeing the shutters of each objective, one after the other.   The most scientific solution of the problem is that which permits of obtaining upon a band of film, and with a single objective, a succession of well-separated images whose number depends only upon the length of the band employed.   The difficulty in using a sensitized band consists in arresting it for the very brief instant in which each image impresses the plate.   The Demeny apparatus which we are about to describe is very simple.   A wooden box having about the dimensions of an ordinary seven by nine inch apparatus is provided with an objective of wide

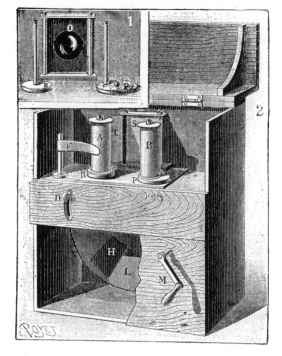

FIG. 1.—AMATEUR'S CHRONOPHOTOGRAPHIC APPARATUS.

aperture, of which only the center is utilized. Back of this objective, and as near as possible to the sensitized surface, the disk shutter is revolved by means of a crank. Up to this point there is really nothing new in the apparatus; but the principal improvement consists in the unwinding and arrest of the sensitized film. Number 1 of our first engraving represents the principle of the system. Two disks, R and P, are each mounted upon an axis passing through their centers; bobbins that carry the films are fixed, one of them at R, upon a spindle mounted in the axis of rotation of the disk, and the other at P, upon a spindle mounted eccentrically to such axis. It is this eccentric position that chiefly constitutes the invention. Let us suppose that the two bobbins are in place, as shown in cut. The film wound upon A, having one of its extremities attached at B, follows the course, C, S, during which it passes behind the objective; the two bobbins cannot have any proper motion in consequence of the method of fixing which is adopted; they and the disks, R and P, that support them, become interdependent. Because the disk, P, revolves, the film coming from A will wind around B; but, in consequence of the eccentric position of this bobbin upon the disk, traction will cease to occur for a very brief instant at the moment at which the bobbin, B, approaches A as closely as possible. Despite this, as the winding always proceeds to a degree proportional to the unwinding, the film remains perfectly taut. It is at this moment that the window, H, of the disk, L, uncovers the objective for an instant. It will be understood that the crank, M, sets the disk in motion, and it is this, through a mechanism of gears, that controls the operation of the bobbins. There is, therefore, an exact mathematical coincidence between the arrest of the film and the passage of the window, and this is essential for the sharpness of the image. This would not always occur if a friction device was depended upon for the rest of the film, for in this case a sliding might occur which would produce a blurring of the image. The solution offered by the Demeney apparatus is, therefore, the simplest and one of the surest known. The simplification of the mechanism has permitted of constructing an apparatus light enough to allow of operating without a tripod, by holding it in the arms, as shown in our second engraving. Each film terminates in a strip of black paper glued to it, and forms a complete covering after the winding upon the bobbin. This arrangement protects the sensitized part from the light, and permits of changing the bobbin in daylight. Twenty of them can be stored in the spaces in the box left by the mechanism, so that one may always have a large supply on hand.

FIG. 2.—METHOD OF USING THE DEMENY APPARATUS.

CHAPTER III.

THE PROJECTION OF MOVING PICTURES.

THE EDISON KINETOGRAPH.

The "kinetograph," which is the precursor of the apparatus for showing moving photographs, is of great interest. The kinetograph as first proposed consisted of a clever combination of a photographic camera and the phonograph, by which the words of a speech or play were to be recorded simultaneously with photographic impressions of all the movements of the speakers or actors. The photographic impression is taken at the rate of forty-six per second. The celluloid film upon which the photographic impressions are taken is perforated along one edge with a series of holes, arranged at regular intervals with as much precision as can be secured by means of the finest perforating mechanism, to secure perfect registry. This was found necessary because the phonographic cylinder must be in exact synchronism with the shutter-operating and film-moving devices of the camera. The phonograph and camera mechanisms are driven by the same motor and controlled by the same regulating mechanism. The greatest difficulty was experienced in devising mechanism for the stopping and starting of the film. It was found that the stopping and starting of the film forty-six times a second required about two-thirds of the time, the remainder being utilized for the exposure of the plate. To take these pictures special camera lenses of large aperture had to be constructed. The reproducing apparatus is practically a reversal of the camera; that is, a superior form of projecting lantern is employed which is provided with a strong light, and mechanism for moving forward the strip with an intermittent motion, corresponding exactly to the motion of the negative strip in the camera. The lantern is furnished with a light interrupter which eclipses the light during the

PHOTO-ENGRAVING OF A PORTION OF THE STRIP NEGATIVE OF THE KINETOGRAPH
(ACTUAL SIZE).

brief period required for shifting the film forward to a new position to show the succeeding picture. The apparatus was largely manufactured on a small scale, without the phonograph, for use in railway stations, cigar stores, etc. It was found to be almost impossible to combine the two instruments. In this case the pictures were not projected upon the screen, but were upon a ground-glass plate which the observer looks at.

REYNAUD'S OPTICAL THEATER.

Up to the time of the invention of this theater, the apparatus that produced the synthesis of the successive phases of an action were limited to reproduction upon a very small scale, which can only be enjoyed by a limited group. The object of the optical theater was to provide an apparatus for the reproduction of a series of actions upon a considerable scale. The continuity of the image obtained by the praxinoscope, invented in 1877 by M. Reynaud, had not up to this time been realized by any projecting apparatus. The effect is produced by using a crystalloid band upon which the images are painted as represented at A in our engraving. The operator can revolve it in one direction or the other by means of two reels. The images pass before the lantern, B, and are projected by the aid of the objective, C, upon an inclined mirror, M, which projects them upon the transparent screen, E. Another projection lantern, B, causes the appearance on the screen of the scene, amid which appear the characters, which change their posture according as the painted band, A, is revolved by the operator.

ELECTRIC TACHYSCOPE.

The apparatus which we are about to describe is an important link in the history of the synthesis of animated motion. The apparatus is the invention of Ottamar Anschuetz, of Lissa, Prussia. A special camera was used, adapted to take a number of photographs in quick succession. The instrument for displaying the pictures is called the "electrical tachyscope." It consists of an iron wheel of sufficient diameter to hold an entire series of positive prints on the periphery. The wheel is arranged upon a rigid standard, and provided with a series of pins which register exactly with the picture. Upon the standard behind the wheel is located a box containing a spiral Geissler tube which is connected with the terminals of a Ruhmkorff coil. The primary coil is provided with a contact maker and breaker adapted to be operated by the pins projecting from the wheel, so that every time a picture comes before the Geissler tube it is illuminated by an electrical discharge through the

REYNAUD'S OPTICAL THEATER.

ANSCHUETZ'S ELECTRICAL TACHYSCOPE.

tube. This discharge, being instantaneous, shows each picture in an apparently fixed position. These pictures succeed each other so rapidly that the retinal image of one picture is retained until the next is superimposed upon it, thereby giving to the observer the sense of a continuous image in constant motion.

THE DEMENY CHRONOPHOTOGRAPHIC APPARATUS.

The chronophotographic apparatus which we illustrate was invented by M. G. Demeny, who is the assistant of Dr. Marey, whose work in chronophotography we have already described. As long ago as 1891, M. Demeny was able to project upon a screen figures which simulated the motion of animal life.

Strips of sensitized films from sixty to ninety feet in length were not available at this time, and it was necessary to employ some makeshift. Images were taken from the chronophotographic apparatus upon a strip four or five yards in length, and were printed as positives upon a glass disk sensitized by chloride of silver, and it was by means of this disk that the projection was made. The

FIGS. 1 AND 2.—THE DEMENY PROJECTION APPARATUS.

1. Arranged for use without electricity or gas.
2. Arrangement for stopping the strip of film.

number of images was limited to forty or fifty, according to the subject, but the advent of the long strips of sensitized film induced the inventor to so modify the apparatus as to be able to take images in long series and for projecting them. The apparatus of M. Demeny, which we show in our engraving, employs strips of any length, but at present the longest that have been used are one hundred and fifteen feet. This gives about one thousand images of the dimensions adopted by the inventor, one and one half by one and three quarter inches. This wide surface of the image has an immense advantage, since, with the electric light, it permits of throwing the moving pictures on a screen sixteen feet high.

For a small screen the oxyhydrogen light will be sufficient. The lantern is provided with an ordinary condenser, in front of which is placed a water tank to absorb a portion of the heat. At the opposite end of the table stands the chronophotographic projector which carries the film wound around its bobbins. The lantern is so regulated that the luminous rays will fall exactly upon the aperture as the image passes behind the objective, O.

After the focusing has been effected, all that has to be done is to turn the crank, M. At P and R are seen guide bobbins that serve to put in their normal direction the films that have been used. As is well known, the principle of all projecting apparatus of this kind consists of arresting the film for an

FIG. 3.—INTERIOR VIEW OF M. DEMENY'S REVERSIBLE PROJECTION APPARATUS.

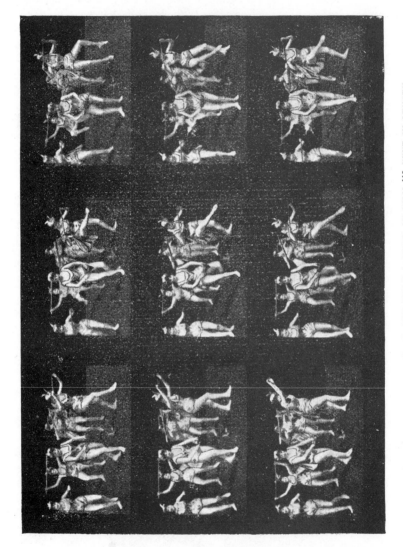

FIG. 4.—FIGURES OF ACTUAL SIZE FROM A STRIP OF FILM 115 FEET IN LENGTH.

instant at the moment it is uncovered by the shutter. The process employed in the Demeny apparatus is very simple. It is shown in Fig. 3 of our engraving. Upon coming from the bobbin the film passes over a guide roller, S, and then over a rod, D, mounted eccentrically; thence it goes to the toothed roller, C, designed for causing the images to register accurately. The film then reaches the magazine roller, B. The mechanism is entirely enclosed in a box, and the shutter disk, which is not shown in the engraving, is situated at the other side of the aperture, F. Beneath the bobbin, A, is a rubber roller, E, mounted upon a spring in such a way that it will bear against the film, whatever be the thickness of the ribbon on the bobbin. It is this roller which is moved by gearing that causes the film to unwind in a continuous manner, and thus prepares it for the eccentric rod, D, which pulls upon a portion of the film already unwound, but does not screen it. The film passing under the guide, S, passes between two velvet-lined frames, H and T, that are provided with an aperture F. It is upon making its exit thence, and passing over the guide, S, that the film is taken up by the rod, D, then runs over the toothed roller, C, and finally over the bobbin, B. All these parts, exclusive of the shutter, are interdependent, and are connected by gear wheels set in motion by the crank, M. None of them have a jerky motion. All of the parts of the mechanism have uniform rotary motion, and the stoppage of the films is prepared for by a graduated diminution of the velocity. One advantage of this apparatus is that it is very tender with the films. Our last engraving represents a few images on a strip made for a spectacular drama at the Châtelet Theater, Paris. This strip is one hundred and fifteen feet long, and embraces a thousand images, each of which was colored by hand. The effect is very pleasing.

THE KINETOSCOPE STEREOPTICON.

Since the time the "kinetoscope" brought the art of moving photography prominently into notice, many inventors have been striving to perfect apparatus for successfully projecting these miniature pictures upon the screen by means of a stereopticon, producing the same effect of motion as in the kinetoscope. In the kinetoscope the successive images are illuminated by reflected light, and are seen through a lens enlarging them considerably, say from half an inch in diameter to about four inches. The problem of the kinetoscope stereopticon was to successfully project these little images several thousand times, and secure sufficient illumination upon the screen to make them appear distinct and clear. The two factors which aided in solving the problem were the use of the electric lamp as an illuminant and of continuous flexible transparent celluloid films. Our first engraving shows some kinetoscopic pictures taken directly from the negative film, by the "phantoscope" invented by Mr. C. F. Jenkins. The successive motions of practicing "putting

KINETOSCOPE PICTURES—PRACTICING PUTTING THE SHOT.

the shot," shown in these fifteen pictures, may be traced by beginning at the lower left-hand corner and reading upward for each column of pictures. The device for taking the phantoscope pictures is shown in Figures 5 and 6.

On a shaft is fixed a disk supporting four lenses, and geared to the shaft is a vertical shaft engaging a bevel gear on the axis of the film-winding reel. As the shaft is revolved by the handle on the outside, the lenses are brought respectively behind the opening in the front of the box and transmit the

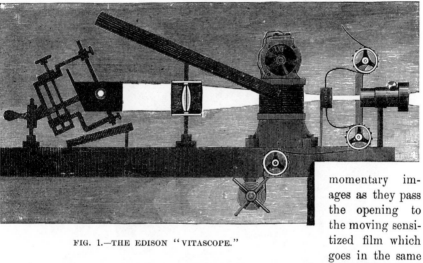

FIG. 1.—THE EDISON "VITASCOPE."

momentary images as they pass the opening to the moving sensitized film which goes in the same direction as the moving lens, and at the same speed. The exposed film is at the same time wound up on the top reel. With the same apparatus the positive pictures may be reeled off of one spool to the other, being projected by the electric light in the rear, illuminated by rotating condensers, one for each lamp. The pictures may be looked at in the box, through a small screen; they are made at the rate of twenty-five to the second, and are about three-quarters of an inch in diameter, and one-quarter of an inch apart, on a continuous sensitized celluloid strip about one and a half inches wide, having perforations in its edges, in which the sprocket wheels of the projecting device engage. The projecting apparatus is shown in Fig. 1, and consists of an electric arc lamp in front of which is a condenser. In advance of that is the motor for operating the feed mechanism, and in front of all is the film traveling device and the objective. Our second engraving is a view of the stand complete, showing the rheostat, switches, etc., for regulating the current. The film, after passing behind the lens, is wound up on the reel below. Our third engraving shows the use of the apparatus in the theater. It is placed in a cabinet surrounded by curtains, in an upper gallery, the images being thrown forward upon a screen upon the stage.

In projecting pictures of this kind it has been usual to employ shutters operating in unison with the movements of the picture ribbon. After a series of experiments it was found that the same effect of motion could be produced by causing the ribbon itself to have an intermittent movement without the use of shutters at all, which greatly simplifies the apparatus. A film-working apparatus based on this idea is shown in detail at Fig. 4. The electric motor operates a

FIG. 2.—THE EDISON "VITASCOPE."

main shaft to which it is geared, a worm engaging a gear on the shaft with the main sprocket pulley, and draws the picture ribbon downward at a uniform speed. Back of this shaft may be seen the main shaft, intended to rotate rapidly, on the end of which is a disk having a roller eccentrically fixed thereto. Behind this is a standard supporting spring-tension fingers behind the lens. As the film is drawn forward by the main sprocket

FIG. 3.—THE "VITASCOPE" IN THE THEATER.

pulley, it is quickly pulled downward by each rotation of the rapidly moving
eccentric roller on the disk. The sprocket pulley meanwhile takes up the
slack of the ribbon, so that at the next rotation the eccentric roller quickly
pulls the film down and makes the change; from the sprocket pulley the film
is carried to the winding wheel operated automatically from the main shaft by

FIG. 4.—FILM PROJECTING APPARATUS.

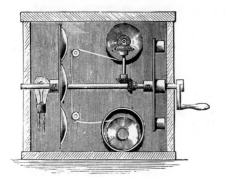

FIGS. 5 AND 6.—THE JENKINS "KINETOSCOPE" CAMERA.

means of pulleys; or, when it is desired to repeat the subject over and over again, the endless film is allowed to drop into folds in a box located under the sprocket pulley, passing out at the rear, upward over pulleys arranged above the spring-tension fingers, then downward between them again to the main pulley.

Fig. 7 is a diagram of a film-moving mechanism of an English inventor, Mr. Birt Acres, which has been successfully operated in London.

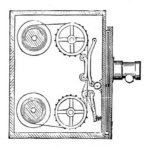

FIG. 7.—ACRES' PROJECTING DEVICE.

The picture film is drawn from an upper reel, passed over a sprocket pulley, downward through a retaining clamp, and over a second pulley to the bottom or winding reel. The film passes over both sprocket pulleys at a uniform speed, between a stationary and swinging clamp operated automatically from the shaft of the shutter and which holds the film stationary when the opening of the shutter is behind the lens, during the interval the picture is projected on the screen. The clamp is released; then the pivoted lever below, with a roller on the upper end, is pulled inward at the other end by a spring and immediately takes up the slack (as shown by the dotted lines), and causes, by such sudden movement, the bringing of the next picture into position.

THE "MUTOGRAPH" AND "MUTOSCOPE."

The "mutograph" and "mutoscope" are names of very interesting machines for presenting moving photographs. The camera frame is mounted, by means of three adjustable legs, upon a triangular turntable, which may be placed upon any suitable support. Upon the top of the frame is bolted a two horse-power electric motor which is driven by a set of storage batteries; the combination of the turntable with a vertical adjustable enables the camera to be shifted so as to take in the required field. In the front of the camera is fixed a lens of great light-gathering quality which produces an image of exceedingly clear detail. Inside the camera is a strip of gelatine film two and three-quarter inches wide, and usually about one hundred and sixty feet in length, which is wound upon a small pulley and drum. The length of the film varies for different subjects. In case of a prolonged scene it may extend several thousand feet. The film is led through a series of rollers, and is caused to pass directly behind the lens of the camera, and is finally wound upon a drum. The object of the rollers is to cause the film to pass behind the lens with an intermittent instead of a continuous motion. At ordinary speeds this could be easily accomplished, but the difficulties are increased when it is remembered that the impressions are taken at the rate of forty per second, and that the film, which is running at the rate of seven or eight feet a second, has to be stopped and started with equal frequency. The film comes to a rest just as the shutter opens, and starts again as the shutter closes. The impressions vary in actual exposure between one one-hundredth and one four-hundredth of

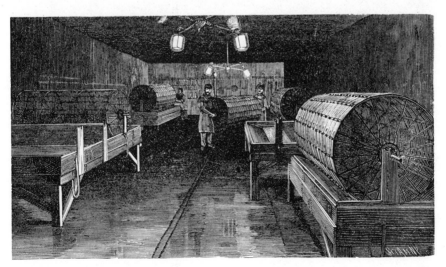

THE DARK ROOM AND REEL FOR DEVELOPING FILMS.

TAKING PICTURES FOR THE "MUTOSCOPE."

DRYING AND RETOUCHING ROOM. "MUTOSCOPE" SHOWN IN THE FOREGROUND.

a second.   While the ordinary speed is forty a second, the mutoscope can take equally good pictures at the rate of one hundred per second, if it is necessary. The highest speed would be used in photographing the flight of a projectile or other object which was in extremely rapid motion.   After the mutograph has done its work, the films are carefully packed and sent to the New York establishment of the American Mutoscope Company.   Here they are taken to the dark room, the interior of which is shown in our engraving.   Arranged along each side of this room is a series of troughs, above which are suspended large skeleton reels three feet in diameter and seven feet long, the axes of the reels being journaled in brackets attached to the end of the trough.   The films are wound upon the reels and subjected to the action of the various solutions for developing, fixing, etc., the reels being transferred from bath to bath until the films are ready to go to the drying-room.   In this room are also prepared positive transparent strips for use in the biograph and the bromide prints for the mutoscope.

THE SAUSAGE FACTORY.

The films are unwound on to large wooden drums about the same size as the reels, where they are carefully dried.   At the far end of the room are seen the machines for cutting up the bromide prints.   Here also is carried on the work of retouching the films and preparing them for use in the biograph and mutoscope pictures.   The biograph is somewhat similar to machines which we have aready described.

The annexed engravings show pictures of clay-pigeon shooting and of the firing of a ten-inch disappearing gun at Sandy Hook.

Upon the roof of the New York establishment of the company there has been erected a large movable stage for taking photographs of celebrated scenes from plays or of individual performances in which it is desired to reproduce the motions as well as the features of the subject.   It consists of a floor of steel I-beams which carries a series of three concentric steel traps.   Upon this rotates the massive frame at one end of which is a stage supplied with the necessary scenery, and at the other end a corrugated iron house, in which

"MUTOGRAPH" PICTURES OF CLAY-PIGEON SHOOTING, AND OF THE FIRING OF A TEN-INCH DISAPPEARING GUN AT SANDY HOOK

is located the mutograph. The stage is bolted to the frame, but the house travels upon a track, so that it may be moved to or from the stage as required. The frame carrying the stage and house rotates about the smaller circular track located beneath the house, and may be swung around so as to throw the light full upon the scene at any hour of the day.

INTERIOR OF THE "MUTOSCOPE."

The "mutoscope" is compact, and the pictures are large. It is not any larger than the cover of a sewing machine. The enlarged bromide prints, measuring four by six inches, are mounted in close consecutive order around the cylinder and extend out like the leaves of a book, as shown in the illustration. In the operation of the mutoscope the spectator has the performance entirely under his own control by turning a crank which is placed conveniently at hand, and may make the operation as quick or as slow as he desires, and can stop the machine at any particular picture at will. Each picture is momentarily held in front of the lens by the action of a slot attached to the roof of the box, which allows the pictures to slip by in much the same way as the thumb is used upon the leaves of a book.

MOVABLE STAGE FOR PHOTOGRAPHING SCENES WITH THE "MUTOGRAPH."

"CINEMATOGRAPH" CAMERA.

The "cinematograph" camera, invented by the Messrs. Lumière & Sons, works on a somewhat different principle from those we have already described. In this camera the film is carried forward intermittently, no sprocket wheel being used. The film-moving mechanism is fully illustrated in Figs. 1 and 3.

The film-moving device consists of two prongs which somewhat resemble a fork. It is shown at D in Fig. 3. The prongs are alternately pushed through or withdrawn from the perforated ribbon by the aid of a rotating bar, C. The film-moving device, D, has really a shuttle movement, having a rapid reciprocating motion. The rotating bar, C, which is secured to the main shaft, is so arranged that its ends, which are bent in opposite directions, strike on alternate sides of the wedge-shaped piece which is secured to the fork, D, and thus impart to the latter a reciprocating motion. The up-and-down motion of the film is accomplished by the aid of a cam which is secured to the main shaft. The reciprocating yoke piece, A, is given a vertical motion when the crank shaft is rotated. The arm, B, is attached to the yoke piece, A, and this carries down the film through the medium of the fork, D. When the film has been lowered the distance of one exposure, the rotating bar, C, strikes the fork and removes the prongs from the film. The yoke piece then raises the prongs, and the other arm of the rotating bar strikes the wedge-shaped piece, and forces the fork, D, through the apertures in the film. On the main shaft is also arranged the shutter, E, which rotates

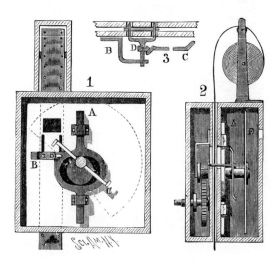

FIGS. 1, 2, AND 3.‑FILM-MOVING MECHANISM.

FIG. 4.—DRIVING GEAR AND FILM SUPPORT.

with the film-moving mechanism. Fig. 2 shows the simplicity of the camera. On the upper end of the box is the sensitized ribbon, which passes downward between guides before the lens opening. The bent ends of the cam operating bar, which give the fork, D, its reciprocating motion, are shown in Fig. 3. Fig. 4 is a general view of the instrument, showing the driving gear and film support. Fig. 5 shows the cinematograph camera in operation. It will be seen that the camera is very portable. The same camera can be converted into a projecting apparatus for throwing moving pictures upon the screen. The images are about an inch square.

CAMERA FOR RIBBON PHOTOGRAPHY.

The camera for ribbon photography which we illustrate is the invention of Mr. C. F. Jenkins, the inventor of the "vitascope," which we have already described. Instead of using a rotary disk shutter, the radial apertures, and a

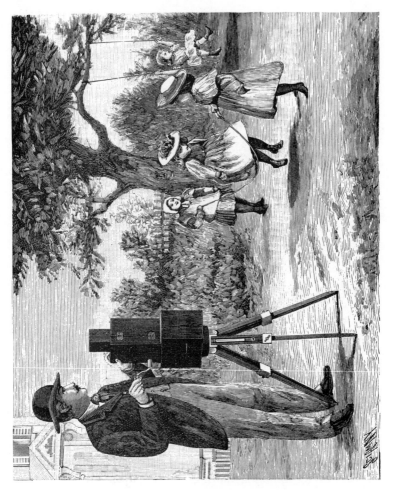

FIG. 5.—THE CINEMATOGRAPH IN OPERATION.

fixed lens, this camera has a single opening in the front, the size of the aperture being regulated at its rear end by a diaphragm disk having radial slots of varying widths cut therein. The operator is thereby enabled to govern the amount of light admitted to the lenses according to the subject to be photographed and the length of the exposure desired. This disk is rotated by hand, like an ordinary stop in a wide-angle lens. Back of the diaphragm disk is the battery of lenses, each of the same focus, arranged in a circle, joining each other, upon a rotating disk which is secured to a shaft which extends rearward and terminates in a bevel gear wheel which meshes with a side bevel gear wheel fixed upon the main shaft, suitably geared to the main driving shaft.

The main shaft may be operated by a crank on the outside of the box, by hand or by any suitable motor. The sensitized celluloid perforated ribbon film may be noticed passing downwards near the front end of the camera, in front of the exposure tension plate, the square aperture in which is exactly in line with the front aperture in the box. From this point the film, after exposure, passes downward between the sprocket wheel and pressure roller to the winding reel in the rear end of the camera, which is rotated by belt-connection to a pulley on the upper shaft and takes up the film ribbon as rapidly as it is exposed. A feed roll for the supply of unexposed film is not shown, but may be located at the rear of the camera, over the winding reel. The operation will be readily understood. The camera is placed upon the tripod or stand; the crank on the outside is rotated, which causes the film to travel downwards continuously, at exactly the same speed at which the lenses rotate, so that at every fraction of a second that it takes for each lens to pass behind the camera aperture an impression of light is made on the downwardly moving film; and as the lenses and film both move in unison, it follows that a sharp picture will be the result while the brilliancy of the illumination is at its maximum. The camera can be carried about as readily as any other camera. In practice it is found that the motion of the hand-operated crank is sufficiently uniform to permit of the proper reproduction of motion by the positive pictures projected upon the screen.

Our next engraving shows how the positive ribbon pictures for the vitascope and other forms of apparatus are printed; this is also the invention of Mr. Jenkins. It consists of reels supported on suitable upright standards holding respectively the sensitized ribbon film and the negative film. The film from the negative supply wheel is carried along over the sensitized film wheel, and both pass in contact, in continuous motion, under an exposing chamber illuminated by any source of white light, as an incandescent lamp or a Welsbach incandescent gaslight, thence over the toothed sprocket driving wheel to the winding wheels, the exposed film being wound first. This will be better understood by reference to our detailed diagram of the mechanism. It will be noticed that the reels are interchangeable, and hence, to make duplicate copies it is only necessary to remove the negative spool from the winding-up end to the supply-spool standard of the apparatus, and begin over again. The perfora-

RIBBON PHOTOGRAPHY—A NEW CAMERA.

tions in the edges of the film are of a special square shape, and give the square sprocket wheel of the propelling pulley a better tension on the film. The teeth pass through the perforations of both films, causing both to move at exactly the same time, and at all times to keep in perfect registry. The speed of the film passing under the exposing chamber must be absolutely uniform; this is obtained by propelling the sprocket wheel by an electric motor or by a spring motor. The electric motor is seen in the large wood cut. The axle of the

RIBBON PHOTOGRAPHY—EXPOSING AND PRINTING APPARATUS.

motor has worm gear operating a cog wheel on the main shaft. The V-shaped elastic band holds the frame in which is a ground glass in contact with the film, producing a kind of tension on the film. To the left of the light chamber is a supplementary tension adjusted by screw nuts, as shown. Referring to the diagram, two slotted diaphragm cards will be seen. These are placed over the ground glass just mentioned, at the bottom of the light chamber, and are for the purpose of regulating the amount of light that acts on the negative. If

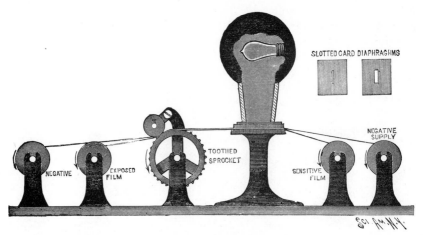

RIBBON PHOTOGRAPHY—DIAGRAM OF THE PRINTING DEVICE.

the negative film, as a whole, should be thin, then a card with a narrow slot is used, which allows a short exposure to be made if the negative and film are passed under it. If the negative is full of density, then the narrow card is removed, and the wider slotted card substituted, which allows a larger volume of light to act upon the negative film. The exposed film is wound around large open reels from a spool and is developed by passing through cloths of developer solution. The novelty in the device which we illustrate consists in the fact that the film moves continuously under a uniform source of light, under any intermittent motion or the use of shutters. The operation of exposing the film is carried out in a room illuminated by the usual ruby light.

THE MICROMOTOSCOPE.*

The principles of the kinetoscope or mutoscope have been applied to the microscope, with some interesting results, by Dr. Robert L. Watkins, of New York City. The instrument, though simple, was made a success only after many experiments and failures in adjusting the objective of the microscope in a line with the right sort of light and a rapidly moving film.

The principal difficulties in making a mutoscope out of so delicate an instrument as the microscope are the light and the lens. Every electric lamp in the market, when its light has been concentrated sufficiently for photography, will, after a short time, with its heat, kill, dry up, or impair almost any kind of life in the microscopic field. The greater the magnification, the

---

* By D. F. St. Clair.

A ROTIFER AS SEEN IN THE MICROMOTOSCOPE.

more intense the light must be and the nearer the microscope. This difficulty was often enhanced by the length of time it took to get a focus on the sensitive film, but most of the pictures taken were good, and show well the various characteristics of the action taking place in cell life, so far as it can be observed with the microscope.

Whatever is to be photographed, once it is put in the field of the lens, is adjusted to a horizontal plane. Near one end of the microscope is placed an electric lantern containing a small arc light concentrated on the object. Near the other end is the box that covers the apparatus for moving the long, sensitive gelatine film. The film runs like a belt, on wheels, and passes in front of a tiny window in the box and on a direct line with the lens and light. This machinery is turned by a crank, and its ordinary capacity is about 1,600 pictures per minute. It is possible to increase it to 2,000 or 2,500, but for most purposes 1,000 or even less per minute will record every motion taking place in most cell life. Dr. Watkins found, however, after a number of trials, that he could not turn the machine fast enough to photograph the motion of the blood circulating in the web of a frog's foot. He simply needed a larger wheel.

The advantages of mutoscopic photography to microscopy are quite evident, especially as regards the action of bacteria and blood cells. Nearly all the numerous families of bacteria have motion, many having motion that the eye cannot always follow clearly. It has already been discovered that the same kind of bacteria will act very differently under different circumstances. For instance, a flash of bright light will suddenly drive some kinds to cover. Some kinds will readily seek the negative pole of the battery. They will also seek food with avidity and reject poison with true instinct. All such phenomena can, of course, be followed with the eye, but not with the same detail in the microscopic field as in a series of clear photographs. The fact is that on account of the motion of some bacteria it has been well nigh impossible to photograph them. The books have had to depend upon the eye and hand of the draughtsman and upon vague description. This may not be of much importance either way, but as yet comparatively little is known about bacteria. It is not yet known whether they are the cause of disease, or its results, or neither. Photography, under the proper circumstances, is most needed for the investigator, and it can be only moving photography.

The capillary or circulatory motion of the blood cells, after the blood has been drawn, is comparatively slow at best ; but the amœboid movement of the white cells and the changes taking place in the nuclei are complicated, and often hard to intelligently watch in the field.   Many of these changes occurring in the white cells are certain to escape attention, but all of them will be clearly recorded on the rapidly moving sensitive film.   These motions in the white cells, though they are as yet imperfectly understood, are full of meaning to the physiologist and pathologist.   The offices that the blood performs in the body are believed to be due mainly to the action of the white cells.   Certainly, the character of their amœboid action is one of the surest indications of health or disease.

But with the micromotoscope it need no longer be impossible to photograph the blood in actual circulation.   With a better light the cells may be seen in the thin tissue of the ear or the web of the fingers.   They have often been examined in the peritoneum during an operation, and Dr. Watkins himself has made a close study of them in the web feet of some birds and the tails of fishes.

Unfortunately, the illustration of blood here reproduced does not show the white cells.   They stuck to the glass, while the red cells, it will be perceived, retain something of their motion, continuing to flow across the field for half an hour after the blood was drawn.

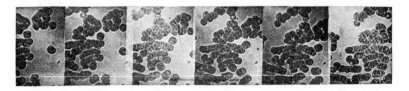

MOVEMENT OF BLOOD CORPUSCLES SHOWN BY THE MICROMOTOSCOPE.

APPENDIX.

APPENDIX.

ADDITIONAL TRICKS.

THE MAGIC TABLE.

This was a trick of the late Alexander Herrmann. In the center of the stage is placed a light table with three legs and a plush top. The prestidigitateur moves his hand over the table; suddenly it rises in the air and follows his hands wherever he moves them. The secret of the trick will be easily understood by reference to our engraving. A small näil is driven in the center of the table. This nail is not noticed by the audience, and the plush top tends to hide it. The magician wears a ring which is flattened on the inner surface and a small notch is filed in it. The ring is placed on the middle finger of the right hand; the hand is spread over the table until the notch fits under the head of the nail. The table can then be lifted with great ease, and it appears to follow the hand of the conjurer in obedience to the magic wand.

THE MAGIC TABLE.

"GONE."

This very clever illusion was designed by Mr. W. E. Robinson, the assistant of the late Herrmann the Great. It has been exhibited in several of the large cities, and is always a great success. When the curtain is raised the square frame is seen ; this frame is braced laterally by side pieces. At the lower part of the frame, within easy reach of the prestidigitateur, is a windlass. Ropes pass from this windlass, over pulleys, to a crossbar in the upper part of the frame. A

THE LADY READY FOR ELECTROCUTION.

lady is now brought upon the stage and for some terrible crime is sentenced to be electrocuted. She is seated in a chair, which she grasps tightly. She is then tied tightly to the chair with ropes, and her hands are chained together. The prestidigitateur now secures the chair, with its fair occupant, to the ropes which are connected with the windlass, by means of hooks which fasten to the top frame of the chair. Wires are now secured to the unfortunate lady so that it really seems as though she was to receive the death-dealing current. The professor of magic now winds away at the windlass and raises the chair until the head of the victim is on a level with the crossbar. He then discharges a pistol, and at the same instant the lady disappears and the chair drops to the floor. Such is, in brief, the mode of operation of the trick called " Gone."

In reality the illusion is a clever adaptation of the " Pepper Ghost " of which we have already described several variations. A reference to our first engraving will show that at the sides of the frame is a row of incandescent lights. While the lady is being secured to the chair, and while she is being hoisted up to the crossbar, these lamps are kept lighted; but the instant the pistol is fired, these lights are extinguished by a stage hand in the side scene. Up over the proscenium arch is arranged a background which corresponds to

RAISING THE LADY BY MEANS OF THE WINDLASS.

the background of the stage. Two wooden bars cross it. Directly below this screen, and carefully shielded from the observation of the spectators, is a row of incandescent lights. As the pistol is fired these lights are turned on, while those in the frame are extinguished. Now, according to the principles of the " Pepper Ghost " which we have already described, the person or thing which is brilliantly lighted has its image projected on a sheet of glass and appears to be real. The front of the frame, from the windlass to the horizontal cross piece, is covered with a sheet of glass which is not apparent to the audience.

THE ILLUSION OF "GONE" EXPLAINED.

The image of the background is projected upon this glass, which hides the lady from view, although she is immediately behind it, and the pieces of wood and this artificial background take the place of the back posts of the frame, thus deceiving the audience. The chair is made in two sections, the lady being tied to the upper, or skeleton chair. She holds a heavy chair with her hand tightly, and at the instant when the pistol is fired she releases the chair, which falls to the floor with a loud noise.

There is another illusion, called " Out of Sight," invented also by Mr. W. E. Robinson, which is somewhat similar, but is not as interesting from a scientific point of view. It is, however, better adapted for a traveling company, as there is no glass to break, the large sheet of plate glass in the front of the frame being entirely dispensed with. When the pistol is fired, a curtain of the same color as the background is released by the prestidigitateur, and it is drawn down quickly by means of rubber bands. It takes only an instant for the curtain to descend, its lower edge being hidden from view by the windlass. The audience is usually deceived as easily by this illusion as by the more complicated one.

THE SPIDER AND THE FLY.

This is one of the most interesting of the series of tricks which depend upon mirrors, and of which the " Decapitated Princess " is a type. When the curtain rises, the scene shows a gentleman's country house set upon the embankment and surrounded by grass plots and shrubbery. This is painted scenery such as is usually used in theaters. The house is approached by a set of stone steps which are built out from the scene proper, or, in other words, the drop. These are what is known in theatrical parlance as " practical " steps ; that is, they may be ascended. The steps are encased by side walls, and these walls are surmounted by vases of flowers and handsome lamp posts. The steps lead to the doorway of the house ; the door is also " practical," and can be opened and shut. The story runs that the house was deserted for such a long time that the steps were covered by a gigantic spider's web, and the spectator is surprised to see this web, which extends from post to post and to the side walls of the steps.

In the center of this gigantic web is seen a spider's body with a woman's head. The steps leading to the doorway of the house are open, and a person starts to descend, but stops on seeing the spider, and retreats after taking three or four steps down the stairs. This adds greatly to the illusion, as it looks as if it could not be produced by a mirror. You can see both above and below the head, and the steps may be seen at any angle you choose. The puzzling part of the trick is the question of the whereabouts of the lady's body.

Reference to our second and third engravings will give the secret of the trick. The mirror lies at an angle of 45° and runs from the base of the posts

THE SPIDER AND THE FLY TRICK.

to the rear of one of the treads of the lower steps. The mirror extends the full width of the steps. A semicircular hole is cut out of the center of the mirror, at the top edge ; this is to receive the lady's head.

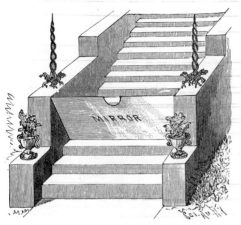

The spider's body is fastened to the network of rope ; the lady has simply to affix this body to her head, and the illusion is complete, as the body of the lady is concealed behind the glass. The mirror reflects the lower steps, so that this reflection really appears to be a continuation of the steps, and the entire flight seems unbroken. When the person appears at the door and descends the steps, he must be careful not to come below the line of reflection, as his legs will not be visible. The

THE ILLUSION EXPLAINED.

top edge of the glass is concealed by a rope of the web, as it is directly in front of it, and for safety is usually cemented to the glass.

In our diagram, No. 1 represents the steps ; 2, the mirror ; 3, the web; and 4, the lady. This trick requires the most careful preparation and adjustment, but when this is accomplished, the results are extremely satisfactory.

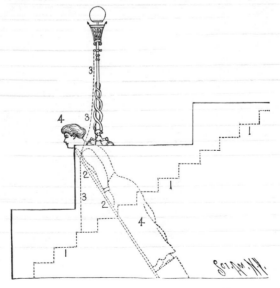

DIAGRAM SHOWING ARRANGEMENT OF MIRROR.

THE TRUNK TRICK.

This trick, which attracted the attention of the world for months, is of English origin, and was presented in England long before it was introduced into Paris. The experiment consists of having a trunk examined, tying it, securing a cover over it, tying it a second time, sealing it with wax, and then showing that in a few seconds a young East Indian has succeeded in getting inside of it without unfastening the cords, breaking the seals, or opening the trunk.

THE TRUNK TRICK.

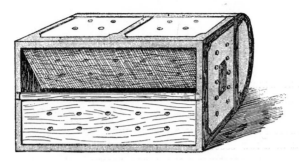

TRAP DOOR IN TRUNK.

Half the bottom of the trunk constitutes a trap door which is opened by inserting a round key in one of the ventilating apertures. As soon as the trunk has been tied, sealed, and placed under a canopy, the curtains of which are let down so as to hide the trunk from the spectators, the East Indian, who is also invisible to the spectators, lays the trunk down as shown in our second engraving, unbuckles the cover and slides it down, takes his key, opens the trap door, gets into the trunk, puts the cover in place, buckles it, and then closes the trap door. To raise the trunk to its proper position, he takes a long screw, something like a gimlet, from his pocket, inserts it in one of the holes under him, and turns it ; the trunk rises slowly, and when it has reached its point of equilibrium, it falls back suddenly on its bottom. The noise thus made is the signal for the operator, who immediately draws back the curtains, finds by the weight that something is in the trunk, and then unties it slowly and presents the mysterious traveler to the audience.

It will be seen by one of our engravings that the Indian appears tied in a bag in the trunk. This is a variation of the trick. The bag is made of some light or soft material, and is provided with a hem at the mouth. In this hem runs a cord or tape ; the performer draws the string tight, and seals the knots at the same time. The bag is then placed in the trunk, and the trunk is secured as above. The assistant who enters the trunk has concealed under

PUTTING ON THE COVER.

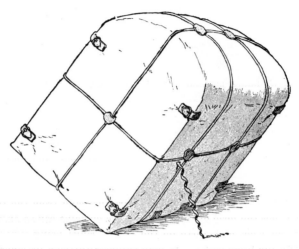

METHOD OF RAISING THE TRUNK.

his blouse a similar bag, the string of which is long enough to correspond in appearance to that of the other bag when it is tied and sealed. There are a couple of stitches missing on each side of the hem, leaving space enough for the assistant to insert his fingers. When he enters the trunk he removes this bag from his blouse, placing the original bag in the place of the duplicate. He now goes into the duplicate bag and places it up over his head, and, inserting his four fingers into the opening in the hem, draws in all the slack of the string, thus closing the bag, which is, of course, to all appearances, tied and sealed as the original.

REMOVING THE BAG FROM THE INDIAN.

"LA STROBEIKA PERSANE."

This illusion, made popular a few years ago by the late A. Herrmann, under the name of "Strobeika" was originally produced at Houdin's Little Hall, in Paris, by the inventors of it, two Germans, Herren Lutz and Markgraf.

The trick is supposed to take place in a prison or dungeon. In the center of the stage, quite near the back scene, stand four upright posts about eight feet high, and set about eight feet apart on the long side, and four on the short. These posts are made fast to a rectangular iron frame at the top, from the four corners of which are chains supporting a plank about an inch and a quarter thick, all in full view of the audience. Curtains hang from the framework to about a foot below the level of the board ; these curtains can be opened or closed by sliding them back and forth on the frame, rings being sewed on them to allow of this being done easily. A man supposed to be a prisoner is stretched upon the plank ; his wrists and ankles are manacled and locked by a committee from the audience, who can furnish, if they desire, locks of their own. His neck is also enclosed in a steel collar and locked to the plank. At a signal the curtains are closed, and, as they reach only a little way below the plank, permit of a full view underneath, to the rear wall of the stage. In less than a minute the curtains are withdrawn again, and a young lady is seen to

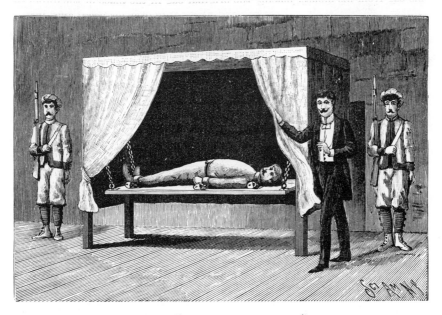

FIG. 1.—"LA STROBEIKA PERSANE."

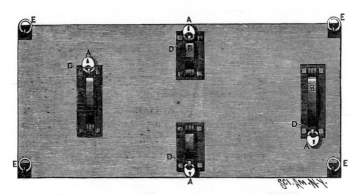

FIG. 2.—TOP OF BOARD, SHOWING LOCKS AND HASPS.

have taken the place of the man, who, at the instant of the girl's discovery, is seen running down the aisle of the theater. Now, let us see how this strange trick is accomplished.

The first thing is the explanation of how the man becomes released from the shackles. It principally lies in the construction of the board. There is no deception about the keys, locks, or manacles, since it is not at all necessary to the deception that there should be. The board is hollow and contains cunningly concealed levers, four in number, which move simultaneously. The eyes that the manacles slip over, and to which the locks are fastened, go into the board and are held fast by the ends of these levers, which enter a hole or notch, as the case may be, in the eye. The shackles and neck piece and their respective eyes are all made fast to an iron plate or bed which is bolted to the board; a bolt at each corner of the plates goes through the board and secures another plate at the bottom of it, making all firm. There is one bolt, however, that does not go through; it is riveted to one of the short levers, and by its means the system of levers is

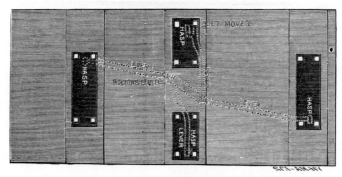

FIG. 3.—BOTTOM OF BOARD, SHOWING PLATES.

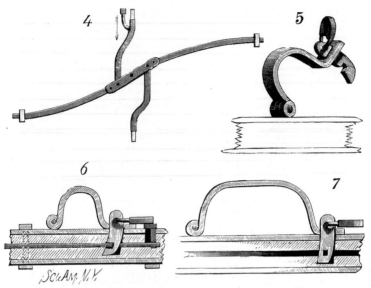

FIGS. 4–7.—DETAILS OF THE MECHANISM.

pushed backward or forward. There is a nut on the bottom plate to make it appear as if this identical bolt went completely through, the same as the others. The levers run in grooves made in any suitable part of the board and covered by a strip of wood or other material, thus rendering the mechanism invisible, and appearing as if the board was solid.

At each corner of the board is a ring or screw eye, into which the chain provided with a hook is secured, by which to suspend the board. The four levers

FIG. 8.—THE ESCAPE OF THE PRISONER.

are pivoted to a rocking lever in the center of the board, which is likewise pivoted. By this means all the levers are moved simultaneously. When the lever is moved it releases all the shackles, and the prisoner is then, of course, free, and it is but the work of a moment to climb out through an opening in the scene at the back, where the lady who is to take his place is now waiting on the end of a long board pushed out through the opening in the scene. The lady gets on the trick board, the man slams the shackles into place, moves the bolt back, thus shoving the levers back into their notches in the eyes, again making everything fast, makes his escape through the scene, and appears a minute later from the front of the theater.

The trick is varied sometimes by using double curtains at the back; concealed between them is the lady. After the exchange the man hides in the same place, and another man, his exact counterpart, is the one who makes his appearance in the audience.

"METEMPSYCHOSIS."

"Metempsychosis" is the name of an illusion which was the joint invention of Messrs. Walker and Pepper, of London. It was devised by the former gentleman, and the latter assisted in perfecting it. It is probably the most mystifying of any of the optical tricks. It has of late years been shown in America, by Kellar, under the title of the "Blue Room." The first effect produced upon the spectator after witnessing the illusion is that he has been dreaming, or seeing ghosts or spirits, for it seems utterly impossible for man to accomplish the wonders produced by it.

Our first engraving shows the stage set as an artist's studio. Through the center of the rear drop scene is seen a small chamber in which is a suit of armor standing upright. The floor of this apartment is raised above the level of the stage and is approached by a short flight of steps. When the curtain is raised a servant makes his appearance and begins to dust and clean the apartments. He finally comes to the suit of armor, taking it apart, cleans and dusts it, and finally reassembles it. No sooner is the suit of armor perfectly articulated than the soulless mailed figure deals the servant a blow. The domestic, with a cry of fear, drops his duster, flies down the steps into the large room, the suit of armor pursuing him, wrestling with him, and kicking him all over the stage. When the suit of armor considers that it has punished the servant sufficiently, it returns to its original position in the small chamber, just as the master of the house enters, brought there by the noise and cries of the servant, from whom he demands an explanation of the commotion. Upon being told, he derides the servant's fear, and, to prove that he was mistaken, takes the suit of armor apart, throwing it piece by piece upon the floor. This is only one of the countless effects which can be produced by this interesting illusion.

FIG. 1.—"METEMPSYCHOSIS."

The working of the illusion will be understood by reference to the diagram, Fig. 2. At A we have the proscenium opening ; B B are two flats of scenery

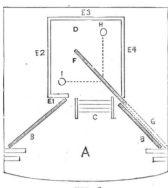

FIG. 2.

which close in the scene from the front wings to the steps, C, which in their turn lead up to the small chamber, D, at the back, in which all the changes occur. The walls of the chamber are lettered E^1, E^2, E^3, E^4. F is a large mirror extending from floor to ceiling, and capable of being wheeled back and forth on a truck or carriage. When this mirror is withdrawn, as seen at the dotted lines, G, the spectators see through the opening of the chamber to the rear wall. The suit of armor is marked H. Now, if the mirror be pushed across the chamber, both the armor, H, and the rear wall disappear, and the walls of the chamber at E^1 and E^2 are reflected so that they appear to be the walls E^3 and E^4. There is another suit of armor at I. It is placed so that, when it is reflected in the mirror, it will occupy the exact position of the other suit of armor, H. When the mirror is shoved forward and hides the suit of armor, H, an actor dressed in a similar suit enters behind the glass by a secret door, removes the dummy armor, and assumes the same place himself. All this time the suit of armor at I is reflected in the mirror, so that a suit of armor is always visible. The mirror is now drawn back, and the suit of armor which the actor wears is seen. When the servant now dusts the armor, it suddenly seems to become endowed with life and chases him around the room ; and when it again mounts the steps in the smaller room, the mirror is shoved forward, the actor making his escape in time to place the first suit of armor where it formerly stood. Now the mirror is again drawn out, revealing the sides of the room, E^3 and E^4, and of course exposing the suit of armor, H. If the walls, E^1 and E^2, and the armor, I, are correctly placed as regards reflection, he can pass the mirror to and fro at will, without any change being detected, as the reflection takes the place of the reality, and we suppose we are looking at the real object.

As the edge of the mirror passes the suit of armor a hard line is to be seen, a distinct vertical line, which would seem to wipe out the object as it passes. To avoid this, the inventors hit upon a novel and purely ingenious expedient. They etched vertical lines in the silver back of the glass at the

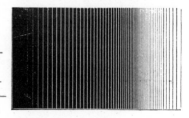

FIG. 3.

end which first passes across the field of view, beginning with thick silvered spaces close together, and tapering, with the lines farther apart as shown in our diagram, Fig. 3. It can thus be seen that the reflected article gradually appears instead of coming suddenly into view, and when the mirror is moved away the real article gradually appears.

In order that the edges of the glass may be better disguised as it moves forward or backward, the edge is cut or ground into steps, as shown in Fig. 4.

By the apparatus described above, many changes can be made, as a living man appearing in a previously empty chair, flowers growing on an empty bush, a change of a man into a woman, a painted picture into a living one, etc. In some effects a table is employed, to all appearances the common square kitchen table. A person is seen sitting at the table, which is empty; suddenly there appears before him a large dish of oranges or a meal. This is arranged by providing the table with a slot which runs diagonally from corner to corner. This allows the glass to travel through it, and thus shuts off one-half of the table. Articles are placed on the table, behind the glass, which is now withdrawn, leaving them to be seen upon the table. The slot in the top of the table is covered with sheet rubber or other material.

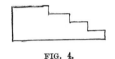

FIG. 4.

BIBLIOGRAPHY OF NATURAL MAGIC AND PRESTIDIGITATION.

BIBLIOGRAPHY

OF

NATURAL MAGIC AND PRESTIDIGITATION.

COMPILED, WITH NOTES, BY

HENRY RIDGELY EVANS.

I.

ENGLISH.

ARNOLD, GEORGE, *and* CAHILL, FRANK. The Magician's Own Book ; or, the Whole Art of Conjuring. New York, 1857. 8vo. 362 pp.

ASTLEY, PHILIP. Natural Magic. London, 1785.

BACON, ROGER. Discovery of the Miracles of Art, Nature, and Magic. (About 1260.)

BAILEY, F. H. Hindu Jugglery. Journal of Education (Boston), vol. xliv. p. 378.

BALL, W. W. ROUSE. Card Tricks. *In his* Mathematical Recreations.

BANCROFT, FREDERICK. Yogi Magic in India. Scientific American Supplement, vol. xliii p. 17845.

BARTLETT, J. Second Sight. Scientific American Supplement, vol. xlii. pp. 17477, 17478.

BECKMANN. History of Inventions. (About 1770.)

BENJAMIN, M. Modern Magic and its Explanation. Chautauquan, vol. xi. p. 731.

BERKELEY. Card Tricks and Puzzles. London, 1892. 8vo.

BERTRAM, CHARLES. "Isn't it Wonderful !" A History of Magic and Mystery. London, 1896. 4to. 300 pp.

BISHOP, WASHINGTON IRVING. Houdin and Heller's Second Sight. Edinburgh, 1880.

BLITZ, ANTONIO. Fifty Years in the Magic Circle. An Account of the Author's Professional Life, his Wonderful Tricks and Feats, with Laughable Incidents and Adventures as a Magician, Necromancer, and Ventriloquist. Hartford, 1871. 8vo.

BRESLAW. Last Legacy ; or, The Magical Companion. London, 1784.

BREWSTER, *Sir* DAVID. Letters on Natural Magic. London, 1832. 16mo.

BURLINGAME, H. J. Around the World with a Magician and a Juggler. Chicago, 1896. 8vo. 172 pp.

BURLINGAME, H. J. Herrmann, the Magician. His Life; His Secrets. Chicago, 1897. 12mo. 250 pp.

—— History of Magic and Magicians. Chicago, 1895. 8vo. 41 pp. (Pamphlet.)

—— Leaves from Conjurers' Scrap-Books; or, Modern Magicians and their Works. Chicago, —. 8vo. 274 pp.

—— Modern Magical Marvels : A Practical Treatise on Magic and Conjuring for Professionals and Amateurs. (In preparation.)

—— Tricks in Magic : Illusions and Mental Phenomena. Chicago, —. 8vo.

A series of entertaining works on modern magic and its professors.

BURSILL, H. Hand-shadows to be thrown upon the Wall ; Consisting of Novel and Amusing Figures formed by the Hand, from Original Designs. Second series, in one volume. New York. —.

CARLYLE, THOMAS. Count Cagliostro. *In his* Miscellaneous Essays.

This is a fascinating sketch of the most famous of charlatans and pretenders to magic. It is written in Carlyle's characteristic style, and is, perhaps, more of a philosophical study of the *genus* quack than an impartial biography of the celebrated necromancer of the old *régime*. A more detailed account of Cagliostro's romantic career is to be found in the series of articles by William E. A. Axon, published in the Dublin University Magazine, vols. lxxviii. and lxxix. (1871, 1872). All biographies of Cagliostro are founded on the work published in Rome, 1790, under the auspices of the Holy Apostolic Chamber. The Italian life contains an elaborate *exposé* of the great magician's system of Egyptian masonry, also the full Inquisition sentence pronounced against him. This highly interesting product of papal jurisprudence makes strange reading for the nineteenth century. In the year 1791 the Inquisition biography was translated into French, under the title of *Le Vie de Joseph Balsamo, connu sous le nom de Comte Cagliostro.* It has for a frontispiece a steel-engraved portrait of Cagliostro. Original editions of this rare and curious old work may be seen in the Peabody Library, of Baltimore, Md.; the Scottish Rite Library, of Washington, D. C.; and the Masonic Library of Grand Rapids, Iowa.

Cagliostro made adroit use of hypnotism, optical illusions, and chemical tricks. He was past master of the art of deception. Modern professors of conjuring are fond of using the name of Cagliostro for all sorts of magical feats, such as the " Mask of Balsamo," " Cagliostro's Casket and Cards," " Cagliostro's Cabinet," etc.

CARPENTER, WILLIAM H. At an Algerian Aissaoua. Current Literature, vol. xix. pp. 409–411.

The Aissaoua are the miracle-mongers of Algeria. For explanation of their tricks, see the concluding chapter of Robert-Houdin's memoirs.

CONJURER UNMASKED, THE : With the Tricks of the Divining Rod, Magical Table, etc. 1790.

CONJURER'S GUIDE. Glasgow, 1850.

CREMER, W. H. Hanky-panky : A Collection of Conjuring Tricks. London, —. 8vo.

—— The Magician's Own Book. London, —. 8vo.

CUMBERLAND, STUART. A Thought-Reader's Thoughts : Impressions and Confessions of a Thought-Reader. London, 1888. 8vo.

DAVENPORT, REUBEN BRIGGS. The Death-Blow to Spiritualism. Being the true story of the Fox sisters as revealed by authority of Margaret Fox Kane and Catherine Fox Jencken. New York, 1888. 8vo. 247 pp.

A rare and interesting work, with portraits of Margaret Fox Kane and Katie Fox Jencken, the pioneer mediums of American spiritualism.

DESSOIR, MAX. The Magic Mirror. Monist, vol. i. p. 87.

—— The Psychology of Legerdemain. Open Court, vol. vii.

Series of articles translated from the German. Of great interest to psychologists.

De Vere, M. S. Modern Magic. 1869.

Evans, Henry Ridgely. Hours with the Ghosts ; or, XIX. Century Witchcraft. Investigations into the Phenomena of Spiritualism and Theosophy. Chicago, 1897. 8vo.

This work, in the main, is a critical study of the phenomena of modern spiritualism. It is divided into two parts—psychical phenomena and physical phenomena. Concerning the first, the author ascribes the manifestations witnessed by him in test séances, with professional and non-professional subjects, to telepathy, etc., not to spirit intervention. As regards the second phase, he takes a decidedly negative view. *Exposés* are given of psychography, or slate-writing tests, had with such famous mediums as Pierre Keeler, Dr. Henry Slade, etc. The alleged miracles of modern theosophy are also treated at length. Interesting features of the book are the biographies of Madame Blavatsky, D. D. Home, Dr. Slade, etc., and the history of the Theosophical Society from its inception to the present time (1897). A Bibliography of the leading critical treatises on psychic phenomena is appended to the book.

Ewbanks, T. A Descriptive and Historical Account of Hydraulic and Other Machines for Raising Water, Ancient and Modern, with Observations on Various Subjects connected with the Mechanic Arts. New York, 1851. 8vo.

Contains many descriptions of magical automata of ancient Greece and Rome.

Fitzgerald, H. A Chat with Mr. Maskelyne and Mr. Charles Bertram. Ludgate Illustrated Magazine, vol. vi. p. 198.

Forbes, John. Card-Sharpers ; their Tricks Exposed. (Translated from Robert-Houdin's *Les Tricheries des Grecs.*) London, 1891. 8vo.

Frikell, G. Hanky-panky : A Book of Conjuring Tricks. London, 1875.

—— Magic no Mystery : Conjuring Tricks with Cards, Balls, and Dice ; Magic Writing, Performing Animals, etc. *Edited* by W. H. Cremer. London, 1876.

Frost, Thomas. The Lives of the Conjurers. London, 1881. 8vo.

—— The Old Showmen and the Old London Fairs. London, 1881. 8vo.

Gale. Cabinet of Knowledge : With Mechanical, Magnetical and Magical Experiments, Card Deceptions, etc. London, 1803.

Ganthony, R. Practical Ventriloquism and its Sister Arts. London, 1893. 8vo.

Garenne, *Prof.* Henri. The Art of Modern Conjuring, Magic, and Illusions. A Practical Treatise on the Art of Parlor and Stage Magic, Illusions, Spiritualism, Ventriloquism, Thought-reading, Mesmerism, Mnemotechny, etc. London, —. 8vo.

Gatchell, Charles. The Methods of Mind-Readers. Forum, vol. xi. pp. 192–204.

Scientific account of the so-called mind-reading feats of Stuart Cumberland, Washington Irving Bishop, and others, showing them to be muscle-reading. Worked in conjunction with certain conjuring tricks, muscle-reading has an all but supernatural effect. Mr. Gatchell explains many of the devices used by charlatans to imitate clairvoyance, etc. See also chapters on similar subjects in Burlingame's " Leaves from Conjurers' Scrap-Books," Carl Willmann's " Moderne Wunder," and Sid. Macaire's " Mind-Reading, or Muscle-Reading ? "

Good, Arthur. Magic at Home : Book of Amusing Science. Translated by Prof. Hoffmann [Angelo Lewis]. London, 1890. 8vo.

Halle, J. S. Magic. Berlin, 1783.

Hart, Ernest. Hypnotism, Mesmerism, and the New Witchcraft. New York, 1893. 12mo. 212 pp.

A new and enlarged edition, with chapters on " The Eternal Gullible," " The Confessions of a Professional Hypnotist," and notes on the hypnotism of Trilby.

Hatton, Henry. Secrets of Conjuring. Scribners, vol. xxi. pp. 304–306.

—— The Art of Second Sight. Scribners, vol. xxi. pp. 65–69.

HEATHER, H. E. Cards and Card Tricks. London, 1879. 8vo.

HENRY, T. SHEKLETON. "Spookland." A record of research and experiment in a much-talked-of realm of mystery, with a review and criticism of the so-called spiritualistic phenomena of spirit materialization, and hints and illustrations as to the possibility of artificially producing the same.

HERCAT. Card Tricks and Conjuring up to Date. London, 1896. 8vo. 123 pp.

HERMON, HARRY. Hellerism : Second-sight Mystery ; Supernatural Vision, or Second-sight. What is it ? A Mystery ; A Complete Manual for Teaching this Peculiar Art. Boston, 1894. 16mo.

A fine *exposé* of Robert Heller's second-sight trick.

HERRMANN, ADDIE. Confessions of an Assistant Magician. Lippincott, vol. viii. p. 482.

HERRMANN, ALEXANDER. Light on the Black Art. Cosmopolitan, vol. xiv. p. 208.

—— Necromancy Unveiled. Lippincott, vol. viii. p. 475.

—— Some Adventures of a Necromancer. North American Review, vol. clv. p. 418.

—— The Art of Magic. North American Review, vol. cliii. p. 92.

Interesting magazine articles by the great Herrmann, giving his personal experiences as a magician.

HOCUS-POCUS, JR. The Anatomy of Legerdemain. Fourth edition. London, 1654.

HODGSON, RICHARD. Indian Magic, and the Testimony of Conjurers. Proceedings : Society for Psychical Research, Part 25, p. 354.

HOFFMANN, *Prof.* [ANGELO LEWIS]. Drawing-Room Conjuring. London and New York, 1887. 12mo. 179 pp.

—— Modern Magic. A Practical Treatise on the Art of Conjuring. With an appendix containing explanations of some of the best known specialties of Messrs. Maskelyne and Cooke. London and New York, —. 12mo. 578 pp.

An elaborate treatise on prestidigitation. Very useful to students. Palmistry in all its branches explained, as well as stage illusions.

—— More Magic. London and New York, 1890. 12mo. 457 pp.

See also under Robert-Houdin.

HOFFMANN, WALTER J. Juggling Tricks among the Menominee Indians. United States Bureau of Ethnology ; fourteenth annual report, 1892–93. Part 1, pp. 97–100.

HOLDEN. A Wizard's Wanderings. London, 1886.

[HURST, LULU]. The Revelations of Lulu Hurst, the Georgia Wonder. —. 267 pp.

JASTROW, JOSEPH. Psychological Notes upon Sleight-of-Hand Experts. Science, vol. iii. pp. 685–689. Reprinted in " Scientific American Supplement," vol. xlii. p. 17488.

Professor Jastrow, at his psychological laboratory, subjected the conjurers Herrmann and Kellar to a series of careful tests to ascertain their tactile sensibility, sensitiveness to textures, accuracy of visual perception, quickness of movement, mental processes, etc. In " Science " he details the results obtained by him in his experiments, the first of the kind ever made with magicians as subjects. Read in conjunction with the highly interesting series of articles on the " Psychology of Deception," Robert-Houdin's memoirs and magical revelations, and Max Dessoir's fine papers, these studies of Herrmann and Kellar are of great interest to all students of experimental psychology. There are no finer illustrations of mental and visual deception than the tricks of prestidigitateurs.

—— Psychology of Deception. Popular Science Monthly, vol. xxxiv. pp. 145–157; 721–732.

KELLAR, HARRY. High Caste Indian Magic. North American Review, vol. clvi. pp. 75–86.

In this entertaining paper, Kellar the conjurer describes some of the magical performances of the Hindu fakirs and Zulu wizards. They not only out-Herod Herod, but out-Haggard Rider Haggard, the prince of romancers, for weirdness and improbability. The article reads as if it had been " written up " for effect, being the product of an elastic and brilliant imagination, though Kellar claims to have been an eye-witness of all the marvels he describes. Some few of them; hypnotic in character, such as the feat of " imitation death," are unquestionably true, as witness the evidence of Sir Claude M. Wade and other eminent Anglo-Indian investigators. The magician Herrmann, who traveled over India, had but a contemptuous opinion of Hindu fakir tricks. Modern theosophists have done much to exploit the so-called miracles of Tibetan and Indian necromancers. Madame Blavatsky's works are full of absurd stories of Oriental magic. See her "Caves and Jungles of Hindustan," " Isis Unveiled," etc., for example. But also see Arthur Lillie's work, " Madame Blavatsky and her Theosophy," London, 1807, for amusing revelations of theosophical marvels.

—— Magic among the Red Men. North American Review, vol. clviii. pp. 591–600.

KUNARD, *Prof.* R. Book of Card Tricks for Drawing-Room and Stage. London, 1888. 8vo.

—— Modern Magic ; a Book of Conjuring for Amateurs. London, 1888. 8vo.

LE ROUX, HUGUES, *and* GARNIER, JULES. Acrobats and Mountebanks. Translated by A. P. Morton. London and New York, 1890. 4to.

A very entertaining work, tracing the history of the mountebank from his inception in the nomadic caravan to his apotheosis in the splendid modern circus and vaudeville theatre.

LEWIS, T. HANSON. The Great Wizard of the West [J. N. Maskelyne]. English Illustrated Magazine, vol. xii. p. 75.

LOCKHART, W. Advanced Prestidigitation. London, 1894.

LOGAN, OLIVE. The King of Conjurers [Robert-Houdin]. Harper's Magazine, vol. lv. pp. 817–831.

MACAIRE, SID. Mind-Reading, or Muscle-Reading ? London, 1889.

A capital little work on muscle-reading and pretended second-sight.

MACCABE, FREDERIC. The Art of Ventriloquism. London, —. 12mo. 110 pp.

MAGIC AND PRETENDED MIRACLES. London, 1848.

MARION, F. Wonders of Optics. New York, 1869. 8vo.

Contains interesting translations from the memoirs of Robertson, the eighteenth-century ghost illusionist.

MASKELYNE, JOHN NEVIL. Modern Spiritualism. London, 1875. (Pamphlet.)

—— Natural Magic. Leisure Hours, vol. xxvii. pp. 5–204.

—— Sharps and Flats. London, 1894. 8vo.

An *exposé* of the multifarious devices used in cheating at games of chance and skill. One of the best works on the subject.

—— The Magnetic Lady ; or, A Human Magnet Demagnetized. Being an appendix to " The Supernatural." London, —. 8vo. 16 pp.

NATURAL MAGIC. Chambers' Miscellany, No. 82.

NAUDÉ, G. History of Magick, by way of Apology for all the Wise Men who have been Unjustly Reputed Magicians, from the Earliest Times to the Present Age. London, 1657.

PEPPER, JOHN HENRY. The Play-Book of Science. London, —. 8vo. 506 pp.

—— The True History of the Ghost, and all about Metempsychosis. London, 1890. 8vo. 46 pp.

Professor Pepper, inventor of the famous "Ghost," gives full details in this little book of the apparatus used in performing the startling optical illusion, together with many amusing personal experiences connected with its stage production. There were spiritualists in London who asserted that Professor Pepper was a powerful medium, and produced his weird phantasms by some occult influence. They deluged him with letters on the subject. The illusion known as "Metempsychosis" is the basis of Kellar's ingenious "Blue-Room" trick, which has puzzled thousands of spectators.

PIESSE, G. W. S. Chymical, Natural, and Physical Magic. Third edition. London, 1865. 16mo.

QUINN, JOHN PHILIP. Nineteenth Century Black Art ; or, Gambling Exposed. With illustrations of all crooked gambling appliances. Chicago, 1896. 12mo. 104 pp.

REVELATIONS OF A SPIRIT-MEDIUM ; or, Spiritualistic Mysteries Exposed. A detailed explanation of the methods used by fraudulent mediums. By A Medium. St. Paul, Minn., 1891. 8vo. 324 pp.

ROBERT-HOUDIN. (JEAN-EUGÈNE). Card-Sharping Exposed. Translated and edited, with notes, by Professor Hoffmann. London and New York, 1882. 12mo. 316 pp.

——— Memoirs of Robert-Houdin, Ambassador, Author, and Conjurer, written by himself. Translated from the French by R. Shelton Mackenzie. Philadelphia, 1859. 12mo. 445 pp.

——— The Secrets of Conjuring and Magic ; or, How to Become a Wizard. Translated and edited, with notes, by Professor Hoffmann. London and New York, 1878. 12mo. 373 pp.

——- The Secrets of Stage Conjuring. Translated and edited, with notes, by Professor Hoffmann. London and New York, 1881. 12mo. 252 pp.

Robert-Houdin's works on magic are genuine classics, and are so regarded by all conjurers. No more fascinating biography was ever written than Houdin's Memoirs. It contains interesting sketches of old-time magicians, such as Philippe, Bosco, Comte, Torrini, and Pinetti, also a great deal of scientific and historical information relating to early inventions, etc. "The Secrets of Conjuring and Magic" (*Les secrets de la prestidigitation et de la magie*), published in 1868, is an admirable treatise on sleight of hand. The French edition is out of print. "The possession of a copy of this book," says Angelo Lewis, "was regarded among professors of magic as a boon of the highest possible value. It is unquestionably the most scientific work ever written on the art of conjuring." The English translation has been received with the greatest favor by amateur and professional sleight-of-hand performers. Students of psychology will find much to interest them in this clever book.

ROCHAS, ALBERT DE. Trials by Fire, and Fire Jugglers. Popular Science Monthly, vol. xxi. pp. 645–650.

ROTERBERG, A. The Modern Wizard. Containing an essay on " The Art of Magic," by W. E. Robinson. Chicago, ——. 8vo. 120 pp.

——— Latter Day Tricks. A sequel to The Modern Wizard. Chicago, 1896. 8vo. 104 pp.
Capital little manuals of the latest marvels in the magical line.

SACHS, EDWIN O. Modern Theater Stages. Engineering, January 17, 1896, to June 11, 1897.

——— Sleight of hand; a Practical Manual of Legerdemain for Amateurs and Others. London, 1885. 12mo. 408 pp.
An excellent work for students. Palmistry carefully explained.

SALVERTE, E. The Occult Sciences ; Philosophy of Magic, Prodigies, and Apparent Miracles. From the French, with notes by A. T. Thomson. 2 vols. London, 1846. 12mo.

SHAW, W. H. J. Magic and its Mysteries. Chicago, 1893. 8vo. 61 pp.

SKINNER, W. E. (*Compiler*).—Wehmann's Wizard's Manual. New York, 1892. 8vo. 122 pp.

SOCIETY FOR PSYCHICAL RESEARCH : Proceedings, vols. i. to xi. London, 1882–83 to 1895.
Contain many *exposés* of pretended mediumship, etc.

STANYON, ELLIS. Conjuring for Amateurs. A Practical Treatise on How to Perform Modern Tricks. London, 1897. 8vo. 122 pp.

TAYLOR, *Rev.* E. S. History of Playing Cards. 48 plates and woodcuts. London, 1865. 8vo.

Contains anecdotes of the uses of cards in conjuring, fortune-telling, and card-sharping.

THAUMATURGIA ; or, Elucidations of the Marvelous. By an Oxonian. London, 1835. 12mo.

TIMAYENNIS, T. T. History of the Art of Magic. With a Sketch of Alexander Herrmann. New York, 1887. 8vo.

TINDAL, MARCUS. Tricks with Pennies. New Illustrated· Magazine, August, 1897, pp. 373–376.

TISSANDIER, GASTON. Popular Scientific Recreations, a Storehouse of Instruction and Amusement ; in which the Marvels of Natural Philosophy, Chemistry, Geology, Astronomy, etc., are Explained and Illustrated, Mainly by Means of Pleasing Experiments and Attractive Pastimes. London and New York, —. 4to. 884 pp.

This monumental work is a translation of Tissandier's *Les récréations scientifiques*, with many additions. It contains a few conjuring feats of a very simple nature, and an *exposé* of the ghost illusion and decapitated-head trick. In the chapter on clocks, the reader will find an interesting description of Robert-Houdin's famous magical timepiece, which ran apparently without works. It will be remembered that one of these wizard clocks was the means of introducing Houdin to the French public as a prestidigitateur, as explained in the introduction—"The Mysteries of Modern Magic."

TREWEY, FÉLICIAN. Shadowgraphy : How it is Done. London, 1893. 8vo. (Pamphlet.)

TRUESDELL, JOHN W. The Bottom Facts Concerning the Science of Spiritualism : derived from careful investigations covering a period of twenty-five years. New York, 1883. 8vo. 331 pp.

Exposés of slate-writing feats and cabinet arts. A valuable work.

WEATHERBY, L. A. The Supernatural ? With chapter on Oriental Magic, Spiritualism, and Theosophy, by J. N. Maskelyne. London, —. 12mo. 273 pp.

WELTON, THOMAS. Mental Magic ; a Rationale of Thought-Reading and its Phenomena. London, 1884. 4to.

WHITE MAGIC. Encyclopædia Britannica, vol. xv. pp. 207–211.

WHOLE ART OF LEGERDEMAIN ; or, Hocus-pocus Laid Open and Explained. [Anon.] Philadelphia, 1852. 18mo.

II.

FRENCH.

ANTONIO, CARLO. Dictionnaire encyclopédique. Avec atlas. Paris, 1792–1799. 4to. 900 pp.

Scientific recreations, illusions, and conjuring tricks, ingenious applications of science to industry, etc. The works of Decremps, Ozanam, Guyot, Pinetti, and Montucla, etc., are largely drawn upon.

—— Trésor des jeux. The Hague, 1769.

Cup and ball conjuring, tricks with cards, etc., illustrated.

CÉPAK, ABEL. Ce qu'on peut faire avec les œufs. Collection complète et variée des expériences faciles et amusantes pouvant être exécutées par tout le monde avec des œufs. Paris, 1889. 12mo. 163 pp.

A work devoted solely to conjuring tricks performed with eggs.

COMBINAISON EGYPTIENNE DU CÉLÈBRE CAGLIOSTRO. Véritable explication des six cents principaux songes. Figures noires et coloriées. Paris, —. 12mo.

35

COMTE, *and* FONTENELLE, JULIE DE. Sorciers, ou la magie blanche dévoilée par les découvertes de la chimie, de la physique, et de la mécanique. Paris, —.

COMUS. Physique amusante. Paris, 1801.

DECREMPS, N. La magie blanche dévoilée. ou explication de tours surprenants qui font depuis peu l'admiration de la capitale et de la province, avec des réflexions sur la baguette divinatoire, les automates joueurs d'échecs. Figures explicatives. Paris, 1784, 1788, 1792. 8vo.

—— Supplément à la Magie blanche dévoilée, contenant l'explication de plusieurs tours nouveaux joués depuis peu à Londres, avec des éclaircissements sur les artifices des joueurs de profession, les cadrans sympathiques, le mouvement perpétuel, les chevaux savans, les poupées parlantes, les automates dansants, les ventriloques, les sabots élastiques. Figures. Paris, 1785, 1788, 1792. 8vo.

—— Eclaircissements à la Magie blanche dévoilée. Paris, 1785. 8vo.

—— Testament de Jérome Sharp, professeur de physique amusante, où l'on trouve parmi plusieurs tours de subtilité qu'on peut exécuter sans aucune dépense, des préceptes, des exemples sur l'art de faire des chansons impromptu, pour servir de suite et de complément à la Magie blanche dévoilée. Figures. Paris, 1786, 1788, 1789, 1793. 8vo.

—— Codicile de Jérome Sharp, professeur de physique amusante, où l'on trouve parmi plusieurs tours, diverses récréations relatives aux sciences et beaux-arts, pour servir de suite à la Magie blanche. Figures. Paris, 1788, 1791, 1793. 8vo.

—— Les petites aventures de Jérome Sharp, professeur de physique amusante, ouvrage contenant autant de tours ingénieux que de leçons utiles avec quelques petits portraits à la manière noire. Avec 18 figures grav. en bois. Bruxelles et Paris, 1789, 1790, 1793. 8vo.

Original editions of the works of this ingenious writer are exceedingly rare. They are genuine curiosities in the domain of magical literature, being the first scientific treatises on the art of sleight of hand written in the French language. Decremps was a pioneer in this line, and hundreds of authors, English, French, and German, are indebted to him for material for their books. He exposed the tricks and illusions of the eighteenth-century wizards, and, according to Larousse, did much to dispel by his revelations the pretended sorcery of Cagliostro. The *Codicile de Jérome Sharp* was published during the " Reign of Terror " of the French Revolution. Its author did not fall a victim to the guillotine, but lived to a good old age, dying in the year 1826. This work contains a portrait of Decremps.

DE MUSON. La Magie blanche dévoilée. Paris, 1855.

—— Manuel des sorciers. Paris, 1802.

—— Récréations de physique. Paris, 1828.

DICKSONN. Mes trucs. Paris, 1893.

DICTIONNAIRE DE TRUCS ; illusions de physique amusante. 1 vol. (with one volume of steel plates). Paris, 1792. 878 pp.

DICTIONNAIRE DES ANA. Paris, 1794. 4to.

DIDOT. Nouvelle biographie générale. Paris, 1859. *See article* Robert-Houdin.

DUCRET, ÉTIENNE. Tours d'escamatoge, anciens et nouveaux. Paris, —.

FAIDEAU, F. Les amusements scientifiques, récréations sur les illusions, ou erreurs des sens. Paris, —.

GANDON, F. A. La seconde vue dévoilée. Paris, 1849.

GRANDPRÉ. Magicien moderne. Paris, —. 570 pp.

GRAND TRAITÉ DES SONGES, ou explication complète des visions et inspirations nocturnes. Paris, 1831. 18mo.

GUYOT. Nouvelles récréations physiques et mathématiques. Paris, 1769, 1775, 1786, 1790, 1799, 1800.

HATIN. Robert-Houdin, sa vie, ses œuvres, son théâtre. Paris, 1857.

HELION. Physique amusante. 1660.

L'ALBERT MODERNE. Paris, 1782. 2 vols. 12mo

LA MAGIE NATURELLE. Lyons, 1787. Figures.

LANDAU. Petit magicien. Paris, 1810.

LA NOUVELLE MAGIE BLANCHE DÉVOILÉE. Amusantes grande initiation à la vraie pratique des célèbres physiciens et prestidigitateurs. Par un amateur. Paris, 1855. 8vo. 324 pp.

L'ESCAMOTEUR HABILE, ou l'art d'amuser agréablement une Société, contenant les tours de cartes, etc. Pesth, 1816.

MAGUS. Magie blanche en famille. Paris, 1895. 352 pp.

MANUEL DES SORCIERS, ou cours de récréations physiques, mathématiques, tours de cartes et gibecière ; suivi des petits jeux de société et le leurs pénitenas. Cinquieme édition, avec figures. Paris, 1820. 16mo. 293 pp.

MARION, F. Magie naturelle, ou optique amusante. *In his* Optique. 1869.

MARLY. Physique amusante. 1626.

MATHIOT, GERMAIN. Nouvelles récréations physiques et mathematiques. Paris, 1799.

MOYNET, GEORGES. Trucs et décors. Paris, 1895. 8vo.

——, M. J. L'Envers du théâtre. Paris, 1875. 16mo.

NAUDÉ, G. Apologie pour tous les grands hommes qui ont esté accusez de magie. Paris, 1669. 24mo.

OZANAM, JACQUES. Récréations mathématiques et physiques. Paris, 1694. 2 vols. 8vo. *Other editions published in* 1720, 1723, 1725, 1735, 1741, 1749, 1750, 1778, 1790.
Contains many curious scientific diversions, besides tricks with cups and balls, pyrotechny, etc.

PINETTI, DE WILDALLE, JEAN-JOSEPH. Amusements physiques. Paris, 1784. 8vo. 95 pp.
—— *The Same.* Nouvelle édition augmentée par l'auteur de six nouvelles grav. Paris, 1785. 8vo.
—— *The Same.* Troisième édition augmentée de quelque nouvelles expériences physiques et de gravures. Paris, 1791. 8vo.
This work by the famous Pinetti, king of conjurers of the eighteenth century, is a little handbook of very simple experiments in natural magic, evidently designed to be sold in the theatre. It contains no sleight-of-hand experiments, or anything of value to a professional. Pinetti carefully preserved the secrets of his tricks, and died without making any revelations. Decremps, however, has sufficiently acquainted us with them in his *Magie blanche dévoilée.* An edition in English of Pinetti's book was published in London. On the title-page the conjurer expresses himself as follows : "Physical amusements and diverting experiments composed and performed in different capitals of Europe, and in London. By Signor Giuseppe Pinetti, de Wilidalle, Knight of the German Order of Merit of St. Philip, professor of mathematics and natural philosophy, pensioned by the court of Prussia, patronized by all the royal family of France, aggregate of the Royal Academy of Sciences and Belles-lettres of Bordeaux, etc. London, 1784." 65 pp.
The most interesting thing about this insignificant booklet is a steel-plate frontispiece containing a portrait of the great magician. Two winged cherubs are depicted, placing the bust of Pinetti in the temple of arts. The motto reads : "Des genies placent le buste de M. le Professeur Pinetti dans le temple des arts, au milieu des instruments de physique et de mathematiques."

PONSIN, J. N. Nouvelle magie blanche dévoilée, physique occulte, et cours complet de prestidigitation, contenant tous les tours nouveaux qui ont été exécutés jusqu' à ce jour sur les théâtres ou ailleurs, et qui n'ont pas encore été publiés, et un grand nombre de tours d'un effet surprenant, d'une exécution facile, et tout à fait inconnus du public et des professeurs. Paris, 1853. 8vo. 312 pp.

Sleight of hand with cards, coins, cups and balls.

PRESTIDIGITATION MODERNE. Figures. Paris, —.

Scientific recreations, tricks with cards, etc. Spiritism exposed.

RAYNALLY. Les propos d'un escamoteur. Paris, 1894.

ROBERT-HOUDIN (JEAN-EUGÈNE). Les confidences d'un prestidigitateur. 2 vols. Paris, 1858. 8vo.

—— Les secrets de la prestidigitation et de la magie. Paris, 1868.

—— Les tricheries des Grecs. Paris, 1861.

—— Magie et physiques amusante. Paris, 1877.

ROBERTSON, ÉTIENNE-GASPARD. Mémoires récréatifs et anecdotiques. 2 vols. Paris, 1830–34. 8vo. (With a volume of plates.)

—— Mémoires physiques et phantasmagorie. 2 vols. Paris, 1840.

Very interesting *exposés* of ghost illusions, phantasmagoria, optical tricks, etc.

ROBIN, D. Histoire des spectres vivants et impalpables ; secrets de la physique amusante. Paris, 1864. 4to.

Ghost illusions explained. Illusions similar to those described by Pepper in "The True Story of the Ghost."

ROCHAS, ALBERT DE. Les origines de la science et ses premières applications. Paris, 8vo. 288 pp.

A very elaborate treatise on the natural magic of ancient times, primitive science, etc.

III.

GERMAN.

ANDERS, FRITZ. Der junge Tausendkuenstler. Leipzig, 1884.

COMTE. Das Gedankenspiel oder die Kunst der Menschen Gedanken zu erforschen; Beitrag zur natuerlichen Magie. Mit 12 Tafeln. Halle, 1782. 8vo.

—— Handbuch der Taschenspielerkunst oder die Geheimnisse der natuerlichen Magie. 2 Bände mit 3 Tafeln. 1834. 8vo.

CONRADI. Zauber Spiegel, monthly magazine.
—— Karten Künstler.

CUMBERLAND, ARTHUR W. Der Experimental-Spiritist als Orakel, Hellseher, blinder Rechner und Gedaechtnisskuenstler. Stuttgart, 1895. 8vo. 125 pp.

DIE KUNST ZAUBERER ZU WERDEN, VON PHILADELPHIA. Leipzig, 1870.

ECKARTSHAUSEN, V. Aufschluesse der Magie. 8vo. About 1790. 4 Bde. Mystische Maechte oder der Schulessel zu den Geheimnissen des Wunderbaren ; Nachtrag zu den Aufschluessen der Magie. Mit Kpfr. Muenchen, 1791. 8vo.

—— Verschiedenes zum Unterricht und zur Unterhaltung. fuer Liebhaber der Gaukeltasche, des Magnetismus und anderer Seltenheiten. 2 Bde. mit Kpfr. Muenchen, 1793. 8vo.

GUETLE, J. Zaubermechanik oder Beschreibung mechanischer Zauberbelustigungen, mit darzu gehoerigen Maschinen fuer Liebhaber belustigender Kuenste. 2 Bde. mit 58 Tafeln. Nuernberg, 1794. 8vo.

GUYOT. Neue physikal. und mathemat. Belustigungen oder Sammlung. von neuen Kunststuecken zum Vergnuegen, mit dem Magnete, mit den Zahlen, aus. der Optik und Chemie. 7 Thle., 4 Bde. mit vielen Kpfrn. Augsburg, 1772–77. 8vo.

HILDEBRAND. Das Buch der alten natuerl. Magie oder Kunst und Wunderbuch, darin enthalten viele wunderbare Geheimnisse, Kunststuecke, etc. Baltimore. 8vo.

JACOBY-HARMS. Illustrierte Zauber-Soirée. Leipzig. 117 pp.

KERNDORFFER, *Prof*. Carl Bosco. Zauber-Cabinet. Leipzig, 1874.

MARIAN, RUDOLPH. Das Buch der Kartenkuenste : in 126 Piecen und 75 Illustrationen. Wien, 1890. 8vo. 158 pp.

—— Das Ganze der Salon-Magie ; in 169 Vortraegen und 220 Illustrationen. Wien, 1889. 12mo. 240 pp.

MOLWITZ, F. Magische Unterhaltungen oder Taschenbuch fuer magische Unterhaltungen. Jahrg. 1809–10.

ROCKSTROH, HEINRICH. Mechanemata, oder der Tausendkuenstler. Berlin, 1831. 8vo. 344 pp.

SUHR, H. F. C. Der Kartenkuenstler. Eine Sammlung neuer leicht ausfuehrbarer Karten-Kunststuecke, mit und ohne Apparate. Stuttgart, 1895. 8vo. 125 pp.

—— Die Magie im Salon. Eine Auswahl neuer, leicht ausfuehrbarer Zauber-Kunststuecke ohne Apparate. Stuttgart, 1895. 8vo. 104 pp.

—— Zauber-Soirée. Ausfuehrliche und genaue Anleitung zur Vorfuehrung von Zauber-Kunststuecken in privaten Kreisen. Stuttgart, 1895. 8vo. 94 pp.

TROMBOLDT, J. Streichholzspiele. Leipzig, 1890.

WAGNER, J. Neuestes Zauberkabinet ; Auswahl von magischen, Karten, Rechnungs-u. anderen Kunststuecken. Wien, 1799. 8vo.

WALLBERGENS. Sammlung. natuerl. Zauberkuenste oder aufrichtige Entdeckungen bewaehrter Geheimnisse nebst vielen Kunststuecken, so zu Haushaltung, Gaertnerey, Wein u. Feldbau gehoeren. Stuttgart, 1768. 8vo.

WILLMANN, CARL. Die moderne Salon-Magie. Leipzig, 1891. 460 pp.

—— Moderne Wunder. Leipzig, 1892. Third Edition, 1897. 8vo. 320 pp.
  "Moderne Wunder" contains interesting *exposés* of pretended mediumship, clairvoyance, second sight automata, and stage illusions.

—— Zauber-Welt.
  A monthly magazine of natural magic and prestidigitation, edited by Willmann.

ZAUBER-BUCH. Natürlicher, oder neu eröffneter Spielplatz rarer Künste, in welchem alle Taschenspieler-, mathemat. und physikal. Künste, Karten-, Würfel- etc. Spiele beschrieben u. mit vielen Figuren erläutert werden. Sehr selten u. interessant. Nürnberg, 1762. 8vo. 752 pp.

IV.

SPANISH.

Gomez, S. R.   Los divertidos, curiosos, juegos de escamoteo.

Krespel, Karl.   Nuevo manual de magia blanca.   Paris, 1888.

Minguet e Yrol, P.   Juegos de manos.   Madrid, 1733.   16mo.

Palonca, D. R.   El moderno prestidigitador.   Valencia, 1887.

V.

ITALIAN.

Giochi Numerici Fatti Arcani Palesati, da Giuseppe Antonio Alberti Bolognese ; seconda edizione adornata di figure.   In Venezia, 1780.   8vo.

——*The Same*   Napoli, 1814.   8vo.

VI.

LATIN.

Hildebrandt, W.   Magiæ Naturalis, 1610.

Hippolytus.   Ref. Om. Haer, iv. 34, 35.

Porta, Giovanni Battista della.   Magiæ Naturalis, sive de miraculis rerum naturalium, Libri iv. 283 ff., 3 l.   Lugduni, apud G. Rovillium, 1561.

Schot, K.   Physica Curiosa.   2 vols.   1667.

—— Thaumaturgus Physicus sive magiæ universalis naturæ.   1659.

INDEX.

INDEX.